PHARMACY MANAGEMENT IN CANADA

PHARMACY MANAGEMENT IN CANADA

SECOND EDITION

General Editors

JOHN A. BACHYNSKY

HAROLD J. SEGAL

Grosvenor House Inc.

The publisher wishes to express its gratitude to the Canadian Foundation for Pharmacy and the Canadian Association of Chain Drug Stores (CACDS) for educational grants which have helped make the publication of this book possible.

Special thanks as well to the CACDS in their role as endorser of this publication.

Canadian Cataloguing in Publication Data

Main entry under title:

      Pharmacy management in Canada
      Second Edition

ISBN 1-895995-20-5

1. Pharmacy management – Canada I. Bachynsky, John A. II. Segal, Harold J.

RS100.4.C3P53 1998   615'.1'068   C98-900914-9

Published by
      Grosvenor House Press Inc.

1456 Sherbrooke Street West   King West Centre
Montréal, Québec   2 Pardee Avenue, Suite 203
H3G 1K4   Toronto, Ontario
      M6K 3H5

Printed and bound in Canada

TABLE OF CONTENTS

LIST OF CONTRIBUTORS

JOHN A. BACHYNSKY, BSP, MSc, PhD (General Editor)
John A. Bachynsky is Professor of Pharmacy Administration at the Faculty of Pharmacy and Pharmaceutical Sciences at the University of Alberta, where he served as Dean from 1981 to 1989.

He received a PhD in Pharmacy Administration from the University of Wisconsin, has served as President of both the Association of Faculties of Pharmacy of Canada and the Association of Deans of Pharmacy of Canada. In 1988, he was appointed Vice-President of the Commonwealth Pharmaceutical Association. He has received the Meritorious Service Award of the Canadian Pharmacists Association and is an Honorary Life Member of the Alberta Pharmaceutical Association.

DONALD M. CAMERON, BScPharm
Donald M. Cameron served as Registrar of the Alberta Pharmaceutical Association for 25 years, and lectured for 18 of those years in Pharmacy Management and Administration and Forensic Pharmacy at the University of Alberta. A former president of the Alberta Pharmaceutical Association and owner/operator of his own pharmacy, Mr. Cameron retired in 1982 and until 1991 marketed the association's pharmacist insurance program.

STEPHEN L. CAPPE, LLB
Stephen L. Cappe practices law in Toronto, having graduated from the University of Toronto Law School in 1975, and has been a member of the Ontario Bar since 1977. His understanding of community pharmacy comes from working in his father's pharmacy. He lectures to pharmacy students regularly on leasing, and advises many pharmacist clients in his law practice.

WAYNE M. CAVERLY
Wayne M. Caverly is President, BakerAPS Canada, "*The Pharmacy Productivity Company*" and its pharmacy design division AutoPharm. Based in Dorval, Québec, Mr. Caverly is an editor of *The Efficient Pharmacy*, a member of the Canadian Pharmacists Association, and an associate

member of The Institute of Store Planners. He has been involved in pharmacy automation, productivity, and design since 1984 and is currently lecturing on those subjects.

JACQUES GAGNÉ, BscPharm, Msc, PhD

Dr. Gagné is a Professor and former Dean at the Faculty of Pharmacy, University of Montréal, and an active member of numerous scientific and professional organizations. He received a PhD in Pharmacology from the University of Montréal in 1971. A former administrator (1977-81) and Vice-President (1978-81) of the Ordre des Pharmaciens du Québec, Dr. Gagné has also served as President of both the Association of Faculties of Pharmacy and the Association of Deans of Pharmacy of Canada.

TOM HICKS

Tom Hicks is past Director of Loss Prevention at PharmaPlus Drugmart. He has been active in the loss prevention field for 22 years.

KEVIN MOODY, BScPharm, MBA

Kevin Moody received his pharmacy degree from the University of Toronto and his MBA from the University of British Columbia. He is currently the Director of Continuing Pharmacy Education and Lecturer of Pharmacy Practice at the University of British Columbia. From 1992 to 1995, he was the Executive Director of the Association of Faculties of Pharmacy of Canada and currently serves in an administrative capacity to the Canadian Council on Continuing Education in Pharmacy.

KEITH MORGAN

Keith Mogan earned a BA in Political Science and a BEd from Acadia University, Wolfville, Nova Scotia. He taught senior high school in Chester, Nova Scotia then served as a police officer in Metropolitan Toronto for 13 years. He has been with Shoppers Drug Mart for the last 11 years and currently is the Director of Loss Prevention working out of the Toronto central office.

JACQUES NADEAU, BScPharm, MSC, MBA

Jacques Nadeau is Vice-President of Professional Services and Development for Pharmaprix in Québec. He has held several management positions in

R & D, production, sales and marketing since receiving his Master's degree in radiopharmacy from the University of Southern California and his MBA from McGill University. He is a former Director General and Secretary of the Ordre des Pharmaciens du Québec.

STAN REMIN

Stan Remin was employed with IBM for ten years before becoming licensed as a life insurance and general insurance agent. He has represented several insurance agencies including the Interprovincial Pharmacy Group Insurance, the carrier for the Alberta Pharmaceutical Association. He has completed several sales-related courses including the Life Underwriters Association Training Course.

GLEN H. SCHOEPP, BScPharm

Glen H. Schoepp is Manager of St. Anthony's Clinic Pharmacy in Victoria, British Columbia. He is also a clinical instructor at the Faculty of Pharmaceutical Sciences, University of British Columbia, Vancouver. He specializes in long-term care and home health-care marketing.

HAROLD J. SEGAL, BSc Pharm, MS, PhD (General Editor)

Harold J. Segal is Professor of Pharmacy Administration at the Faculty of Pharmacy, University of Toronto and holds a part-time appointment at the School of Pharmacy at the Memorial University of Newfoundland, where he teaches. A former community pharmacist, he earned his PhD in Pharmacy Administration from Purdue University. He is a co-author of a marketing textbook, several booklets on pharmacy management, and numerous journal articles. Dr. Segal also consults and lectures widely to provincial, national, and international conferences on pharmacy management.

DANA WELIN, BS, MBA

Dana Welin holds a Masters in Business Administration from Oklahoma City University (1984) and a Bachelor of Science (Pharmacy) from Southwestern Oklahoma State University (1979). She is a registered professional pharmacist who has worked both in industry and as a clinical pharmacist. Ms. Welin has a broad-base experience in improving productivity through automation and technology. Ms. Welin also holds a patent for co-inventing a pharmacy automation system.

PREFACE

The Canadian Foundation for Pharmacy (CFP) is a national Canadian foundation that provides opportunities for members and friends of the profession of pharmacy to support education and research projects designed to generate progress in Canadian pharmacy. The foundation was founded in 1945 and supported over the years by individual pharmacists, pharmaceutical manufacturers, and pharmacy-related businesses that identify with the profession. The Board of Directors, comprising 16 volunteers from the different provinces who truly represent the various disciplines of pharmacy, has accepted a long-term financial plan to support major programs related to pharmaceutical education and research. This support will enable the profession to move forward as a recognized leader in Canadian health care.

The major programs supported by the CFP are:

- research in pharmacy practice and education which promotes progress;

- special lectures and continuing education programs which enhance both community- and hospital-based pharmacy practice;

- awards, grants, and fellowships to pharmacy students to encourage the pursuit of excellence;

- special projects such as the foundation executive workshop, establishment of drug information centres, faculties of pharmacy, chairs in pharmacy, and special surveys and studies;

- recognition award (Pillar of Pharmacy) for outstanding support of community pharmacy and of the foundation.

The CFP is pleased to be able to provide our latest contribution to pharmacy education, a second edition of *Pharmacy Management in Canada*, a textbook designed to serve as a resource for professors and practicing pharmacists, pharmacy students at all nine pharmacy schools, and new practitioners wishing to start up practice in Canada. The contributors to this textbook and reviewers are recognized nationally as experts in their various disciplines. The ultimate result will be a more efficient, effective, and successful provision of health care by pharmacists for the Canadian public.

The CFP would like to thank two major sponsors, the Canadian Association of Chain Drug Stores and the Canadian Society of Industrial Pharmacists, as well as the pharmacy associations, societies, and colleges, and the pharmaceutical industry. We also appreciate the personal support of all individual pharmacists across our country who saw this book as an extension and reaffirmation of their ongoing commitment to continuing pharmacy education. The foundation hopes that it will be a source of information for you in your pharmacy management endeavours.

Acknowledgements

The second edition of *Pharmacy Management in Canada* could not have been successfully accomplished without the support, contribution, and constructive suggestions of many people.

The CFP is to be congratulated for its foresight in providing an ongoing legacy to pharmacy students. The committee responsible for the second edition of the textbook deserves recognition: Barry Phillips (Chairman), John A. Bachynsky, David Fielding, Marianne Greer, Jacques Nadeau, Stuart Ryan and Harold J. Segal. They obtained the support of the CFP, which in turn raised the funds for the publication.

Stuart Ryan was instrumental in obtaining funding and arranging for the publishing of the textbook by Grosvenor House Press. His commitment to the project and continuing support for the contributors made the project a reality.

The financial support and expert input from the Canadian Association of Chain Drug Stores (notably Marty Belitz from Shoppers Drug Mart, Carole McKiee from Medical Pharmacies, and Roxanne Veloso, from Wal-Mart Canada) and individuals such as Len Marks, London Drugs, was vital to the success of the publication.

In the first edition, the original authors created an excellent base on which to build and expand, notably the chapters on financial concepts by Graham Cunningham, especially materials appearing in chapters 5 and 6. We began this second edition as an extension of the original work. We are indebted to the authors of the first edition, and list them here in recognition of their contributions:

André Archambault
Lynda G. Brown
John A. Bachynsky
Donald M. Cameron
Graham Cunningham
David W. Fielding
Norma M. Freeman
Jacques Gagné
Marianne Greer
Donald F. Kyte
Claude Lafontaine
Jacques A. Nadeau
Ken Ready
John James Ryan
Glen H. Schoepp
Harold J. Segal
Pierre Tremblay
William R. Wensley

In addition, we would like to acknowledge the valuable role of the knowledgeable reviewers who participated in critically appraising the draft manuscript: Guy Belisle, Don Cameron, Serge DuLaine, David Fielding, Len Marks, Barry Phillips, Norman Puhl, Harold Lopatka, Bill Wilson, and Jerry Ziedenberg.

Much of the material was typed with skill, patience, and understanding by Jennifer Brown at the University of Toronto.

While this has been a joint effort with many participants, as editors we take full responsibility for any mistakes or inaccuracies.

John A. Bachynsky   *Harold J. Segal*
Edmonton, Alberta   *Toronto, Ontario*

1

PHARMACY AND THE HEALTH-CARE SYSTEM— UNDERSTANDING THE ENVIRONMENT

INTRODUCTION

The pharmaceutical system in Canada is an integral part of the overall health-care system. To understand the distribution and use of pharmaceuticals in Canada, one needs to understand the system in which it operates. Canada has an international reputation for its health-care system and other countries often look to our system when planning changes to their own system. Within Canada, the health-care system is looked upon with pride and, in some ways, it serves to identify the values and culture of Canada.

Many believe that Canada has a national system and that most health-care services are provided by the public sector to the patient at no charge, or minimal charge. In reality, Canada has ten provincial health-care programs and two territorial programs that provide interlocking health-insurance plans. At the heart of the program are the insured hospital and medical care services, which incur the majority of the expenditures, receive most of the publicity, and generate debate. The health-care system also has programs in both the private and public sectors that contribute to health care and are attracting more attention as their costs increase. To better understand the structure of the pharmaceutical system and its place in health care in Canada, look at the following examples of different users of health-care services and medications.

———————————— *EXAMPLE 1* ————————————

George, age 53, is an active man who tries to keep fit by exercising regularly. He has noticed that his foot is sore and swollen. As a prudent person he makes an appointment to see his family physician at a nearby shopping mall where there is a clinic of four family physicians in practice. They have his health insurance number on file so that they can bill the provincial health plan. If George lives in Alberta or British Columbia, he is required to pay monthly health-insurance premiums to be eligible for insured services.

Although it normally takes a few days to get to get an appointment to see a physician, in cases that are potentially serious physicians will see the patient immediately, ahead of other patients who are waiting in the physicians' waiting area, who will then have a longer wait.

George's condition is diagnosed as an opportunistic infection that developed in the area where athletes' foot (a fungal infection) had split the skin. A prescription order for amoxicillin is given to George and he is instructed to continue taking the medication until it is finished. He does not have to pay anything to the physician for the care he received. Under the health-care system in Canada, George has first-dollar coverage for his visit to the physician.

To get the medication, George goes to his community pharmacy near his home. It is open evenings as well as on weekends and is readily accessible. He has the medication dispensed by the pharmacist who gives him instructions on how to use it, after asking about any allergies to penicillin and counseling George on the prescription. The pharmacist also provides information on the results George should expect. George pays for the medication based on a fee-for-service and the cost of the medication. The medication prescribed is a standard product that has been available for some time and it is relatively inexpensive. The medication cost plus the pharmacist's fee is less than $20. George has health-insurance coverage for medication through a drug benefit program as part of his employment. He will submit the receipt and receive full reimbursement. This program is more generous than many that cover only part of the cost.

Unfortunately, the medication is not effective and the foot continues to swell and becomes more painful. George notifies his physician and returns for a second examination. The physician gives him another prescription order, this time for intravenous medication to be administered at the hospital. It requires that George go to the hospital Emergency Department every eight hours for medication that is infused into a catheter, which is placed in his forearm. The medication is administered by a nurse and, because the staff give priority to the injured who arrive in Emergency, they did not have time until his third visit to provide George with information on the medication.

The hospital staff use his health insurance number as authorization to provide service at no charge. Because it is a hospital service, it is an "insured service" and there is no charge for the medication. Detailed records of his treatment are maintained. After four days of therapy, the foot is much better and the treatment discontinued. The information on his treatment will be retained in the hospital but neither George's physician nor the community pharmacist will see it unless they have a specific need for it, in which case they will make a request to the hospital. The hospital may or may not provide the information in a timely manner. George is responsible for managing his own care by remembering the services that he receives and by linking the services provided. This is an important aspect of the quality of care in the Canadian health-care system, which is not well understood or appreciated by many Canadians.

Questions

1. Why are physicians' services provided at no charge to George?

2. How are physicians reimbursed for the services that they provide to patients such as George?

3. Why does George take his prescription order to a community pharmacy? Where else could he get medication?

4. Why does George have to pay for his medication at the community pharmacy?

5. How is the pharmacist reimbursed for the services he provides to George? Are there other mechanisms for reimbursement?

6. Why is the medication provided in the hospital provided at no charge to George?

7. How is the nurse reimbursed for the services that she provides to George in administering the medication?

8. How is the hospital reimbursed for the services provided to George?

9.   Does the money from health-insurance premiums cover the cost of providing services in those provinces that require payment of premiums?

10. Where does the money come from to cover the services provided at no charge to the patient?

11. Why is the information from physicians and hospitals separate, with no ongoing linkage?

12. Does George's physician have access to a record of all the medication taken by George?

ANSWERS

Most Canadians can provide general answers to the above questions. Answers are provided in the sections entitled "Health Care in Canada" and "Changes in Health Care in Canada" (respectively, p. 20 and 27). In reading these sections, refer to the above questions and try to understand how they "link together."

——————————————— EXAMPLE 2 ———————————————

Sally is a university student. She is an active person and in excellent health. Since her senior year in high school she has been taking birth control pills (oral contraceptives—or OCs to pharmacists). They had been prescribed by her family physician who had performed an assessment before prescribing them. There was no charge to her for the physician services.

She had taken the prescription order to a community pharmacy and had them dispensed for about $10 each month. The pharmacist charged only a small amount over the cost of the medication due to intense price competition on this group of products.

At the university, Sally goes to a student health clinic where physicians provide services to students. Sally does not need to see the physician, but she takes her prescription order from her family physician to the pharmacy in the student health clinic where she obtains the OCs at a very low price. The clinic is treated as a hospital or government agency by the pharmaceutical firm that markets the product and is able to purchase the OCs at extremely low prices. The practice of giving low discriminatory prices to the public sector encourages the development of public sector programs, with an obvious goal to take advantage of these low prices.

The pharmacist in the clinic would provide her with information about the medication should she indicate that she does not know about its use. The charge by the pharmacy for providing the information and medication is quite low since the pharmacy operation is subsidized by the students and university as part of a sexuality program. Some other medications are also available to Sally should she have them prescribed at the clinic.

QUESTIONS

1. If Sally had a physician assessment at the clinic would she have had to pay for the services?

2. How are physicians reimbursed for their services?

3. How is the clinic reimbursed for the services it provides?

4. How is the pharmacy reimbursed for the services it provides?

5. How can a pharmacy operate with low prices and low-cost products?

6. Why is the student health clinic allowed to compete with community pharmacies? Is it a licensed pharmacy?

7. Are there other publicly funded programs that provide OCs at low cost or no cost?

ANSWERS

In this case, the university health clinic comes between the direct relationship between the physician and the government health program. The clinic also operates within the scope of the overall principles of the Canada Health Act. In addition to payments being made by the patient, other organizations make funding contributions to health services and programs. Many programs take responsibility for organizing physician and other services, and for subsidizing the out-of-pocket cost of services to the patient.

The pharmacy may or may not be licensed, as the requirements vary from province to province. OCs are often dispensed from sexuality programs and family planning programs in public health clinics. There is usually a very low charge, or no charge, for the medication. Dispensing is often done by nurses, theoretically under the general supervision of a physician.

——————————————— EXAMPLE 3 ———————————————

James is 85 years old. He has several chronic conditions for which he is taking medication. He sees his physician monthly, at no charge, and the physician closely monitors the effects of his medication.

He obtains his prescribed medication and nonprescription drugs at a community pharmacy near his home. The cost of the medication is covered in part by a drug program. The total cost of the covered medication is about $155 per month, most of which is covered by the provincial government drug benefit program. James pays only a small portion of this cost. One prescription drug that he takes for depression is not covered by the provincial drug benefit program and he must pay $78 per month. This is difficult for him as he receives only a small, fixed pension. He has little money left over to cover medication, and even less for exceptional health expenditures such as dental care, which he requires from time to time and which are not covered by any provincial government benefit program.

The high cost of the depression medication and its side effects lead him to discontinue it from time to time, sometimes resulting in hospitalization. He incurs no out-of-pocket costs for hospital services or medication when he is admitted to hospital. The last time he left the hospital he had difficulty adjusting to his independent functioning due to the prolonged period in hospital. He now benefits from home-care services provided by the provincial health department but these are insufficient to keep him safe. He often falls and needs increasing levels of care. He will in all likelihood soon be assessed as needing chronic care and will be admitted to a nursing home. There is no charge to him for home-care services but if he is admitted to a nursing home, he will have to pay the nominal costs of accommodation and meals.

It is likely that he will be admitted to a nursing home where he will have continuous nursing care. In some provinces, the medication will be covered in total by the nursing home through grants from the provincial government and he will no longer have to pay for his depression medication. In other provinces, his medications may require a co-payment and his depression medication will not be covered unless included in the provincial drug formulary. All other health costs will be covered as is required under the Canada Health Act for insured services.

QUESTIONS

1. Why are the full costs of hospital care covered but not the cost of James' medication for depression?

2. What other health services, in addition to dental services, are not covered by provincial health authorities?

3. How are home-care services reimbursed by the provincial government program?

4. Why are costs for accommodation charged in nursing homes but not in hospitals?

5. Are pharmaceuticals part of the home-care program benefits?

6. Is there continuity of pharmacists and of pharmacy records in James' treatment? Who is in a position to coordinate his medication?

ANSWERS

In the current health-care system, each program is isolated from other programs, and decisions pertaining to budgets are often made without consideration of their effect on other programs. In many cases, expenditures related to pharmaceuticals are not covered by the provincial drug benefit program because of budgetary decisions, which may result in costly hospital admissions. The administrators of the drug benefit program may not be directly concerned with the impact of these decisions on other systems, as they are responsible only for their own budget. If they are "over budget" it reflects on their managerial performance, irrespective of what happens in other programs.

It was once thought that if all programs were managed by a single organization such as a provincial department of health, there would be better coordination and an easier shifting of resources. This has not yet happened, although problems have been acknowledged and some activities aiming at integrating programs are being developed, in large part through regional organizations. Where a program approach is taken with a budget for comprehensive care for a group of patients, it is easier to allocate funds in a more appropriate manner (this is the basis for managed care in the US).

Community pharmacists provide medication to patients in home-care programs as the program is intended to help them to remain independent and in their own home. The pharmacy reimbursement is based on the provincial drug benefit program. Some nursing homes also receive services from community pharmacies, although it is likely that a patient moving from home care to a nursing home would obtain the medication from a different pharmacy. Hospital care would be even more separate in terms of records and service providers.

Patients in nursing homes are charged for accommodation, as this is seen to be their permanent residence and they would pay rent for it. In contrast, hospital care is seen as a short stay during which patients must continue to maintain their own residence.

HEALTH CARE IN CANADA

The health-care system in Canada is one that Canadians are proud of and one to which they are willing to commit a sizeable portion of their tax revenue. Most provinces spend one-third of their annual expenditures on health care. At the federal level, transfer payments for health are a major expenditure. The total health-care expenditure in Canada, combining both governmental and private expenditures, is about ten percent of the gross domestic product. This is considerably more than the 7.13 percent in 1970 and 7.73 percent in 1981.

Pharmaceuticals including both prescribed and nonprescribed medication account for about 13.2 percent of the total expenditures for health.[1]

Currently, the key legislation in health care is the Canada Health Act (1984). It sets out penalties for provinces that allow patients to be charged for "insured services." These insured services are hospital care, diagnostic services, and physician services. In effect, any person who goes to see a physician will not be charged over and above the amount that the government plan pays for physician services. Additional charges are now prohibited in Canada through action taken in each province. These additional charges have been called "extra-billing" and "user fees."

The federal legislation is designed to ensure that all residents of Canada have access to needed medical care on a prepaid basis. For Canadians, this means that medically necessary hospital services, physician services, and certain surgical dental procedures are available to everyone on an equal basis. Although the term "insured" is used, the program is primarily funded from general revenue rather than insurance premiums.

Hospital services include inpatient care at the standard ward level, unless private or semi-private accommodation is medically necessary, and all necessary drugs, biologicals, supplies, and diagnostic tests, as well as a broad range of outpatient services.

Physician services include all medically required services provided by medical practitioners in hospitals, clinics, or physicians' offices where such services are rendered. All ten provinces and the territories are participating in this national program, which provides health-insurance coverage for every eligible resident.

The provincial governments have asked that the Canada Health Act be modified so that it covers only "medically necessary" services. Some services, such as elective cosmetic surgery, have already been removed as benefits by the provinces. By further limiting benefits, the provinces would save money and be able to shift some resources to higher-priority health programs. It is worth noting that the National Forum on Health (1997) uses the term "medically necessary" services in referring to maintenance of the current health-care system.

The Canada Health Act was enacted to deal with ambiguity in the interpretation of the insured services that arose from the Established Programs Financing Act, or EPF (1977). Up to 1977, the provinces were required to submit documentation on their health-care expenditures for "insured services" (hospital, diagnostic, and physician services) in order to receive federal transfer payments which totalled 50 percent of national insured-service expenditures, according to a formula.

The EPF was enacted to provide more flexibility to the provinces in restructuring their health-care systems. Under the cost-sharing arrangement, prior to the EPF, if a province decreased hospital care and shifted patients into community care, its federal funding would be reduced even though the shift was cost-effective and the care more appropriate. Under the EPF, the provinces receive a similar total amount of funding in cash transfer and tax points (a larger share of the income tax collected in the province) than they would have under the Hospital Insurance and Diagnostic Services and Medical Care Act, but they do not have to document expenditures.

Soon after the EPF came into effect in the early '80s, there was an increase in extra-billing by physicians resulting in a public and political upheaval.[a] This led to the Canada Health Act, which clarifies the require-

[a] For a personal and insightful description of the events leading to the Canada Health Act see Begin, M. *Medicare: Canada's Right to Health.* Montréal: Optimum Publishing International, 1987.

ment to adhere to five principles and imposes penalties if these are not adhered to. The principles are:

1. accessibility—reasonable access to insured services without impedi-
    ment by way of user fees and extra-billing;

2. comprehensiveness of insured services covered;

3. universality of population covered;

4. portability of benefits;

5. public administration on a non-profit basis.

The authoritative reference to the decisions leading to our current
system is a book by Malcolm Taylor[2], in which he states that the process of
developing a unique health-care system resulted in the creation of a new set
of values which, in part, define the values of Canadians. These values are:[2]

• that health services be available to all Canadians on equal terms and
  conditions;

• that the indignities of the means test no longer be imposed on the
  medically indigent;

• that the costs of health services for the indigent be assumed by the
  senior government and not by municipal governments;

• that the costs of health services no longer be borne by the sick but by
  all income earners, roughly in accordance with ability to pay;

• that the "Robin Hood" function of equalizing health-care costs to
  patients be accomplished through the tax system;

• that the programs be administered by public agencies, accountable to
  legislatures and electors.

In the political arena, the debate continues over public programs and
their adequacy or as to whether there is a need for "two-tier" programs. This
debate will continue as public program funding is constrained and the US
system of health care is used to compare services in the private sector.[3]

Provincial Role in Distribution and Use of Pharmaceuticals

Under the Canadian system of government, the health-care system is the
responsibility of the provincial government, which determines the nature of
the programs and the extent to which it wishes to establish publicly funded

programs. The federal role has expanded into health care through its ability to make contributions (spending powers). The Hospital Insurance and Diagnostic Services Act and National Medical Care Insurance Act were implemented (respectively in 1957 and 1967) in order to share up to 50 percent of the total cost of each program with the provinces. As long as provincial programs met the criteria of accessibility, universality, comprehensive coverage, portability, and non-profit administration, they were free to administer the programs as they wished.

In terms of control over the health professions, all provinces have very similar systems for designated self-governing professions under provincial legislation. They also have similar systems of hospital care, physician services, nursing-home care, and public-health care. Some significant differences exist in other areas of health services.

Because health is a provincial responsibility, each province has a structure in place to control the pharmaceutical system and link it to the governmental process. Two main functions are involved. The first is the regulatory function, by which control is exerted over pharmacy as a self-governing profession with the primary goal of protecting the public. This system sets out how pharmacists are licensed, their scope of practice, and the standards of practice.

The other aspect of provincial-government involvement in pharmaceuticals is related to programs. Until recently, pharmaceuticals represented a very small portion of government health-care programs. Initially, health-care programs that had a pharmaceutical component consolidated purchasing of pharmaceuticals for specific programs and hospitals, in which bidding process for larger quantities generated substantial savings. Also, by providing additional discounts to governments and hospitals, pharmaceutical firms encouraged the development of public programs of which pharmaceuticals were an important component.

Historically, welfare benefits were provided to welfare recipients through an uneven variety of municipal programs. A patchwork of social assistance programs existed through the '50s and '60s, some of which provided pharmaceuticals, although many did not. It was not unusual for patients to have to travel to the teaching hospitals located in cities in order to obtain their medications. The hospitals assessed the patient's financial situation and provided medication at lower prices or without cost.

In some provinces, programs were developed to provide medication for specific diseases that require life-saving drugs. For example, some provinces provided insulin and antidiabetic drugs. This program approach continued with the distribution of drugs for cancer, tuberculosis, and HIV, and of anti-rejection drugs for transplant patients. From 1955 to 1970, a number of provinces established province-wide social assistance programs.

In the same period there were no programs for seniors, although the problem of high drug costs for this group was known and publicized from the late '50s onward. In the '70s and into the '80s, the provinces developed major drug benefit programs for seniors, as well as for social assistance recipients and other designated groups, which greatly increased the size of the programs and changed their method of administration. This experience with drug benefit programs and province-wide uniform benefit standards was invaluable in the development of later programs.

The development of provincial drug benefit programs has led governments into a complex set of organizational, scientific, and political issues. Governments are now involved in cost of drugs, equitable treatment of firms that invest in research, cost of distribution through pharmacies, cost of administering programs, as well as attempts to influence the factors influencing utilization, and to meet the political goal of constantly improving benefits for more people. This means that a structure to deal with pharmaceutical manufacturers, pharmacists, physicians, drug wholesalers, claims processing, and pharmaceutical policy has had to be developed. Concurrently, the programs have needed to maintain links to the rest of the health-care system and the political process. As the cost of drug benefit programs has rapidly increased, the complexity of the issues and the need for coordination and consultation has resulted in bureaucratic structures and convoluted policy development. On those occasions where a major new program was rapidly implemented, such as the comprehensive, universal benefit program in Québec (1997), there was immense confusion and difficulty. The truncated planning and rapid implementation at the front end were later on followed by adjustments, discussion, and changes.

Pharmacy Organizations and Their Role

In most provinces, except Alberta and Newfoundland, a pharmacy professional organization exists, in addition to a regulatory organization, to serve the needs of the pharmacists, including negotiating with the provincial government about the terms and conditions of reimbursement for providing pharmaceutical services. This has become the major function of the organizations, although other functions are carried out, such as representing the interests of the pharmacists in proposed legislation. The organizations also conduct various programs to help the pharmacist, such as group insurance programs, educational programs, public relations, and innovative practice initiatives.

Professional organizations are voluntary and exist because pharmacists see them as valuable in advancing their own interests. As a result, these organizations address a wide range of issues. In contrast, regulatory organizations have narrower responsibilities conferred through legislation and are generally precluded from economic activities.

The negotiation with government is focused on reimbursement for services in the provincial drug benefit programs. It does not normally extend to discussions of the public sector pharmacy services provided by hospitals—other than when outpatient dispensing by hospitals is used to generate profits for hospitals in competition with community pharmacies— or to the regulatory aspects of pharmacy practice.

Professional associations, which have regular meetings where methods of reimbursement and other professional activities are discussed, are linked through the Canadian Pharmacists Association (CPhA). A national voluntary organization of pharmacists committed to providing leadership for the profession of pharmacy and whose vision is to establish the pharmacist as the health professional whose practice ensures optimal patient outcomes, the CPhA (as indicated in its mission statement) serves its members through advocacy, facilitation, provision of knowledge, participation in partnerships, research and innovation, education, and health promotion. Issues that are national in scope are the focus of the CPhA.

Other national pharmacy associations (e.g., the Canadian Association of Chain Drug Stores [CACDS], the Canadian Society of Hospital Pharmacists [CSHP], and the Canadian Association of Pharmacy Students and Interns [CAPSI]) serve members by providing leadership to the profession and more specifically representing their interests in various health-care matters to both national and provincial levels of governments and other stakeholders.

The CACDS, representing retail chain pharmacy whose members fill approximately 50% of all prescriptions in Canada, works to promote pharmacists as primary health-care providers, influencing individual health out-comes and reducing health-care costs through patient interventions and education, and bringing together retailers and suppliers creating efficiencies for mutual benefit and enhanced customer satisfaction. Other pharmacy organizations focus on specialty areas to improve patient care and consult-ant pharmacy services to long term-care facilities.

Community Pharmacy, Growth, and Change

Community pharmacy is the major sector in the profession, with 6,027 pharmacies and 17,047 pharmacists in 1997.[4] In 1996, the average sales of a community pharmacy were reported at $1.86 million, with 63 percent of the revenue coming from prescription sales.[5]

The distinguishing characteristic of community pharmacies is their uniform distribution across Canada so that the great majority of the popu-lation have a pharmacy easily accessible to them. For the most part, the pharmacies are open long hours and offer a wide range of health products. This is somehow taken for granted in Canada but is appreciated when one travels to less developed countries and finds that the pharmacies have diffi-culty obtaining medication and health products. In Canada, the products listed in the *Compendium of Pharmaceuticals and Specialities (CPS)* are avail-able immediately in a pharmacy or, if not in stock, the next day when the wholesale order arrives.

Institutional Pharmacy

Institutional pharmacy is defined as the area of pharmacy in which pharma-cists are employed in health-care institutions that have a primary responsi-bility for the treatment of patients. This field consists primarily of hospital pharmacists, although some pharmacists are employed in other institutions such as prisons, military clinics, and universities. The following discussion deals specifically with hospital pharmacists in acute care and long-term care institutions.

Institutional pharmacy had 4,078 pharmacists in 1,007 institutions in Canada in 1997.[5] Downsizing of hospitals from 1995 to 1997 has re-sulted in a slight reduction in the number of institutional pharmacists. The reduction in the number of beds, in some cases, has resulted in a higher level of activity and a wider range of services provided by the pharmacists.

The major changes and opportunities facing pharmacy managers in institutional practice are reported to be:[6]

- an increased use of technicians and automation to free up pharmacists to perform clinical functions;

- changes associated with the merger or centralization of services;

- adaptation to program management structures;

- implementation of pharmaceutical care;

- installation of new computer systems.

Shrinking resources have given managers the difficult task of trying to improve services with less resources.[6] In spite of this, the following improvements in patient care have occurred:

- increased inpatient monitoring activities;

- development of clinical pathways to assist practitioners in effective medication selection and dosing;

- improvements in drug distribution systems with resultant increases in patient safety;

- decentralization of clinical services;

- increased involvement in home-based care;

- improved pharmacist education and expanded in-service programs.

These changes and improvements are often required while resources are shrinking. Pharmacy managers today need to have strong managerial and business practice skills.

CHANGES IN HEALTH CARE IN CANADA

Rapid growth in health expenditures from 1970 to 1985 resulted in a number of studies into the health-care system and health expenditures by task forces and royal commissions. These studies were the basis of a number of incremental organizational changes up to the present time. The National Forum on Health was created in 1994 to advise the federal government on innovative ways to improve the health-care system and the health of the people. The report published in 1997, *Canada Health Action: Building on the Legacy: Final Report of the National Forum on Health*,[7] concluded that the Canadian health-care system as a whole was fundamentally sound and adequately funded but could be improved. The report recommended that first-dollar coverage (i.e., no user fees) for "medically necessary" services should be provided through general taxation. It also stressed the need to address the social and economic determinants that influence health.

The national forum stressed the need for the following key features:[7]

- public funding for medically necessary services;

- the "single payer" model;

- the five principles of the Canada Health Act;

- a strong federal/provincial/territorial partnership;

- expanding public funding of home care and pharmaceuticals;

- reforming the organization and delivery of primary care;

- a transition fund to support evidence-based innovations.

The changes advocated by the national forum are congruent with the issues faced by physicians over the past decade. Physicians have been under enormous pressure to reduce health-care expenditures. A limit (called a "cap") has been imposed on the total budget for physician services, restrictions have been placed on physician fees, hospital access is more limited, increasing pressures are put on physicians to conform to treatment guidelines, and physician prescribing is constrained by formularies and drug benefit lists. In the case of pharmaceuticals, physicians are expected to work more closely with pharmacists to design the best drug therapy for patients within the confines of the benefit programs. Overall, the influence and judgment of the physician in patient care and in health-system design had been significantly "eroded."

CURRENT ISSUES AND CHALLENGES IN PHARMACY

As society undergoes change, so does pharmacy. Because pharmaceuticals come from research and technology, these changes are more rapid than the economic and social changes that are occurring simultaneously. Newer products are enabling more patients to be treated for diseases for which there was previously no effective therapy. Some new products permit more intensive treatment and allow patients to be treated in their homes for serious conditions. More interactive support for these patients by pharmacists is required and necessitates significant changes in the health-care system, as well as to the operations of a community pharmacy.

One of the many challenges in pharmacy is to provide effective treatment for the elderly. Although the elderly represent about 12 percent of the population, it is commonly believed they utilize close to more than a third of all pharmaceuticals. Increasing utilization is one of the reasons behind the increase in pharmaceutical expenditures and poses a difficult problem in cost control as it is resistant to the mechanisms that have been used in the past (cheaper drugs, cheaper dispensing, larger quantities). Problems of drug costs, compliance with therapy, appropriate monitoring and integrated care are all being addressed by the health-care system, often without substantial pharmacy participation. The major challenge of pharmacy is to become fully integrated into the health-care system and part of the decision making process.

On the organizational side, the growth of corporate pharmacies has changed the nature of pharmacies from small, mainly local businesses to large, national, or international organizations. Often the pharmacists can focus on dispensing and patient care, while the administrative functions (i.e., accounting, security, human resources, legal, and advertising) are left to the organization's management. The advantages can include greater emphasis on clinical, educational, and promotional programs being provided by the corporate management.

A challenge to organized pharmacy is to mobilize individual pharmacists—whether corporate employees or independent owners and staff pharmacists—to be active members of professional organizations. In 1997, the Canadian Pharmaceutical Association was facing this challenge. They initiated a major organizational change, a change in name to the Canadian Pharmacists Association, and a vigorous recruiting program to attract members to this new, voluntary pharmacists' organization.

Reimbursement for services is a major issue for pharmacies. The provincial drug benefit programs have been reluctant to increase professional fees and in some cases these have been reduced. Professional organizations are moving to make claims for "cognitive services," i.e., professional services that go beyond traditional dispensing and counseling. Some success has been achieved in receiving payment for prescriptions that are not dispensed and in providing trial prescription programs. Innovative reimbursement systems are expected to proliferate over the next decade. Also, the provinces are expected to continue to reduce the dispensing fees in the provincial drug benefit programs. Similarly, the private drug benefit programs will enact restrictions on benefits and attempt to reduce the dispensing fees through exclusive arrangements with selected pharmacies.

Logistic systems are changing the way pharmaceuticals are distributed. The wholesale firms and chain-distribution systems are becoming much larger and more efficient. Rapidly developing technology is allowing just-in-time ordering, direct computer link-ups and immediate sales history, which makes the ordering and stocking much more efficient and cost-effective. Larger chains and purchasing groups are taking full advantage of these opportunities, while smaller pharmacies may be somehow at a disadvantage.

Niche markets are proliferating as the size and scope of organizations expand. Many individual patient needs are identified by pharmacists and products and services are being designed to meet those needs. In some cases, pharmacists are specializing in durable medical equipment, custom compounding, certain disease areas such as palliative and geriatric care, or contracting to provide pharmacy services to patients in institutions such as group homes or elder hostels.[7]

The movement towards a national pharmacare program will be an important issue for organized pharmacy. The proposal by the National Forum on Health for a comprehensive drug benefit program provides an opportunity for developing innovative approaches to care. Historically, the emphasis has been on the least expensive approach to distributing medication to the public. The political complexity of this problem makes it highly likely that the debate will continue for several years. In the interim, there is a movement towards a more uniform drug benefit list for all provinces and a standard reimbursement program. Emphasis will be on the unique needs of special groups in the population that are currently not well served by the uniform list of services and benefits, i.e., approximately 12 percent of Canadians. Pharmacists in each province will need to work together to have a voice in shaping the eventual outcome of the national system.

PHARMACEUTICAL CARE

The concept of "pharmaceutical care" has become an important concept in pharmacy practice. One description is: "pharmaceutical care is that component of pharmacy practice that can be performed by no one other than a competent pharmacist committed to establishing a reciprocal relationship of truthfulness, confidentiality, and loyalty with patients whose pharmacotherapeutic needs are met through the application of knowledge and humanistic principles."[8]

In Canada, the professional and regulatory pharmacy organizations have adopted the concept of pharmaceutical care as the basis of patient care in pharmacies. This concept has a strong conceptual base and is well suited for improving patient care. However, problems with its implementation are slowing its acceptance and use in practice.

Some of the problems with implementing pharmaceutical care are:

- the time-consuming nature of the process;

- limited understanding and demand from the public;

- lack of a suitable reimbursement system;

- difficulty in obtaining complete information on all medications;

- inappropriate operating systems in the community pharmacy.

This latter point—operating systems—is one that is most directly concerned with management in terms of organization, staff, and systems.

To implement pharmaceutical care, the pharmacy must establish an education program for both professional and non-professional staff. The duties will be different from in the past and patients' expectations will be different also. Pharmacists will be expected to work at a high level of knowledge and proficiency with a link into an appropriate drug information system. Most pharmacists will be expected to develop specialist knowledge and skills for some groups of patients with specific needs. The information system for patient care will be extensive and linked to therapeutic outcomes.

With pharmaceutical care, the market served will be for services rather than products, and marketing will shift to include physicians, drug benefit programs, third-party payers, and pharmaceutical firms. A working relationship with these groups will evolve into a partnership to make patient care more effective and efficient.

Only when the operating systems in pharmacies will be designed to support pharmaceutical care and, perhaps, when the individual pharmacists will be reimbursed for providing this care will we see it become the norm rather than the exception. Over the next few years a dynamic process will unfold to implement pharmaceutical care that will eventually lead to better patient care.

The acceptance at the provincial government level of the underlying concepts of pharmaceutical care will be important to the future of pharmacy. For government policies to be influenced, improvement in the health care provided and strong public support by the patients must be demonstrated.

HEALTH OUTCOMES

Health programs are now emphasizing the use of outcome measures. It is intended that program funding and program design will eventually be based on outcome measures. Pharmacies may have to demonstrate improved patient outcomes in order to qualify for programs and justify reimbursement. As a beginning, pharmacies will have to acquire software systems that maintain and utilize treatment information as part of the professional services provided. Linkage of this information with physicians and hospitals will be the next step and will pose a major challenge for the profession. Integration of services through program management (mainly in institutions) and disease management (mainly outside institutions) holds both opportunities and threats to pharmacists. In both cases, initiative and leadership are needed.

IDENTIFYING YOUR ENVIRONMENT

To be a successful manager you must understand the business and professional environment in which you practice. The political and economic climates, pertinent demographics, and Canadians' health-care perceptions and changing lifestyles all need to be taken into account. In recent years, federal and provincial politicians have implemented many policies and concepts such as financial restraint, privatization, free trade, and devolution of government. How significant are these public policies to a pharmacist's environment?

Government-Spending Restraint

From 1940 to 1980, the public sector in Canada grew steadily, initially as a result of the war effort and the need to develop social programs. By the late '70s, Canada came under severe criticism from other Western industrialized countries for having too large a public-sector program and a correspondingly excessive public debt.

Faced with burgeoning deficits, the various levels of government were obliged to introduce considerable fiscal restraints in the early '80s. Provincial and federal governments alike found it politic to respond to taxpayer demands for real decreases in government deficits, even if it meant a marked reduction in spending and service levels. These changes in fiscal policy at provincial and federal levels have resulted in significant changes in the delivery of health-care services and the expectations of the public about health-care services.

Privatization

Economic pressures grew as costs rose and politicians had to look at administrative remedies that would enable them to maintain needed health care while decreasing expenditures. One such administrative remedy was a policy of privatization, defined as the act of reducing the role of government or increasing the role of the private sector in an activity or in the ownership of assets. Privatization has come to symbolize a new way of looking at society's needs and represents a rethinking of the role of government in fulfilling them. It means relying more on private business and less on government to satisfy citizens' demands. Proponents of privatization envisage the government providing the proper political environment, while small businesses carry out transactions on the public's behalf. In essence, privatization is more a political than an economic act.[9]

Privatization was first proposed as a deliberate public policy to improve government performance in 1969.[10] Since then, there has been a worldwide political push in this direction as it is seen to be a more efficient use of governmental funds.

When it comes to the ability to get things done, the North American public considers the private sector superior to political institutions.[11] People believe that the long-term well-being of society will be maximized if economic decisions are left mostly to the marketplace. The argument is that competition within the private sector produces pressure for greater efficiency. Privatization, then, is a strategic approach to improving the productivity of government agencies, thereby giving people more for their tax dollars.

However, when individuals are deprived of benefits that they have come to see as a right, the party in power generally pays a high political price. This makes it very difficult to roll back established programs, particularly those with a high profile, such as health-care programs.

With privatization, the strategy of imposing user fees or co-payments wherever practicable is now more acceptable. The fundamental objectives of a user charge are to cut costs by having the consumer share in the cost or to decrease utilization by making the consumer aware that there is a cost to service. The fees may also stimulate consumers to shop around for the best deal. For instance, in Ontario in 1996, the user fee for seniors with income below a certain level was set at $2 per prescription, and at $6.11 for seniors with higher incomes, leading some pharmacies to reduce the fee, or not charge it, in response to consumer demands.

In the end, the challenge in privatization will be to achieve a better division of responsibilities and functions between government and the private sector in order to take advantage of the strengths and overcome the limitations of each.

Governments as Payers

Without question, the most significant change to occur in the economics of pharmacy practice in the last 20 years has been the increasing involvement of third-party agencies—mainly provincial governments—as payers. In 1996, 47 percent of all prescriptions dispensed were paid for by public (government) drug programs.[12]

Each provincial government's prescription-drug plan possesses unique features that directly influence pharmacies' professional, business, and economic climate. The National Pharmacy Coalition on Managed Care was formed in 1994 under the auspices of the CPhA to address the challenges posed by the growth of managed care and to monitor the provincial government programs. The coalition has the mission "to design, develop and promote the implementation of drug benefit plan management strategies by pharmacists to ensure that people in Canada have access to appropriate, affordable drug therapy to achieve optimal patient outcomes."[13]

Provincial third-party drug programs vary widely across the country. The terms and conditions of the contracts in each province evolved through the bargaining process between pharmacy organizations and governments, as well as through the evolution of government policies. As a result, we see wide variations in the number of days supply is authorized to be dispensed, the amount of the deductible or co-payment, the use of a markup on the cost of drugs before applying the professional fees, and the authorization in some provinces of a "purchasing advantage" as an additional markup.

Insurance Companies as Payers

Private insurance firms are now more aware and active in pharmaceutical benefits as a result of the substantial increase in pharmaceutical claims.

Private firms now account for about 15 percent of prescription volume.[5] A 1997 survey of pharmacies by *Pharmacy Post* and Eli Lilly Canada estimated that 23 percent of the prescriptions were covered by private third-party programs.[5]

Economic Competition

Pharmacies face competition from other pharmacies, some of which are in grocery stores, department stores, discount stores, and publicly owned institutions. They also have competition from a wider range of retailers for front store business. Results of a *Pharmacy Post* survey of community pharmacies in 1997 regarding sources of competition for their goods and services[5] are shown in Table 1.1.

Table 1.1   Sources of Competition to Community Pharmacies

	Percent Reporting	
Major Competitors to Community Pharmacy	*Dispensary*	*Front Store*
Supermarket pharmacies	70.0	88.0
Chain store pharmacies	70.0	78.0
Department store pharmacies	50.0	64.0
Other community pharmacies	52.0	38.0
Mail order pharmacies	18.0	—
PPO (Preferred Provider Organization) pharmacies	10.0	2.0

In the prairie provinces and British Columbia, it is reported that respectively 90 percent of the competition for dispensary revenues, and 94.8 percent of the competition for the front store revenues, originate from supermarket pharmacies.

The large corporate chains (Safeway, Wal-Mart, Zellers, Westons) have established pharmacies, mainly within the past decade, and are competing vigorously on the basis of price and convenience (one-stop shopping). This model is now prevalent in the US and it appears that the model will dominate pharmacy in Canada in the next decade.

PUBLIC PERCEPTION OF HEALTH-CARE PROFESSIONALS

The public's perception of pharmacy's services is of vital interest to the profession. A survey in 1997 by Roger Reports Canada gives an insight into consumer views.[14] In an assessment of professional attributes the results were uneven. Table 1.2 illustrates how the public perceives pharmacists and physicians on selected attributes.

Table 1.2   Public Perceptions of Pharmacists and Physicians

Professional Attribute	Pharmacists (%)	Physicians (%)
Knowledgeable	81	78
Dependable	76	71
Helpful	75	62
Professional	70	71
Trustworthy	69	71
Approachable	62	57
Easy to understand	61	56
Readily available	60	42
Accessible	55	45
Caring	50	58
Ethical	50	54
Provides value	42	35

These results show the strengths of the community pharmacist who is seen as being knowledgeable, dependable, helpful, professional, and trustworthy by most consumers. They are perceived as somewhat less accessible, approachable, available, and easy to understand. This sets out challenges for the profession in making services available.

More disconcerting is the low proportion of the public who see the pharmacist as caring, ethical, and providing value. In comparison with physicians, the pharmacists are not perceived as well, except in providing value, where physicians are not seen as providing a valuable service by the two-thirds of the public! An important task for pharmacy managers is to change the nature of the services provided so that pharmacists are seen as caring and ethical.

Consumer perceptions of the quality of service provided by pharmacies is more reassuring. Two-thirds (66 percent) of the respondents indicated that they were "very satisfied" with the quality of service received, while 27 percent indicated that they were "fairly well satisfied."

EMERGING HEALTH-CARE TRENDS

Physician-Oriented Pharmacy Practice

Physician-oriented pharmacy practice is made possible when pharmacists are encouraged, through the specific management polices of the pharmacy, to develop their professional skills for the purpose of counseling physicians in the optimal use of drugs. The introduction of a drug-information hotline for physicians is one example of such management policy. Environments suitable for the development of physician-oriented practice include pharmacies in clinics or medical buildings, pharmacies in small communities, and pharmacy departments in hospitals—the common feature is an environment that fosters one-to-one personal contact between the physician and the pharmacist.

Home Health Care

The aging of the population, combined with the trend to move patients into community care rather than institutional care, has resulted in a rapid, sustained growth of home care and the demand for home-care supplies. One example of a home-care program is hospice care, which is designed to provide a caring environment for the physical and emotional needs of the terminally ill. Palliative care offered by hospitals is intertwined with care of the patient in the home by members of the immediate family.

Providing home health-care supplies is a very different form of enterprise and requires unique marketing strategies, product knowledge, and selling skills. The bulk of the business is generated from referrals from key health-care personnel, such as enterostomal therapists, hospital emergency departments, physiotherapists, or community-care facilities. A home health-care pharmacy typically draws from a trading area three times larger than the prescription drug trading area.[15]

Home health-care products are in two main groups: durable medical equipment (DME) and durable medical supplies (DMS). Products such as lumbosacral braces, walkers, anti-embolism stockings, cervical traction kits, or ostomy equipment cannot be purchased off the shelf, person-to-person selling, counseling, or fitting is required.

In addition to providing home health-care supplies, some community pharmacists are now providing to patients services such as home infusion therapy. This is largely for pain management but it also includes antibiotics as well as nutritional products for intravenous or enteral therapy. Pharmacists may also conduct home visits to ensure compliance, or provide education on the administration of medication or the proper way to use glucometers. These are growing areas of service that are being stimulated by the focus on community rather than institutional care.

Supplementary (Alternate) Health Care

Patients are interested in, and searching for, alternative (better described as supplementary) forms of health care. Among others, trends toward "natural" foods, psychological counseling, and acupuncture, are growing and challenging the traditional health-care system. As these alternative forms of care are having a significant impact on the environment in which pharmacists operate, some pharmacies are now incorporating them into their practices.

The Aging of Our Population

The increasing proportion of the elderly in our society is a phenomenon that will have a profound impact on the health-care environment. Not only is the proportion of elderly increasing but, more importantly, the number of elderly is growing rapidly.

While more than half of our non-institutionalized population suffers from health problems, the proportion of persons in poor health increases with age. In addition, women have more health problems than men in adulthood and old age.[16]

Epidemiological Trends

Some interesting epidemiological trends are emerging. For instance, the incidence of Crohn's disease and, therefore, the number of ostomates, has been on the rise for the last 20 years.[16] Also, more high-risk patients such as premature infants and cancer patients are surviving than ever before, placing new demands on our health-care system. This is resulting in a growth in the chronic-care sector in relation to acute-care prescriptions in community pharmacies—a trend bound to continue. Pharmacies will have to realign their communications and operations so that they work more closely with institutions and ensure that their information systems are able to monitor patients on a long-term basis and to report on their progress.

Changes in Lifestyle

The importance of self-care is being recognized as people learn to eat better, exercise more, and smoke less. To reinforce positive attitudes, the provincial governments have embarked on new legislative approaches and public-awareness campaigns. Despite pressure from tobacco lobbyists, the federal government made significant changes to the Tobacco Products Control Act to limit advertising, especially advertising linked to sports. The restrictions on cigarette advertising contained in the legislation signal a growing concern over smoking and society's attitudes toward smoking.

For many years, pharmacists have been encouraging healthful behavior with innovative programs such as the CPhA's "Stand Up and Be Counted" program, conducted in conjunction with the federal government. Similarly, many pharmacies supply information on diet and exercise on the request of physicians and nurses.

SUMMARY

A successful manager understands the health system and pharmacy's place in it, as well as monitors the environment to determine the scope of practice and the opportunities generated by environmental changes. Given the current political, economic, demographic, and lifestyle trends, it is clear that if pharmacies are going to flourish in the marketplace, they will have to offer their professional services wisely and aggressively to governments and consumers.

References

1. "Health Expenditures in Canada 1994." As cited in *PMAC News* (February 1997), p. 4.

2. Taylor, M. *Health Insurance and Canadian Policy*. Montréal: McGill-Queens University Press, 1987.

3. Stingl, M., and Wilson, D. *Efficiency vs. Equality: Health Reform in Canada*. Halifax: Ferwood Publishing, 1996.

4. "Canadian Pharmacy Licensing Authorities Information Survey." Members, January 1997.

5. Anon. "1997 Pharmacy Business Trends Report." PharmaScience, *Pharmacy Post*. Toronto: Eli Lilly Canada, 1998.

6. McKerrow, R. ed. *Hospital Pharmacy in Canada, 1995/96 Annual Report*. Toronto: Eli Lilly Canada, 1997.

7. National Forum on Health. *Canada Health Action: Building on the Legacy. Final Report of the National Forum on Health*. Ottawa: Minister of Public Works and Government Services, 1997.

8. Strand, M., Cipolle, R.J., Morley, P.C., and Perrier, D.G. "Levels of Pharmaceutical Care: A Needs-Based Approach." *American Journal of Hospital Pharmacy* 48 (1991):548.

9. Savas, E.S. *Privatization: The Key to Better Government*. Chatham: Chatham House Publishers, 1987.

10. Drucker, P.F. *The Age of Discontinuity*. New York: Harper and Row, 1969.

11. Lipset, S.M., and Schneider, W. *The Confidence Gap*. New York: Free Press, 1983.

12. Anon. *IMS Academic Reference Manual for 1997*. Montréal: IMS Canada, 1997.

13. Anon. *Managed Care, A Wake-Up Call for Canadian Pharmacists?* Ottawa: National Coalition on Managed Care.

14. Roger Reports Canada. *Altimed Pharmacy Services Study*. Altimed and The Canadian Foundation for Pharmacy, 1997.

15. Schoepp, G. "Home Sweet Home: First-Hand Tips on How to Make it in Home Health Care." *Drug Merchandising* 66, 22 August 1985.

16. Peron, Y., and Strohmenger, C. *Demographic and Health Care Indicators: Presentation and Interpretation*. Ottawa: Statistics Canada, Cat. #82E–543E, 1985.

2

MANAGEMENT AND THE PROCESS OF CHANGE

INTRODUCTION

Increasingly, modern society is becoming more complex, more regulated, and more integrated. To function in this environment, a professional must understand how organizations function, and be able to influence the organizations and have them adjust to their environment.

As part of their responsibilities, pharmacists are called on to bring together people with skills and knowledge to accomplish some task. Few pharmacists can avoid this organizational aspect of management. Pharmacists who are proficient and have good patient communication skills will be asked to take part in committee work or chair a committee. More commonly, pharmacists accept supervisory and managerial responsibilities at an early stage in their career. The non-professional staff will look to the pharmacist working an evening shift as the only pharmacist for decisions and information. Over time, pharmacists gain experience and are able to develop managerial skills.

ROLE OF MANAGEMENT IN ORGANIZATIONS

The role of a manager is to get things done through others, using the resources provided, by setting objectives in a planning process, allocating resources to accomplish the objectives, and making decisions to achieve the objectives. They then evaluate the results and begin another cycle. The key to effective management is making good use of allocated resources and accepting responsibility for the outcomes. Good managers are able to accomplish amazing feats based on the performance of highly motivated and trained staff and the innovative use of financial and organizational resources. In short, managers work through people, allocate scarce resources, and achieve goals.

When a pharmacist accepts a position as manager of a community pharmacy, there is an implicit set of expectations. Firstly, legal obligations imposed by the provincial licensing authority must be met. Secondly, there are the responsibilities for personnel—some legal, some cultural, and some concerning usual commercial practices. Finally, there are the commercial responsibilities for financial and physical assets. While the physical assets are the most visible, and the financial assets the most clear-cut, the challenge is on the "people" side of the operation. Organizing staff into an efficient operating team that produces effective results is the essence of management. Equally important is to understand the environment, so that the efforts made are able to achieve the objectives that have been set.

As a pharmacist there are managerial responsibilities in a number of areas. As an educated person with technical skills, the pharmacist is expected to assume a leadership role in several organizations. The management skills learned in community pharmacy are generally applicable to positions in related areas, and could be employed in the pharmaceutical industry and hospitals, as well as in pharmacy professional organizations, wholesale, educational institutions, purchasing groups, and communications.

Each field of endeavour has its individual characteristics and unique requirement for skills. A general requirement in management is that the manager be responsible for making the most effective use of the people and facilities in these environments. Common managerial approaches underlie the activities performed. For example, there is a budget for staff. Irrespective of the kind of staff, the budgeting process is similar; a specific amount of money is allocated that is not to be exceeded. As well, if someone needs to be hired, the recruiting process will be similar.

In an organization a manager has many roles. The manager is the figurehead for the organization and speaks on its behalf. The manager is the leader to the employees in a pharmacy. The manager has a liaison function to other organizations such as suppliers. Being responsible for the organization, the manager is required to make decisions that deal with day-to-day problems, as well as major decisions on such issues as renovations, relocation, adding services, or reducing staff.

In performing these roles, the manager does not have complete freedom of action. In reality, the manager is responsible to the owner. Also, the manager is responsible to the customers, government, pharmacy licensing authority, suppliers, employees, and society. These constraints limit the scope of decision making and provide a challenge to managers.

Management Functions

Classical management theory is based on the managerial functions of planning, organizing, directing (leading), and controlling.[1] Management textbooks follow this general outline and most managers who have taken managerial courses are familiar with these functions. While management textbooks are useful to understand the management functions in a general way, they are not a useful guide for day-to-day management problems.

Planning is the determination of the work that must be done. It includes the defining of roles and missions, setting objectives, budgeting, scheduling, policy-making, and the establishment of procedures.

Organizing is the classifying and dividing of work into manageable units. It includes the grouping of work in the most effective manner and determining how the units will work together. It also includes determining the number and kind of staff, and their recruiting.

Directing (leading) is the use of human resources to achieve the objectives set. This involves assigning responsibilities, motivating staff, co-ordinating activities, and establishing a system of communications.

Controlling is the methods used to determine if the objectives are accomplished. This may involve setting standards, measuring performance, and taking corrective action.

In addition to the classical theory of management, a number of methods of management have emerged over the past few decades. A large body of literature and a number of approaches now exist for specific areas such as industrial relations, finance, international marketing, and risk management.

Books on management are popular and many of them advocate a particular approach, often described as "revolutionary." Some of these concepts have become popular among managers, some have even survived to become part of the conventional wisdom in management. The growth of popular literature in management has resulted in a succession of fads and a growing weariness of managers with the attempts to utilize them in practice. Each of the approaches has some value but individual managers will have to find the method that works best for them in the context in which they operate.

The popularity of management books and articles is an outcome of the desire of managers who want their organization to change; in size, structure, and effectiveness, as well as culturally. One approach that illustrates current thinking is the work of Peter Senge, *The Fifth Discipline: The Art and Practice of the Learning Organization.*[2] Senge proposes an organization where people expand their capacity to create the results they desire, where new and expansive patterns of thinking are nurtured, and where people are continually learning how to learn together. Underlying this approach is the notion that the firm that learns more rapidly has a competitive advantage over its rivals.

In the newer concepts of management, corporations and other organizations are increasingly viewed, not as hierarchical structures reflecting the organization chart, but as adaptable organisms that exist in, and interact with, the larger organization. In this system, organizational purpose is set by the larger organization as a policy function, whereas the component organization fulfills an operational role while receiving the support of the larger organization. This system calls for autonomy and empowerment of employees so that they can react to change. Management, which is sometimes defined as the direction of resources to accomplish a predetermined task, has now more to do with empowering individuals to respond creatively to a changing situation by aligning staff activities around a shared vision and purpose.[3]

Mobilizing staff and ensuring that they are trained and motivated to assume more responsibility as empowered workers is the challenge for managers in the next decade or two.

Management in Pharmacy

Management in pharmacy differs from other fields in that the outcome of the activity is the health of the patients dealing at that pharmacy. Because this process involves distribution of "controlled medication," it is highly regulated by a provincial licensing authority. There is also a code of ethics that guides the decisions of pharmacists in making decisions. Some decisions that may be commercially desirable may not be professionally acceptable. (This is illustrated to some extent in the discussion over the sale of tobacco products.)

Another aspect of pharmacy management is that the products sold are complex, highly technical substances that depend on proper use to achieve their purpose. This requires a high level of patient communication and service—a professional service. There is also a high level of technical communication with physicians, suppliers, and educational institutions. Requirements based on competency are set as a minimum standard by the licensing body and are expected to be upgraded over time through the process of lifelong learning. Pharmacists on staff are assisted by trained technicians, support staff, and specialists. The manager has the responsibility of ensuring that the group works together efficiently as a team.

The actual distribution aspects are relatively simple as a sophisticated system of suppliers do a remarkable job of supplying the medications and front-store merchandise. In a community pharmacy, the sale of products is relatively simple. The professional challenge consists in establishing a system that improves the health of the patients in a way that can be documented. The front-store challenge is to provide products wanted by the customers, in competition with many other competitors, in a way that encourages them to return and be loyal to your pharmacy.

Community pharmacy staff have traditionally been clerical retail staff with little post-secondary education, hired at a low wage, and predominantly part-time, this situation resulting in a high turnover rate which creates a weak base on which to build an organization that performs well over time. Thus, it is a significant managerial challenge.

In larger pharmacies the front store is separate from the dispensary. As a result, pharmacy managers are often responsible only for the dispensary and are less involved in front-store issues. Front-store managers take responsibility for this area in these stores. In corporate organizations, pharmacists increasingly work only in the dispensary and see their advancement in the context of the dispensary.

Pharmacy managers have a difficult task in providing high-level personal service in a competitive market that focuses on high volume and low prices. They, also, are increasingly regulated and burdened with requirements for reports, both professional and business. In this context they make progress by setting objectives such as: establishing a new department for infant products, decreasing the number and percentage of rejected third-party billings, cross-training staff to minimize disruptions when staff are absent or leave, or increasing sales by a certain amount over the next year.

The scope for changes and decision making at the operational level provides a challenging training ground for pharmacists, not only in setting and achieving objectives, but also in training staff in a way that enhances their effectiveness (empowerment).

MANAGING IN AN ENVIRONMENT OF CHANGE

In today's rapidly changing world, the pharmacist manager faces changes in medical technology, the health-care system, third-party payer policies, and increasingly knowledgeable patients. To anticipate and adapt to change, the manager will have to learn to manage the financial and human resources required to meet these challenges.

Changes will occur irrespective of the action of managers. The challenge is to manage the changes through planning. Pharmacists need to understand the process of change before they are able to manage it. Successful change can be predicted by examining whether certain preconditions exist that reduce the possibility of resistance to change. The pharmacist manager's role in planning for and implementing change will influence patient care and the financial health of the pharmacy.

There are many kinds of change. At the individual level, the manager could try to influence the behaviour of an employee. At the pharmacy level, there could be a change in group behaviour. There are also organizational changes that influence how the pharmacy is structured, authority delegated, communication established, and technology incorporated.[4]

In looking to the future, those pharmacies which embrace change will have learned how to continually adapt in an ever-changing environment. These organizations will achieve success in the long run.

The Process of Change

Change is not an event: it is a process.[2] The need for change is identified by individuals who see a discrepancy between where their organization is now and where it should be. This discrepancy is called "creative tension" or "cognitive dissonance."[5] Whenever there is tension or dissonance, individuals strive to reduce the discrepancy, or performance gap. Change is the process of resolving the creative tension and moving to the more desirable state.

The need for change is often the result of outside forces and is presented to the manager as a problem. To resolve the problem, a variety of options are available to the manager. The selection of the most appropriate course of action will represent the vision to be communicated to the staff and will be the basis for staff and organizational change.

If we examine pharmacy history, we see that some major events often resulted from years of incremental changes that culminated in a need to review the function of the profession in a major way. The result was a new model of practice that was called pharmaceutical care, defined in Chapter 1 (p. 30). Hepler and Strand articulated their concept of pharmacists taking responsibility for patient outcomes in a paper published in 1990.[6] As previously noted, this concept has been accepted by Canadian pharmacy organizations as the basis of practice. Yet, very few pharmacists practice pharmaceutical care as defined by Hepler and Strand. Some pharmacists have embraced patient-centered care, while others have yet to do so. Why has the profession not completely changed since the publication and acceptance of this groundbreaking concept? Let's examine the process of adopting technological change.

Rogers described technological change as a "diffusion of innovation."[7] An innovation is a new idea or concept that can lead to a change in the way things are done. When groups in society are presented with an innovation, change occurs within them in a predictable pattern. Initially, change is adopted by the "innovators," individuals who identify a problem or situation and suggest an innovative solution. An innovation could be an invention of some kind. Just as likely, however, the innovation may be a new way of doing something or managing an organization. Innovators communicate their ideas within their sphere of influence. This could be the workplace, home, or community. Then, a small group of "early adopters" buy into the concept and follow the lead set by the innovators. Thereafter a group of individuals named the "early majority" adopt the innovation, followed by the "late majority." Finally, a group of traditionalists called the "laggards" adopt the innovation. At this time the change has occurred completely.

Why does change occur in this way? Why would the laggards wait so long to adopt the change? The innovators propose new ways of approaching a problem, whereas the laggards hold on until there is proof that the innovation is better than the status quo. By diffusing sequentially among the various groups of adopters, the innovation, or change, is tested and fine-tuned so that, by the time the majority and laggards join in, the change that has occurred is accepted and enduring.

Resistance to Change

It is commonly thought that people resist change. This is not necessarily the case. Everyone embraces the changes that they initiate themselves. People move to new cities, change their hairstyles, buy new cars, and listen to new music. When individuals identify a difference between where they are now and where they want to be, they initiate change. In other words, they resolve the creative tensions in their lives. They compare the benefits from the change and the costs of the change. So, why do people in the workplace resist change?

Some people cling to the old, comfortable way of doing things. Change almost always involves giving up something and the personal sacrifice may be substantial. Others resist change because they want to retain personal control over their activities. Still others resist to punish the organization for making changes. Some resist change because they believe that it is not in the best interest of the organization.[8]

In most cases, there are compelling reasons for the changes to be made. The staff, however, may see only that the changes have been "thrust upon them." Managers who have decided that a change must occur often have planned for it in isolation from the people who will actually implement the change. Changes require effort, time, commitment, false starts, revised plans, and evaluation to deal with the unexpected outcomes and inevitable errors that occur in establishing new systems. The need for change and the input of staff must be explained and justified to the individuals so that they are willing to make the effort to implement changes. For a leader's vision to lead to successful change, the environment in which the change will occur must be taken into account. This includes the people, resources, and physical location.

Change will be resisted if certain preconditions are not present.[9] Firstly, there must be general agreement that a change must occur. In other words, the leader's vision must identify a problem that most people feel needs to be solved. If the vision is not common to the people within an organization, resistance to the change will result. Second, the leader, or his or her designate, must become the champion for change. The champion, or change agent, must be empowered to manage and be responsible for the change from inception to implementation. The lack of an identifiable champion will reduce the likelihood of successful change. Thirdly, change will not be resisted if trust exists within the organization. Trust between management and employees increases the chances of successful change and decreases the possibility of resistance. Fourthly, sufficient financial and human resources must be available to accommodate the change, as otherwise the workers may feel burdened and resist the proposed change. Finally, resistance to change decreases in organizations with a history of successful change. Therefore, it is wise for organizations with no track record to begin with small successes. Modest changes will set the groundwork for more complicated change activities.

Therefore, pharmacy managers can avoid resistance by carefully crafting a strategy for change addressing the conditions that meet the needs of the people affected and the organization in general.

Pharmacy Managers as Change Agents

Successful leaders are innovators, or change agents. Think of people whom you know can effect change in others. What are the qualities they possess to get things done? What do people like Nelson Mandela, Mother Theresa, and Wayne Gretzky have in common? Nelson Mandela once exerted his leadership from the confines of a prison. Mother Theresa, a nun in the Catholic church, was capable of arranging cease-fires in the middle of fierce battles. Wayne Gretzky led his teammates to championships and attracted huge crowds; however, he was neither the owner nor the coach of the team.

Change agents may be managers operating in a normal manner who respond to the need for change, or consultants or experts brought in to deal with the problems. These change agents determine the intervention strategies and prepare a plan. The values and background of the change agents determine the kind of plan that will be prepared. In all cases, however, they will formulate a clear vision of the needed changes and communicate this vision to the staff. Based on this vision, people and resources are mobilized to achieve the identified goals.

How do leaders get others to follow? Employees will more readily adopt change when they clearly understand the vision and receive appropriate and frequent reinforcement that they are on the way to reaching the final goal. In planning for changes, the intervention strategy describes what is to be changed. Then the plan will indicate the specific action to be taken by staff, changes in organizational structure, application of technology, and the organizational processes.

What does this mean to a pharmacist manager? Pharmacist managers within a pharmacy organization have the capability to react to problems by formulating and communicating a vision of their plan. They then have to motivate the staff to implement the plan.

Implementing Change

Implementation of change requires a decision on what is to be done and how it is done. The process of change in a sector will require that the status quo be visibly altered or destroyed, the changes in process and structure being then implemented and, finally, built into the institution so that they will "continue in the new mode." This process of organizational change is sometimes described as "unfreezing," making changes, and "refreezing."[11]

In unfreezing the organization, both individual and group resistance need to be overcome by positive incentives and/or by using restraining forces. Once the unfreezing has been accomplished the changes can be introduced. This is a very complex and demanding phase and requires skill, perseverance, and tact.

The tactics suggested for use by managers in dealing with resistance to change are:[10]

- education and communication;
- participation;
- facilitation and support;
- negotiation;
- manipulation and co-option;
- coercion.

Once the change has been implemented, it needs to be refrozen so that it can continue as the new operational system. The change may be threatened by employees wanting to revert back to the previous system. Until the group culture accepts the new system, reinforcement, rewards, and restraining forces are needed. The many links to other sectors and stakeholders affected by the change also need to be taken into account in the consolidation phase.

To visualize the change process, imagine changing a pharmacy from a traditional dispensing system to a pharmaceutical-care system. The staff would need training, the information system would have to be changed, the communication with physicians and patients would have to change, the relationship with payers would be different, advertising would be aimed at a different audience, and suppliers would be different. The decision to change is easy. The process of making the change is very complex. A planning process lasting a year or more would be necessary to deal with the preconditions for change. Then the incremental changes would be implemented leading to a complete transition. The wonder is not that pharmacists have not changed to pharmaceutical care but, rather, that they have not begun planning for the change.

Evaluating Change

Perhaps the most important aspect of implementing change is evaluating whether the implementation is successful. This is also the case with patient therapy. A pharmacist must carefully identify drug-related problems, evaluate alternative therapies, and determine the most appropriate therapy in consultation with the individual. How does the pharmacist know whether the treatment was successful? A crucial step in the pharmaceutical care process is monitoring and follow-up. The evaluation plan must identify the key therapeutic outcome measures so that the pharmacist can determine the degree of success of the therapeutic intervention. What is the point of sending a patient home on antihypertensives if the pharmacist never finds out if the patient's blood pressure is actually being reduced?

Once the pharmacist manager has ensured that all preconditions for change exist and that there are key outcomes that can be monitored at each stage, the plan can be implemented incrementally, making changes along the way. The outcomes should be objective and based on data that can be collected as the change is implemented. If feedback shows no evidence that the desired change is occurring, the manager will need to reevaluate the implementation plan, the change itself, or both. Often small alterations to the plan will correct the course of change. In some cases, however, the plan or the change itself needs to be completely revised. Regular monitoring of objective outcomes gives the manager the necessary information to make adjustments along the way, as opposed to waiting until it is too late to avoid disaster. If several failures occur in implementing change, motivating the staff to adopt new measures becomes more difficult.

Embracing Change

Successful organizations embrace change as an integral part of their core business. These companies are the "learning organizations" defined by Senge. They have identified change as a learning opportunity that will position them favorably in the market in the long run. In other words, by constantly learning new skills to meet new opportunities in the marketplace, learning organizations change constantly. They use their ability to adopt changes more quickly as a competitive advantage. The core vision of the organization does not usually change; however, the products, services, or target markets may. Learning organizations encourage their employees to continually explore and learn new skills that can be applied to their work setting. These organizations foster an environment where learning is valued so that the learning outcomes can be used to achieve the company's mission.

For example, 3M allows its scientists to spend 15 percent of their time working on projects of their own choosing. They can use the time to pursue whatever interests them. This policy has resulted in the invention of Post-It Notes, among other products that have given 3M a clear strategic advantage over other companies.[11]

For pharmacist managers, the concept of the learning organization provides two important lessons. Firstly, the manager should approach change as a learning opportunity. Learning leads to change that leads to more learning. This endless cycle develops practice and management expertise and gives the organization a competitive advantage. Secondly, the manager should give the organization's employees the opportunity to learn. When employees are allowed to pursue learning activities, they feel they have more control over change events. This empowerment reduces resistance to change and improves the overall skills base of the organization.

The more pharmacist managers and employees identify learning needs, pursue learning activities, and implement new knowledge and skills, the more change will be perceived as a normal state. Continual change can lead to sustained strategic advantage. Change can be perceived as either a hindrance or an opportunity. The pharmacist manager can embrace change by instilling a culture where learning is valued within the organization.

SUMMARY

Pharmacists will be expected to develop knowledge and management skills during their careers. They will have the responsibility to reach objectives through staff. They will be held accountable for making good use of the resources provided to them.

Pharmacists will have managerial opportunities in many pharmaceutically related fields. Although the technical nature of the areas differs, many managerial roles are similar and a person who is a good manager in one field is likely to be a good manager in other fields.

Management is taught from the classical base of the functions of management: planning, organizing, directing (leading), controlling. This approach is useful to understand the management concepts. In practice, managers use more applied concepts and try to stay abreast of changes in management through reading and taking classes.

Managing a community pharmacy requires specific knowledge and skills. Community pharmacy is a highly regulated field, deals with technical products, demands a requirement for high service levels, faces intense competition, and has a large part-time staff with a high turnover. To be successful requires strong managerial abilities and a willingness to apply management methods.

A clear vision of change events required in response to issues and problems, coupled with clear communication strategies, sets the foundation for successful change. The pharmacist manager needs to be able to implement planned changes successfully. Objective outcomes measured at regular intervals will give the manager useful feedback to adjust the implementation plan.

The most successful organizations embrace change as an opportunity to gain strategic advantage. They do this by creating learning organizations that value the learning activities of their employees. The more employees learn, the more skills they can transfer to the activities that help the organization achieve its mission and sustain its success.

References

1. Robbins, S.P., and Stuart-Kotze, R. *Management.* 2nd ed. Toronto: Prentice-Hall Canada, 1990.

2. Senge, P. *The Fifth Discipline: The Art and Practice of the Learning Organization.* New York: Doubleday, 1990.

3. Harman, W. "21st Century Business: A Background for Dialogue." In J. Renesch, ed. *New Traditions in Business.* San Francisco: Berrett-Boehler Publishers, 1992.

4. Robbins, S.P. "Organization Theory: The Structure and Design of Organizations." In *Managing Change.* Englewood, NJ: Prentice-Hall, 1983.

5. Festinger, L. *A Theory of Cognitive Dissonance.* Stanford: Stanford University Press, 1957.

6. Hepler, C.D., and Strand, L.M. "Opportunities and Responsibilities in Pharmaceutical Care." *American Journal of Hospital Pharmacy* 47 (1990): 533–543.

7. Rogers, E.M. *Diffusion of Innovations.* New York: The Free Press of Glencoe, 1985.

8. Pritchett, P., and Pound, R. *The Employee Handbook for Organizational Change.* Dallas: Pritchett & Associates, 1994.

9. Resnick, H. "Managing Organizational Change in Youth Care Agencies." *The Child and Youth Care Administrator* 2, Fall 1988.

10. Kotter, J.P., and Schlesinger, L.A. "Choosing Strategies for Change." *Harvard Business Review*, March-April 1979.

11. Bennis, W., and Nanus, B. *Leaders: Strategies for Taking Charge.* New York: Harper Business, 1985.

Recommended Reading

Covey, S.R. *Principle-Centered Leadership.* New York: Fireside, 1990.

Fedder, D.O. "The Process of Change in Pharmacy." In C.H. Knowlton and R.P. Penna, eds. *Pharmaceutical Care.* New York: Chapman and Hall, 1996.

Kanter, R.M. *The Change Masters, Innovation and Entrepreneurship in the American Corporation.* New York: Simon and Schuster, 1983.

3

FORMS OF BUSINESS ENTERPRISE

INTRODUCTION

In addition to being a profession, community-pharmacy practice is a business. Because this is a basic fact, it is important to recognize that businesses do not operate themselves—people operate them. What then is business and who are these people?

Business has been defined as "all profit-seeking activities and enterprises that provide goods and services necessary to an economic system."[1] The two key elements of this definition—profitability and the provision of goods and services necessary to an economy—are applicable to pharmacy practice.

Firstly, profitability is important because, unless a practice is financially viable, it is of no value to anyone. Profits provide the basis on which pharmaceutical services are delivered. Because pharmacists have historically made themselves available to answer questions and provide their clientele with services and suggestions regarding health care that might be unavailable elsewhere, pharmacy clients have come to expect it. However, in the past, these services rarely, if ever, generated income and as a result were supported out of the profits earned by the business.

Currently, pharmacists are beginning to explore alternative methods of charging for pharmaceutical or medication management services, which is justified by the provision of expanded services that require professional judgment, and by the opportunities created when pharmacists intervene in managing their patients' response to medication.

Profits are also important because, when reinvested into the business, they allow new equipment and fixtures to be purchased, inventory replenished, repairs made, and bonuses and salaries paid. Profits also create new jobs. In short, if a pharmacy practice is not profitable, it falters and closes, thus depriving a segment of the population of pharmaceutical care as well as employment.

Secondly, certain goods and services are unique to pharmacy. In the case of prescription medication and certain non-prescription products, this exclusivity is regulated by law. It is considered to be in the public interest to have these products distributed in a controlled manner by individuals with specialized education and training. Related or companion services, such as initiating and maintaining medication histories, patient counseling, and monitoring a patient's compliance, are becoming increasingly important pharmacy services.

The products and services provided by pharmacies are certainly necessary to our economic system. This system is based on free enterprise, which allows firms to operate in a competitive atmosphere that, in turn, allows for success or failure depending in part on factors of supply and demand. Community pharmacies participate in this system as part of the private sector, since they are owned and operated by individuals or corporations who contribute to the economy by creating jobs, providing steady employment, paying taxes, and distributing products and services that are essential to maintaining health among the country's citizens and for which there is invariably a strong demand. An indication of the economic contribution from community pharmacies can be estimated by looking at the sales data from 39 pharmacies in Ontario. These pharmacies had average sales of $2,164,553[a] which extrapolates roughly into $4,980 billion for the 2301 pharmacies in the province.

Starting a business is fraught with challenges. Among the challenges are those arising from governments—taxes, regulations, interest rates, and the general state of the economy. Another concern to be aware of is the balance between optimism and reality. From a 1992 Statistics Canada survey of almost 1,500 small businesses, three reasons emerged that small and medium businesses grow—good management, good labor, and good marketing.[2]

In addition to these reasons for growth, Brian Tierney identified the following criteria as a "realistic approach to startup success:"[3]

• identify and prioritize personal and family goals that the business can achieve;

[a]In 1994, there were 2,301 pharmacies in Ontario, with average annual sales of $2,164,553.

- test the business concept on everyone whose opinion you value;

- take the time to identify potential problems;

- assess your personal strengths and weaknesses, and acquire needed skills or hire personnel with needed skills;

- consider a working partner with talents to complement your own;

- consider a joint venture with a firm that supplements your own strengths;

- create an advisory board with at least an accountant, lawyer, and banker;

- plan capital needs via a conservative budget and a worst-case scenario;

- develop a business plan;

- secure financing—more than you think you will need.

During the '80s, an increasing number of women started small businesses. The results of a study conducted by the Foundation for Future Leadership in Washington indicate that women perform slightly better than men in 28 of 31 categories.[4] These categories were grouped in seven areas—problem-solving, planning, controlling, leading, communicating, managing relationships, and managing self. Only in the last area did men do better. These findings are based on responses (from people working in US firms of all sizes in all types of jobs) to over 6,000 questionnaires about perceptions of men and women as managers.

In a free enterprise system, businesses, including pharmacies, are usually originated by entrepreneurs. Essentially, an entrepreneur is a person prepared to take a risk upon identifying an opportunity to generate a profit. This usually involves organizing capital and personnel into one of three or four recognized forms of business enterprise: a sole proprietorship, a general or limited partnership, or a corporation.

SOLE PROPRIETORSHIP

A sole (or single) proprietorship is the original and simplest form of business ownership. Its advantages and disadvantages are reviewed in Table 3.1 (p. 58).

Legally, the business and its proprietor are one and the same. As the proprietorship is wholly owned by one individual, its assets, earnings, and debts are those of the proprietor. This is an easy form of business to initiate, usually requiring only the registration of the firm's name with provincial authorities (simply a mechanism to prevent two different firms from using the same name); there is an exception to this, in that registration is not required if the business uses the proprietor's name. In the case of a pharmacy, however, all permits and licences required under the provincial Pharmacy Act have to be obtained before the firm can legally open. As each province has its own Pharmacy Act, it would be necessary to investigate the applicable regulations before opening the business. Also, a sole proprietorship can be discontinued simply by closing it up. In this form of organization, all decisions rest with the owner, who, consequently, is in absolute control. All the rewards of the enterprise accrue to the owner.

However, since the business is considered to be inseparable from its owner, —that is, since the earnings of the business are viewed as the owner's personal income on which he or she pays tax—, all business profits are taxed at the personal tax rate. If the income of the business is very small, this could be a tax advantage, in that a lower rate of taxation than the lowest corporate rate may apply. Also, any losses incurred by the business can be offset against personal income, whether it derives from the business or other sources. However, with greater earnings, a sole proprietorship is at a tax disadvantage because it is not eligible for the small business tax rate that applies only to corporations.[5]

Table 3.1   Advantages and Disadvantages of the Sole Proprietorship

Advantages	Disadvantages
Low start-up costs	Unlimited liability
Greatest freedom from regulation	Difficult to raise capital
Owner in direct control	Lack of continuity
Tax advantages if earnings are low	
Minimal working capital requirements	
All profits belong to the owner	

Source: Adapted from *Starting a Small Business in Ontario,* Toronto: Government of Ontario, Ministry of Economic Development, Trade and Tourism, 1997, p. 47. © Queen's Printer for Ontario, 1997.

A sole proprietorship has some further disadvantages. The most important is unlimited liability. This means that if the business incurs financial obligations that it cannot meet, the owner is required to pay them out of personal assets. This could involve having to sell personal property such as a home or cottage. Some sole proprietors protect themselves from such an eventuality by signing all their assets over to family members or close friends—in itself a potentially risky business.

The financial resources of a proprietorship are limited to the owner's personal wealth and, possibly, borrowed funds. As a result, initial capital for the enterprise may also be limited because financial institutions are reluctant to loan large sums when there is little or no collateral beyond the owner's personal assets.

Furthermore, since expansion and growth in a sole proprietorship may be constrained by limited financing, it can be difficult to retain effective employees. There is seldom any opportunity for promotion, perhaps few fringe benefits, and often little job security. Consequently, good employees leave either to start their own businesses or take other jobs that offer more potential for growth. Finally, proprietorships have a limited life span, terminating upon the bankruptcy, retirement, or death of the proprietor. There are few, if any, pharmacies operating as a proprietorship.

PARTNERSHIPS

Partnerships take one of two forms: general partnership or limited partnership. Partnerships are essentially groupings of two or more people coming together to operate a business. The partners become co-owners through a voluntary legal agreement that usually defines the nature of the business. The major difference between a general and a limited partnership is that, in a general partnership, each partner is individually liable for the business debts, while in a limited partnership, there are general partners and limited partners—the latter being liable only to the amount of capital that they invest. Limited partners must refrain from taking an active role in the management of the business; otherwise, they may be deemed to be general partners and, as such, must assume unlimited debt liability. Limited partnerships are required to register with the appropriate provincial government department. It is important, in general, to be aware of and check current provincial legislation as stipulated in each province's Partnerships Registration Act. In addition, some provincial Pharmacy Acts have provisions regarding partnerships of pharmacists with non-pharmacists in pharmacy practice, which must be thoroughly explored.

Partnerships are easy to organize, provide an opportunity to bring together diverse skills, and, by pooling partners' financial resources, gather more of the capital needed to initiate the enterprise. In addition, partnerships may have a better chance of securing financing than sole proprietorships, since lending institutions have recourse to the unlimited liability of each general partner as opposed to that of a single owner.

In order to prevent misunderstanding between or among partners, it is important to have a written and signed partnership agreement. This agreement, completed with the assistance of a lawyer, should identify the roles and responsibilities of each partner. This may provide some legal protection for general partners who would otherwise have to assume debt because of the unauthorized actions of another partner. Also, the name of the business should be registered with provincial authorities.

Although the unlimited liability of general partners affords the advantage of easier access to financing, it can also be one of the biggest disadvantages of a partnership. It can be the source of conflicts between partners, lack of continuity, and complexities in dissolving the business. The partnership ceases to exist when one partner is unwilling or unable to continue, which can occur through disagreement, illness, or death. In such cases, the equity of that partner is sold to another individual, and the partnership agreement must be renewed. This may not be as simple as it seems.

To preserve the successful make-up of the partnership, any new partner, in addition to having capital, must be acceptable to and compatible with the existing partner(s). Even if these criteria are satisfied, the original partnership agreement might specify that the existing partner(s) have the first option to buy the interest of the partner who is leaving the business. If this occurs, each remaining partner will have a greater equity in the firm. If nothing else, this situation should serve to illustrate the importance of a partnership agreement that clearly sets out such contingencies.

A summary of the advantages and disadvantages of a partnership appears in Table 3.2.

Table 3.2   *Advantages and Disadvantages of a Partnership*

Advantages	*Disadvantages*
Easily formed	Each general partner has unlimited financial liability
Management skills or interests of partners can be complementary	Potential for personality conflicts
Opportunity to raise a greater amount of initial capital	Lack of continuity in the business
	Potential for complicated dissolution

Source: Adapted from *Starting a Small Business in Ontario,* Toronto: Government of Ontario, Ministry of Economic Development, Trade and Tourism, 1997, p. 47. © Queen's Printer for Ontario, 1997.

CORPORATIONS AND LIMITED COMPANIES

The corporation, as a legal entity, exists with the legal rights and privileges of an individual. Corporations are granted charters upon incorporation, either by federal or provincial legislation, that set out the regulations by which the corporation must operate.

Ownership of a corporation is represented by stock or shares in the firm. The shares can be held publicly or privately. Publicly held corporations have their shares traded (bought and sold) on the open market, for example, at stock exchanges in major financial centres. Privately held corporations, such as those established by families or other small groups of people, rarely trade their shares. When they do, it is usually within the confines of the original group of shareholders.

The major advantage of incorporation is limited liability. Shareholders are not financially liable for the business beyond the cost of the shares they have purchased. Corporations are sometimes called limited companies to indicate the limited liability of the shareholders. An incorporated pharmacy will usually identify itself as "XYZ Pharmacy Limited," "XYZ Ltd.," or "XYZ Pharmacy Company Ltd."

Corporations—large ones at least—can more easily obtain personnel with specialized managerial skills because the firm is perceived to offer stability and long-term careers. Similarly, employees can specialize in a particular area or function because of the large size of the firm. Corporate ownership can also generate more capital through increased investor participation; that is, it can raise money by selling more shares in its ownership. It does this successfully because ownership can be divided into small units (shares) and can attract many investors, each with a modest amount of money.

The stability and the financial strength of corporations allow them to borrow funds more easily and, often, obtain more favorable rates than are available to smaller firms, including sole proprietorships and partnerships. It must be remembered, however, that not all corporations are large and that small businesses can also be organized in this way.

There are disadvantages to the corporate form of enterprise that should be noted. Incorporation is the most expensive form of ownership to establish and involves the greatest number of legal restrictions. Because each province has slightly different laws of incorporation, it is wise to use the services of a lawyer in order to avoid pitfalls unperceived by the layman. Keep in mind, however, that legal fees and incorporation costs levied by the provinces add to the total cost of establishing this type of business entity.

As legal entities, corporations are subject to taxation on profits earned. Canadian-controlled private corporations are eligible for a special small business tax rate, ranging from 16 to 23 percent depending on the province, that applies to income under $200,000 per year; above that amount, the firm will be taxed at the full corporate rate of approximately 46 percent.[b] Taxation is different for sole proprietorships and partnerships because the income or earnings of these businesses are treated as personal income and taxed accordingly. Within the corporate structure, certain methods of tax deferment and tax savings are available that do not apply in other forms of enterprise. Also, since corporate tax rates on retained earnings (profits reinvested in the corporation) above certain amounts are lower than personal tax rates for similar income levels, many small businesses choose this form of organization.

Other disadvantages of incorporation center around its legal requirements. For example, the corporate charter may restrict the corporation to certain types of activity. In addition, various reports about business operations must be filed with specific government departments.

Table 3.3 summarizes the advantages and disadvantages of the corporation as a form of business enterprise.

[b] The income-tax rates cited here are applicable at the time of writing and include surtaxes (temporary taxes that are periodically imposed by the provincial and federal governments). Also, note that the basic tax rates can change with each federal budget.

Table 3.3   *Advantages and Disadvantages of a Corporation*

Advantages	Disadvantages
Limited liability	Closely regulated by government
Greater opportunity for specialized management functions	Expensive to organize
	Activity restricted as per charter
Ownership easily transferred	Required record-keeping can
Existence is continuous	be extensive
Legal entity	
Easier to raise capital	
Possible tax advantages	

Source: Adapted from *Starting a Small Business in Ontario,* Toronto: Government of Ontario, Ministry of Economic Development, Trade and Tourism, 1997, p. 47. © Queen's Printer for Ontario, 1997.

FRANCHISES

Basically, a franchise is a particular method of operation used by a company to distribute foods and services. The company (franchiser) grants the operator (franchisee) the right to use its name, sell its products, use its symbols and trademarks, and adopt its operating methods.

Just as there are identifiable personality traits of entrepreneurs, those individuals who select a franchise system of business enterprise exhibit a series of identifiable traits. In both cases, these traits are revealed either through the types of questions asked by prospective franchisees or tests administered to determine personality profiles.

Franchisers look for team players, not individuals. "True entrepreneurs will die of frustration in a franchise system because they want to do everything their own way."[6] Entrepreneurs exhibit a high degree of independence, are risk-takers, and do not require anyone to manage or motivate them. Franchisees, while being self-managers, like to work within guidelines and along with other people.

Six essential issues should be considered before signing a franchise agreement:[7]

1.   location;

2.   reliability of the franchiser in dealing with franchises;

3.   product should have a good record and be in demand;

4.   territorial exclusivity;

5.   visibility of the product and the system;

6.   contract defining the rights of the franchisee and duties of the franchiser, including a formula for any buyback of the location, and specifying leasing and landlord relationships.

A franchise can offer the best of both worlds for many individuals; the freedom to operate as an entrepreneur within a proven group system, and the purchasing and advertising power of chains. Signing a franchise agreement gives you certain benefits but it also puts you at risk.[8] For example, if a dispute with the franchiser winds up in court, a judge may well expect that you have read and understood the contract thoroughly—and hold you to it. Therefore, one should read it and decide if one can live with it. Whereas no single item may make an agreement good or bad, the "bad" franchiser may refuse to put verbal representations into writing.

In order to bring some structure to the marketplace, Alberta enacted the Alberta Franchises Act that came into force on November 1, 1995. Essentially, the Act "assists prospective franchisees in making informed investment decisions by requiring the timely disclosure of necessary information."[9] It deals with the issues of franchiser information, rebates and supply purchasing, financing, trademarks, offences and remedies, misrepresentation, right to associate, relationship rights, self-government, and plain language. It is anticipated that these standards of disclosure, the duty to deal fairly, and the opportunity for franchisees to file civil suits if they feel wronged will be enough to police the industry.

Ontario has been planning to bring similar legislation forward since 1997.[10] It is the province's intention, however, to propose an independent regulator or ombudsman who would rule on disputes. Franchisers are concerned because they want to protect the integrity of the contract and are of the opinion that the franchise agreement should not be subject to external interference. As franchisees and franchisers form groups to lobby for their self-interests, both wait for draft legislation to appear.

COLLECTIVE OWNERSHIP

No discussion of forms of enterprise would be complete without mentioning the concept of collective ownership. This form of business is popularly known as a co-operative or simply a co-op. It is a banding together of interested parties to buy or sell products or services. In western Canada, for example, wheat and dairy farmers form co-ops to market their produce more effectively. For many years, in Ontario, the largest drug wholesaler was Drug Trading Company Limited.[c] It operated as a co-op and was supported by its member pharmacists who shared the firm's profits in proportion to their individual purchases from the wholesaler. In consumer co-operatives, members buy a share in the co-op and receive a rebate based on their purchases. Some large co-ops may operate pharmacies for the benefit of their members. Today, co-ops can be big businesses and must face the same constraints as the businesses with which they compete.

SUMMARY

Determining the legal form of one's business is a critical decision. The prospective pharmacist-owner must consider the advantages and disadvantages of the major forms of private business—the sole proprietorship, partnership, and corporation—in the light of his or her own business and professional objectives. Not to be taken lightly are the issues of liability and the relative potential for continuity and longevity of the business.

[c] Drug Trading Company Ltd. went out of business several years ago.

References

1. Applebaum, A.H., Beckman, M.D., Boone, L.E., and Kurtz, D.L. *Contemporary Canadian Business.* Toronto: Holt, Rinehart and Winston of Canada Limited, 1984.

2. Little, B. "Management Skills Rank High." *The Globe and Mail,* 7 March 1994.

3. Tierney, B. "Planning a Startup? Get Real!" *The Globe and Mail,* 8 August 1994.

4. "Women Score Top Managing Marks." From the *San Francisco Examiner* as reported in *The Globe and Mail,* 23 September 1996.

5. James, Jack D. *Starting a Successful Business in Canada.* 9th ed. Vancouver: International Self-Counsel Press Ltd., 1986.

6. Southerst, J. "If You're Entrepreneurial, Forget Franchises." *The Globe and Mail,* 8 May 1995.

7. Goldenberg, C. "Six Essential Issues for Any Franchise Deal." Small Business Week in *The Globe and Mail,* 23 October 1995.

8. Southerst, J. "The Warning Signs in Franchise Deals." *The Globe and Mail,* 21 August 1995.

9. Sotos, J. "Alberta Franchises Act, Life under the New Regime." *Food Service and Hospitality* (July 1966): 85.

10. Southerst, J. "Ontario Proposals Hit Sore Point with Franchisers." *The Globe and Mail,* 25 November 1996.

4

LOCATION ANALYSIS AND LEASING CONSIDERATIONS

INTRODUCTION

As many retailing experts will tell you, the key to a successful business is location. Community pharmacies are unique among retail enterprises because of their peculiar mix of commercial and professional products, and their varied sizes, layout formats, and approaches to merchandising. The choice of location for a community pharmacy will depend on the nature of its objectives: a professional-oriented pharmacy is more likely to locate in a residential neighborhood and attract a clientele interested in receiving professional services as well as pharmaceutical products, whereas a merchandise-oriented pharmacy might locate in a major thoroughfare to attract clientele looking for a wider variety of products. Therefore, rather than having a fixed formula for selecting a location, it is more useful to explore certain methods and techniques for evaluating alternative locations. In this way, new sites can be assessed and existing ones reevaluated.

Each time a lease is renewed, a pharmacy owner "locates his practice," and each time a pharmacist who owns the building in which his practice is established turns the key in the lock, he too "locates his practice." This may seem oversimplified, but the point is that a subconscious decision is being made because of an unwillingness to move. The astute businessperson analyzes location periodically, taking the same care that was applied in doing so the first time. The need for relocation may arise because additional space is required, the existing location is no longer adequate, rent has increased to an unreasonable rate relative to sales, a lease cannot be renewed, or the building is destroyed by fire or otherwise damaged.

Location analysis has been described as a hierarchy of decisions focusing on a region, a market area, a trading area, and, finally, a site.[1] This method can be applied to locating a community pharmacy in Canada.

REGION

Regional analysis simply divides the country into regions that represent broad geographic areas. For example, Canada can be divided into the regions of British Columbia, the Prairies, Ontario, Québec, and Atlantic Canada. These regions are distinct in their economies, attitudes, and consumption behavior. Although they share many characteristics with their colleagues across Canada, pharmacists will usually locate their practices in the region where they received their pharmacy education and practical training, as they will hold a licence in a particular province within that region, and be familiar with the culture.

MARKET AREA

The basic information about a market area that is of interest to both retail business and professional practice is its population. Population data are readily obtainable from the Canadian Census. The Decennial Census, originated in 1851, is conducted every ten years (most recently in 1991). In 1956, the Quincennial Census—occurring every five years between decennial censuses—was introduced to track statistical information on demographic and socio-economic developments. The most recent was completed in 1996 and is so detailed that population characteristics are available by city block for large cities. These data are often accumulated into census tracts that describe a small section of the city, typically with a population of approximately 5,000 to 10,000.[a]

Two terms that are used in the censuses require explanation: Census Agglomeration (CA) and Census Metropolitan Area (CMA). A CA is a large urbanized core with adjacent urban and rural areas that have a high degree of economic and social integration with that core. Essentially, a CA is the main labor market of an urban area of a population of at least 10,000.

---

[a] For a full description of a census tract, see the *Dictionary of the 1986 Census*, Catalogue 99–101: the *Market Research Handbook 1993-1994*, Catalogue 63–224 Annual. Ottawa: Statistics Canada. Population data by census tract include income, occupation, education, housing, family structure, mobility, etc. Census data published by Statistics Canada are available at many local libraries and at Statistics Canada's User Advisory Centres in major cities across Canada.

When a CA reaches a population of 100,000, it becomes a CMA, which in turn refers to the main labor market area of an urban area of at least 100,000 people. Table 4.1 lists the top ten of Canada's 25 CMAs as of 1991. These data can be used to describe a central city and its surrounding area by population density.

Table 4.1   The Ten Top CMAs in Canada, 1991

CMA	Population (thousands)
Toronto	3893.0
Montréal	3127.2
Vancouver	1602.5
Ottawa-Hull	920.9
Edmonton	839.9
Calgary	754.0
Winnipeg	652.4
Québec	645.6
Hamilton	599.8
St. Catharines-Niagara	364.6

Source: Market Research Handbook, 1993-1994, Catalogue 63-224 Annual, Ottawa: Statistics Canada.

Table 4.2 (p. 70) lists some categories of information that are useful to consider when analyzing the location potential of a geographic area or unit such as a municipality. Such data should be available from local Chambers of Commerce, census tables, banks, and local governments. In addition, much can be gleaned from close observation of the area and its surroundings.

It is important to research the general population parameters of an area, such as size, growth, and density, which characterize a unit base. Such factors can determine the density of consumer traffic in an area and are therefore critical to the success of a pharmacy. Within these parameters, target markets of pediatric, geriatric, or other populations, which represent the potential for specialized services and products, can be identified. Trans-

Table 4.2   *Geographic Data to Consider in Location Analysis*

Data Categories

General population parameters

Target-market parameters

Transportation networks

Economic characteristics

Purchasing power

Potential sales of specialized products

Degree of competition

Compatibility of nearby businesses

Environment uniqueness

Area rental costs

Retail improvement trends (permits issued for remodeling, expansion, etc.)

Source: Adapted from W.F. Davidson, D.J. Sweeney, and R.W. Stampfl, *Retailing Management*, 6th ed. © 1998 John Wiley and Sons, p. 240.

portation networks are also important to consider. For example, the cost and scheduling of public transit may affect the ability of potential clients to get to the market area under consideration. Economic characteristics of the area—its diversity of industry or dependence on only one type or source of employment—must also be examined closely. Related to this concept, and equally important, is information on the disposable income and spending patterns of the population.

It should be obvious that if a particular geographic location is attractive to one pharmacist, it may also appeal to another. In other words, consider the degree and intensity of competition in the area now, as well as what it might be in the future. The uniqueness of the surrounding area, in terms of its health-care facilities or extended-care facilities (such as nursing homes) and the presence of retirement communities or new subdivisions, is an important aspect to explore. Finally, the occupancy cost or rent that will be demanded in the area must be considered in light of the pharmacy's expected sales levels.

It should of course be mentioned that zoning by-laws must be investigated to determine if they are restrictive or compatible. A real estate agent specializing in retail business properties can clarify local by-law regulations and, in addition, assist in the rental of the premises.

No single category of information should sway a decision; rather, the balance of all the indicators must be carefully considered. Furthermore, available information that pertains more specifically to pharmacies should be explored. An example of such information is the nature of consumer spending on health services and products. Table 4.3 (p. 72) shows selected annual per capita expenditures, by province, for "drugs." With this kind of information, the pharmacist will be better equipped to identify the optimal geographic area (in this case, at least the optimal province) in which to locate.

While national or regional pharmacy chains are able to maintain a listing of specific potential market areas ranked in order of location priority, individual pharmacists do not have the resources for such detailed analysis. Nonetheless, individual pharmacists can avail themselves of similar procedures in selecting specific pharmacy locations within the general geographic market areas they have chosen.

Selecting a precise location within a chosen market area necessitates narrowing down the geographic area further, according to the scope of commercial services provided either in unplanned business districts or in areas planned for shopping and personal services. The choice between an unplanned and planned area will partly be determined by the nature and objectives of the pharmacy.

Unplanned Business Districts

Unplanned business districts come into existence through the "uncoordinated site decisions of individual merchants,"[1] and include:

- central business districts that contain a high concentration of retail businesses, offices, and services and have a high traffic flow;

- secondary business districts and strong street districts where the former may service portions of the central city core or suburbs and the latter are located on arterial routes into and out of the central core;

- clusters of neighborhood stores, particularly convenience stores and service outlets for a particular residential area, in which neighborhood pharmacies are usually found, along with other independent retailers.

Table 4.3   *Total and Per Capita Expenditures for Drugs in Canada: 1994*

1994	Total* (millions)	Per Capita
Newfoundland	$176.0	$302.29
Prince Edward Island	49.3	366.34
Nova Scotia	319.8	341.38
New Brunswick	239.7	315.75
Québec	2,163.6	297.16
Ontario	3,848.3	352.16
Manitoba	303.5	268.37
Saskatchewan	296.1	291.41
Alberta	724.0	266.53
Northwest Territories	23.7	368.41
British Columbia	1,027.8	280,17
Yukon Territory	7.4	245.75

* Includes expenditures on prescribed drugs, non-prescribed drugs, and personal health supplies (medical devices used to promote or maintain health) bought in retail stores.

Source: National Health Expenditures in Canada 1975-1994, Full Report, Policy and Consultation Branch, Ottawa: Health Canada, January 1996.

Shopping Areas

Planned shopping areas or shopping centres evolved as cities grew and became surrounded by suburban housing developments. Shopping centres are differentiated primarily by size, location, and the class of merchandise sold. They can be small, with a few stores situated along one side of a street in what is called a "strip layout." This type of center is oriented toward the sale of convenience goods, such as foods, sundries, and drugs, and of personal services, such as laundry, dry cleaning, and barber shops. Larger strip centers may have an anchor store—a major tenant, usually a supermarket—to attract traffic to the center.

Community shopping centers are the next step up in size. In addition to convenience stores, these centers usually contain a small department store and sporting goods, jewellery, and discount stores. They usually service a fairly well-defined neighborhood or housing development and are located at intersections of major arterial roads.

Regional and super-regional shopping centers are the largest in size. They are found at intersections of, or along, major expressways. There are several large full-line department stores that serve as anchors and the other stores sell a wide variety of convenience, shopping, and specialty goods.

The last two categories of shopping centers are often referred to as "malls" or "plazas."

TRADING AREA

Once location decisions are made regarding regional and market areas, it is necessary to select a particular trading area. This involves identifying sub-areas within market areas that contain target-market populations. At this stage of location analysis, it is necessary to consider the type of retail operation that is desired—a destination store or an intercept store. Destination stores generate most of their own traffic; that is, customers consciously choose the store as their destination, whether as a result of promotional efforts, breadth of merchandise, services offered, or store personality. Any one of these factors or some combination of them can create a destination store. Outlets such as supermarkets, discount stores, national department stores, and pharmacies can belong to this category.

Intercept stores are generally located between the people in the trading area and their traditional source of goods or services. The principle of business interception simply involves intercepting customers or pulling them "off the beaten path." Pharmacies, for example, could be located between residential areas and medical clinics or physicians' offices. The principle of interception would be at work when patients stopped in on their way home to fill the prescription they received at the physician's office.

Locations within a trading area can benefit by sharing the customer traffic of retail outlets that are already well established there. Banks, beer and wine stores, and food stores may attract people to an area, but, once there, these consumers will also patronize other businesses.

Another principle to consider in location analysis is that of suscipient business, which holds that a store need not generate its own traffic nor depend on neighboring stores for its customers; rather, its location in a place where people circulate for reasons other than shopping brings in its business.[2] An example is the busy newsstand located in a hotel, a train or bus station, or an airport. Pharmacies, too, may be found in locations such as the underground shopping complexes of large office buildings. They serve the working population of these specific sites and do not rely on attracting people directly from their homes or on their way from a physician's office.

In fact, pharmacies operate and derive satisfactory sales volume in all locations and situations described here. A pharmacist analyzing one location must do so as in the context of analyzing all potential locations.

SITE CONSIDERATION

Among the actual sites that should be considered for the pharmacy are shopping complexes, free-standing buildings, and empty land on which to build. An important consideration in site selection is the relationship of cost to productivity.

The physical characteristics of the space in a building under consideration should be scrutinized. The shape of the space, its width and depth, the absence of supporting pillars, exposed pipes, and duct work, and its general appearance are all factors determining the effectiveness of the space for sales purposes and the cost that will be involved to furnish it. Windows at the front of the building that would offer passers-by a view of the interior are an important feature as well. The position of entry and exit doors and whether they are located above, at, or below ground level will also serve to attract or discourage people from entering the pharmacy.

Parking is a key concern: is the site relatively accessible from the parking lot and is the lot itself convenient for passing traffic to enter and exit? Is parking free or pay-by-meter or pay-to-attendant? Are parking discounts available to customers? Although the traffic that passes by a site en route to and from work is a less valuable site asset than shopping traffic, it is still important to remember that people are more likely to stop on their way home than on their way to work. Hence, one-way streets should be assessed carefully. The prospective owner should conduct counts of both pedestrian and automobile traffic at each site under consideration.

Principles of proximity must not be ignored. Proximity to anchor stores in malls and plazas is important with regard to pedestrian traffic. The distance from medical clinics, outpatient departments of hospitals, and physicians' offices will have a direct bearing on prescription sales as well. (If we can assume that general practitioners write approximately 20 to 25 prescriptions per day, a rough calculation based on the number of physicians' offices and the number of competing pharmacies in the area can help to estimate the percentage of the prescriptions that may be expected at a given location.) Nearness to bus, streetcar, and subway stops, will also add to ambulatory traffic, hence to the number of potential customers.

Obstacles to pedestrian traffic can make a site less desirable. Accessibility to a site could be jeopardized by busy driveways or wide or congested streets that have to be crossed; by sidewalks that end abruptly; by excessive noise, odor, or unsightliness in the vicinity of the site; and by natural barriers such as ravines or rivers that would cause people to have to take lengthy detours.

TECHNIQUES TO ASSESS SITE LOCATIONS

Techniques used to assess site locations range from quite basic rules of thumb to sophisticated mathematical formulations. The retail industry is rife with rules of thumb that have evolved from observed relationships between store performance and certain specific criteria. They are useful as general guidelines and as aids to decision making.

The use of ratios as rules of thumb is fairly common. One such ratio is sales per square foot. In Canadian pharmacies in 1990, the average sales per square foot were $560, with the front store generating $325 per square foot and the prescription department $2,040.[3] Other ratios include the number of prescriptions per patient and the average price per prescription. Such data help to estimate prescription sales.

Another rule of thumb deals with convenience and distance. It suggests that the average consumer's travel time to a retail destination is ten minutes or less. Therefore, to estimate the trading area of a particular site, simply drive in several directions from the proposed site for ten minutes and mark the boundaries on a map. Once this is done, census tract data can be used to estimate the population of the trading area and, with this information in hand, a rough estimate of the potential prescription sales at the site can be made with the aid of such statistics as given in Table 4.3 (p. 72). Say, for example, the proposed site is located in Nova Scotia. From Table 4.3, we see that per capita expenditures on drugs in Nova Scotia in 1994 were $341.38. Let us say that the prospective owner has determined the population of the trading area to be approximately 7,500. The potential drug sales for all pharmacies in the trading area would therefore be approximately $341.38 × 7,500 = $2,560,350. Let us say further that three pharmacies (including the one at the site under consideration) are located in or near the trading area. The potential drug sales at any one of the pharmacies would therefore be roughly $2,560,350 ÷ 3 = $853,450. Adjustments should be made to the estimate to reflect:

- other unique features of the trading area, such as level of income and average age of the population (e.g., a trading area with a high percentage of senior citizens would have higher per capita drug sales than the provincial average);

- apparent advantages or disadvantages of the proposed site (e.g., proximity to a medical clinic) and of the planned pharmacy (e.g., in pricing, shopping convenience, and range of services to be offered).

Similar calculations can be made for potential non-drug product sales as well.

Surveys are sometimes used in assessing site locations to determine the types of products purchased by the respondents in the area, the frequency of pharmacy patronage or visits to a physician, and the distance normally traveled to retail outlets. Such information is then used to evaluate the potential of the trading area.

One of the early mathematical models used to analyze site location was developed in 1929 by William J. Reilly. His approach has since been referred to as a gravitational model because it attempts to explain the patterns in which potential consumers gravitate toward an identified site. Reilly's work formalized empirical observations about consumer shopping movements between cities. The basic principle of his model is that a retail center's attraction for a consumer is directly related to the size of the retail center and inversely related to the consumer's distance from the center. In other words, a larger center suggests a greater assortment of products and therefore holds more attraction for the consumer. Distance, however, represents a cost in time and/or money; thus, the farther the shopping center is from the consumer, the less attraction it holds.[4]

In the early '40s, the theory was further refined by Paul D. Converse, who made it possible to calculate the approximate distance between two competing cities that held equal attraction for consumer shopping. Finally, in the '60s, David L. Huff reformulated the model in probabilistic terms because the original model, designed to identify the market areas of competing cities, was unable to develop accurate estimates for individual store sites. Huff's model, however, has also been criticized as inaccurate, in that "individual store size per se has not been found to have great influence or drawing power."[5] Size, then, is a more important factor with regard to shopping centres.

PHARMACY RELOCATION

Relocating a pharmacy practice is just as important as locating it initially. Reasons to relocate can be as simple as a lack of sales growth, exhausting the renewable options on a lease, outgrowing the space, being displaced by fire or physical damage to the premises, or a changing trading or market area that makes the present location less than ideal.

A voluntary decision to relocate should be based on an analysis of the practice. If a different site within the area is being considered, it should be compared carefully to the present site. Information from the practice can be used to aid in the comparison. For example, an analysis of prescription files will identify the location of major prescribers and patients, and personal charge accounts, if kept, will identify the location of non-prescription clients. If charge or credit card courtesies have not been extended, a free draw that requires customers' names and addresses can be used to determine where they live. If it is found that the proposed site is closer to the majority of patients and physicians, the decision to relocate will clearly become easier.

Regardless of the method used to determine the ongoing advantages of the trading area and the present site, there are several factors that should be considered: Has the population for prescriptions shifted relative to the current site? Have the physicians moved from the area? Has the surrounding neighborhood deteriorated? Has a major industry shut down or moved away? If a major change is identified, the merits of a potential new trading area must be carefully examined, and the owner must make the decision whether or not to relocate. In addition, the activity of competing pharmacies must be taken into consideration: for example, is there a risk that another pharmacy might open on the site or in the area under consideration, with the effect of diminishing your existing clientele? Good judgment, based on as much information as can be collected and tempered by reasonable advice from one's advisers, should lead to the correct decision.

AIDS TO LOCATION ANALYSIS

A location analysis worksheet (Figure 4.1) and a location analysis checklist (Figure 4.2, p. 80) may be useful in summarizing the attributes of various locations. Although simple in approach, these forms do allow for a ready comparison of sites. And, as one gains experience in this type of analysis, such aids can be revised and refined to suit specific needs.

Location then, is one of the most important determinants of the success of a business. A thorough location analysis must include consideration of factors such as population, disposable income, the distance customers must travel, and traffic patterns. Also, periodic location analyses of an existing pharmacy should be conducted, and then compared to alternative locations to help the pharmacy owner or manager stay attuned to the movements and needs of the clientele, and to prevent competitors from gaining a foothold in the trading area.

LEASING THE SITE OF THE PHARMACY

Following a thorough location analysis, the choice of the site of the pharmacy, and a decision on the legal form of the business—a sole proprietorship, partnership, or corporation— as detailed in Chapter 3 (p. 57), the pharmacist-owner or manager would then purchase the site or enter into a lease of the site.

Offer to Lease

In practical terms, the offer to lease is a starting point where the landlord is prepared to make concessions to a prospective tenant in order to make a deal. In drawing up an offer to lease, the tenant should not hesitate to request all—not some—of the items that he/she would like included in the lease, such as a reasonability clause, where the landlord's consent to any request by the tenant is not to be unreasonably withheld; a rent-free period; a leasehold improvement allowance; an option to extend; a first right of refusal; an exclusivity clause; a restrictive covenant; a waiver of subrogation; and a non-disturbance agreement. If prospective tenants do not ask, they will not get.

Figure 4.1   Location Analysis Worksheet

1. Define trading area of the proposed site by:
   a. driving ten minutes in each direction from the site;
   b. marking boundaries on a map;
   c. listing census tracts within the identified boundaries.

2. Population estimate:

Census tract and population	×	Percentage of tract in trading area	=	Estimated trading area population
a. _____	×	_____	=	_____
b. _____	×	_____	=	_____
c. _____	×	_____	=	_____
				Total _____

3. Estimated pharmaceutical and related expenditures in trading area:
   Trading area population × Per capita expenditures
   = Estimate of purchases*   _____
      (prescribed medication   _____
      non-prescribed medication   _____
      other pharmacy-related merchandise)   _____
                                                   Total $_____

4. Estimated market share:

Estimate of total purchases in trading area	÷	Number of pharmacies in trading area	=	Potential purchases at proposed store site
$ _____	÷	_____	=	$ _____

Adjust the resulting estimate upward or downward to reflect the peculiarities of the trading area and of the proposed site.

*For an example, see Health Canada, *National Health Expenditures in Canada 1975-1994, Full Report,* January, 1996 (Table 4B: Total Health Expenditures by Category of Expenditures, Canada, 1975-1994).

Source: Adapted from V. Cardinale, "Are You Living Up to Your Full Market Potential?" *Drug Topics* (6 January 1986), p. 28.

Figure 4.2   Location Analysis Checklist

1. Demographic variables (percentage estimates):
    - predominant age groups:
        - pediatric _____
        - geriatric _____
        - young families _____
    - ethnicity (specify) _____
    - specific needs:
        - language _____
        - products _____

2. Economic variables:
    - per capita income _____
    - average family income _____
    - predominant industry _____

        agricultural: _____ one crop _____ diversified
        industrial base: _____ one industry _____ diversified

3. Institutions (commercial, professional):
    - numbers and types
    - supportive or competitive
    - schools
    - hospitals, clinics, extended-care facilities
    - proximity to proposed site

4. Parking:
    - street—free or pay
    - lots—free or pay
    - width of curb cuts
    - proximity to proposed site

5. Traffic:
    - ambulatory
    - vehicles
    - public transportation
    - location of stops and stations
    - transfer points
    - shelters
    - one-way streets
    - congested streets
    - crosswalks

6. Other observations or comments: _____
    _____

Source: Adapted from V. Cardinale, "Are You Living Up to Your Full Market Potential?" Drug Topics (6 January 1986), p. 28.

A standard clause in a landlord's form of offer to lease requires the tenant to sign the landlord's form of lease. If left unchanged, the clause does not allow the lease to be amended to reflect all changes contemplated in the offer to lease. The tenant must clarify this and stipulate that the lease be negotiated "subject to such amendments as may be negotiated and mutually agreed upon between the tenant and landlord both acting reasonably and in good faith."[6] A "sunset clause" should also specify a time when the lease must be signed or the offer becomes null and void. Although an offer to lease and a lease are distinct documents, the offer to lease ultimately indicates what is to be contained in the lease.

DEFINITIONS AND OBLIGATIONS

The offer to lease/lease is a specific form of contract that may be defined as "a grant of space for a term certain the occupation of which is restricted on express terms and conditions. It is an exchange of promises displayed by the solemn covenants of the parties all supported by consideration."[7] (See Appendix 4A: Sample Offer to Lease, p. 89.) In order to better understand this unique type of contract, we shall look at each part of the definition.

- *A grant of space:* The landlord (the lessor) owns the property or has the right to grant a lease(s) for the same, granting the tenant (the lessee) a right to possession—not ownership, but a right to occupy. One of the first considerations will likely be the amount of space. If one's location objective is an existing corner store, it is easy to define as "the space delimited by the four walls or the existing blueprint."

  Alternatively, if one's location objective is a new shopping centre, one's square footage requirements must be carefully assessed. Depending upon one's budget and financing constraints, it may be possible to lease more space at the outset than one may require. This could be cheaper in the long run, than if one leases too little space and is forced to find additional space at higher cost as one's requirements grow. Alternatively, the prospective tenant may try to negotiate for an "option" on neighboring, vacant space so it is available when required.

- *For a term certain:* This means for a definite period of time. The offer to lease/lease shall state a commencement date which should be the date occupancy commences. If this period commences from the date of the offer to lease/lease document, then one's actual occupancy period is less than what was bargained for. It is prudent to specify the date of lessee occupancy as the date of term commencement to be certain of when one's term matures, when one is obliged to give notice if one intends to renew the lease, and to be aware of any other time-measured obligations.

The term period is usually stated in years. It may be for a minimum of five years, but, if one is in a booming location, one may wish to negotiate for a longer term. Alternatively, if the landlord is not inclined to grant a longer initial term, then always negotiate to provide for one or more options to renew. The options require one to give written notice of one's intention to exercise them, and usually does not fix the rent rate until negotiations ensue. This allows the landlord to maintain a market rent without being locked in for too long. These prevailing higher rent costs are usually a future certainty, but it is intended that with one's success, one's business should be able to support it. Along with the options to renew, it is good practice to have a standard arbitration clause that provides for dispute resolution in deciding the rent to be charged upon renewal of the lease.

Another important consideration in defining the term and renewal options in one's offer to lease/lease is the requirement of one's principal lender. The bank or asset financier shall require a reasonable lengthy term of lease, or certainty of renewal options in order to consider lending significant capital loans. The lender wants a business to succeed, and that the tenant has sufficient time in the same location to repay financial obligations as the business is growing.

- *Occupation of this space is restricted on express terms and conditions:* "Express" means written. If an offer to lease/lease is not stated in writing, it simply does not exist, regardless of the type and frequency of verbal representations, assurances, and promises one may have been given.[8] The offer to lease/lease should state clearly and precisely what one expects the lessor to provide. Conversely, the offer to lease/lease should clearly state what the lessor expects the lessee to do, and the amount the lessee is required to pay.

- *It is an exchange of promises displayed by the solemn covenants of the parties:* This indicates that an offer to lease/lease is to be taken seriously as it sets out the rules of the business relationship between a landlord and a tenant.
- *All supported by consideration:* Consideration is the good faith payment made periodically for the right to use or occupy the property, that is, the payment of money in the form of monthly rent. The legal tender paid by the tenant to the landlord validates the contract of offer to lease/lease as a proper agreement enforceable in law.

TERMS AND CONDITIONS: TERMINOLOGY

Parties to a lease should be aware of terms and conditions that generally appear when writing up an offer to lease/lease. Some of the most prevalent terms and conditions that one needs to understand follow.

- *The covenant to pay rent:* In all leases, the lessee must agree to pay rent. There are several different ways in which rent is calculated and paid. In a corner store location, the rent obligation to the lessor may be limited and simple—for example, $1,000 per month—, and the tenant pays his own hydro, water, and business taxes. This usually does not include realty tax owed by the lessor on the building of which the tenant occupies a portion.

  In a shopping mall, the rent is calculated as a certain sum per square foot, and charged out per year and paid monthly—, this being usually referred to as base rent. In addition, there is an escalation rent, which covers insurance, maintenance, and taxes, as well as a landlord's administrative charge of about 15 percent. Here, taxes—or one's pro rata share—are not only one's own business taxes, but also realty taxes based upon the bill charged to the lessor by the local municipality. One's tax sum is a proportion of the total tax bill for the building, based upon the amount of space leased as a proportion of the total leasable space.

  Depending upon demand and the popularity of the location, the lessor may expressly require the lessee to agree to one of different types of lease formats: a gross lease, a semi-gross lease, or a net lease. A gross lease is also called "turnkey," where everything is included by the landlord in the lease cost—rent, taxes, common area maintenance, utilities, and leasehold improvements.

In addition to a base rent per square foot, a semi-gross lease provides a base year that is stated, giving the lessor an opportunity to escalate the hydro, taxes, water, and heating. The tenant pays the charges on these items based on the difference between a current and future cost. For example, in 1997, taxes amounted to $10,000 and one's proportionate share was $1,000, based on the amount of space occupied (10%). If taxes do not increase, one pays nothing more. If taxes do increase so that one's proportionate share is $1,200, one pays $200 in the lease year of increase. Since taxes (plus such other charges) always go up, it is wise to negotiate for a future base year.

A semi-gross lease may also expressly provide that the tenant must pay a percentage rent. There are several ways to negotiate the impact of a percentage rent obligation. Firstly, as gross sales are both a number and concept, one should try to negotiate so that the percentage rent does not commence until the gross sales breakout level is maintained consistently for some number of months. Secondly, it would be both sensible and practical to exclude certain things from the calculation of the concept of gross sales, such as low profit-margin items. These may include, for example, drugs sold to physicians, sale items, magazines, paper goods, soft drinks, post office, and sales to employees.

A net lease stipulates that the tenant pays for everything such as water, hydro, taxes, etc. This is particularly popular in shopping mall locations. In addition to rent paid per square foot per year, an additional sum is paid based on the performance of the business, which is called a breakout level. For example, the percentage rent provision may state that if gross sales for the month rise to $50,000, a percentage in the range of three to five percent is to be paid to the landlord. The lessee is obligated to submit monthly sales figures so the landlord will know how well the business is doing.

- *Sublet clause:* In the event that one finds that one has excess space or wishes to sublet space to other parallel business functions that may enhance one's business, a sublet clause is required. The clause provides that the landlord's written consent is required and such consent may either be arbitrarily withheld, or not be unreasonably withheld. The preferred format for the lessee is the latter, of course.

- *Leasehold improvements and allowance:* In an offer to lease/lease, when dealing with a blank, empty-shell space comprising concrete walls, floors, and pillars, one must decide what is to be constructed. One will require ceilings, walls, partitions, air-conditioning and heating, and perhaps even carpeting or tiled floors. If the landlord is not providing some or all of these items, one should ensure provision of an allowance representing so much money per square foot for what has to be installed by the lessee. No doubt there may be many other things one may want to include. Shelving, partitioning, and display cases are all likely to be obtained at one's own expense. Therefore, one should try to have the actual space prepared at the landlord's expense up to the point of installation of these other items. It is worth noting that one may have to submit an architect's plan indicating how one wants the store to appear. The planned layout may also require the landlord's consent.

- *Adequate signing:* The lessee must provide in the offer to lease/lease that signage of a certain dimension be made available. This would also include tenant directory and pylon name-plating. It may be created and installed at one's own expense, but the right to have it is a matter of negotiation between the landlord and the tenant. In many mall locations and some strip plazas, the landlord reserves aesthetic control and total discretion on color, size, and features to maintain a consistent appearance.

- *The use clause—exclusive rights:* It is advised to have the use clause as broad as possible. For instance, this provision could read "full service drug store and pharmaceutical dispensary and ancillary uses," so that front-store operations are virtually unrestricted. It is also prudent to try to obtain exclusive rights to being the only pharmacy in the mall. In addition, one may attempt to obtain exclusivity on certain product lines, such as greeting cards, so that it is not granted to another merchant in the mall.

- *Contingency on financing clause:* In order to provide greater certainty in the development of this business project at the offer-to-lease stage, protection is available by inserting a condition that the terms of the offer are conditional on financing. This protects one to ensure that one has the financial backing in place before signing the lease.

- *Definite occupancy date:* In the situation where the landlord is constructing the premises, it is prudent to obtain a reduction in rent for construction delays. It should be noted that where leasehold allowances are provided to a tenant and the tenant has not completed the premises by a specified date for an organized mall opening event, severe penalties are imposed for failing to be open for business on time. Solid planning and strategy are the solutions for these potential problem areas.

- *Definite and accurate description of store location within the shopping center:* This express term addresses the specific dimensions of the premises one intends to rent, so that where rent is payable per square foot, there is certainty as to what is being leased and exactly where it is located. For example, a pedestrian entrance is provided on the main mall thoroughfare, not merely at a side entrance. Usually, an architect's certificate is provided certifying precise measurements once the premises are fully constructed.

- *Waste removal provisions:* It may seem obvious, but it is prudent to ensure that specific provision is made for garbage removal as part of the landlord's maintenance and janitorial obligations. Usually there is also a general standard of care stated that is reasonable for the landlord to require of the tenant.

- *Warranties on major equipment:* It may appear surprising that, even if tenants do not own major mechanical items, they are responsible for the maintenance and repair costs for damage to same. The objective is to pay only maintenance and repairs. Items of a capital nature should be paid for by the landlord. For instance, an air conditioning system on the roof of the building premises will usually have a warranty available. The terms of this warranty should be reviewed to ensure the tenant is adequately protected.

- *Parking privileges:* Depending upon the type of location, the need for this provision varies. In a mall, arrangements may be available for a certain number of guaranteed parking spaces for staff but unassigned. In addition, specific customer parking may be available if the location provides an entrance/exit door to the parking lot area. It is always useful to negotiate free parking for customers.

- *Contribution to maintenance of common areas:* In a mall, or even strip plaza location, the tenant may be obliged to contribute to a fund to maintain common areas, including pedestrian walkways and parking facilities based on a charge per square foot of space occupied.

- *Contribution to mall merchants association:* This is seen as a form of local advertising and community outreach. Either a flat rate per merchant is levied or it can be based upon a charge per square foot occupied.

- *Insurance:* In a mall location, one pays for the costs of the landlord's insurance. If, as a result, one is able to increase one's own coverage, it is advisable to get as much as one can. Good insurance coverage provides a more secure business future. Also, through the insurance obtained, one has in writing a complete code or rulebook of specific areas of responsibility, and a healthier relationship with one's landlord.

- *Rent adjustment based on a number of physicians:* In a medical clinic location you may wish, in addition to paying a base rent, to tag the rental rate to the number of full-time equivalent physicians in active practice in their respective areas of specialty on the same premises as the pharmacy. Full-time is considered to be at least 32 hours per week. This would allow for the adjustment in rent in the event the clinic prospers, remains static, or declines. The success in obtaining and building the pharmacy business in such an environment rests with your own marketing style, service, and charisma. This would apply in general terms to all types of locations.

- *Guarantee and indemnity:* In the event the landlord determines that greater financial backing is required in order for the tenant to obtain the lease sought, a form of guarantee or indemnity should be provided. This may occur when a newly formed limited corporation is the proposed tenant, and the individual principals thereof are requested to provide their guarantees. In a start-up operation this is not unusual. The tenant best agrees to provide the guarantee but should try to limit same to the first two or three years of the term of lease negotiated. The landlord would then release the guarantees so long as the tenant is not in default and the lease is in good standing.

- *Right of assignment:* The offer to lease should provide that the named offering party as tenant, when submitted in trust, has a right to assign the benefit of the offer and subsequent lease to a limited corporation to be formed for the purpose. On assignment, the offering party is thereby relieved of any personal responsibility.

- *Roof and parking lot:* The roof of the building and the parking lot are the landlord's responsibilities and cost of repairs are not to be charged back to the tenant in the common and maintenance costs.

- *Continuance occupancy:* There should not be a continuance occupancy clause so that the tenant can vacate the premises and sublet it. The original tenant may have to remain in the lease and be responsible to the landlord.

- *Receiving door:* It is critical that the pharmacy have access to a receiving door.

- *Vista:* There should be some guarantee that visibility of the premises is maintained and not blocked by additional construction of buildings or signs.

SUMMARY

A lease is a written contract. Once agreed to and signed by lessor and lessee, it is difficult to change. Therefore, it is extremely important that all issues are considered carefully and included in writing. Remember that if a lease is not in writing, it does not exist. In order to achieve a reasonable lease, it is always useful to use appropriate professionals who will negotiate on one's behalf.

References

1.   Davidson, W.R., Sweeney, S.J., and Stampfl, R.W. *Retailing Management.* 6th ed. Toronto: John Wiley and Sons, 1988.

2.   Nelson, R.L. "Principles of Retail Location." In R.D. Gist, ed. *Management Perspectives in Retailing.* New York: John Wiley and Sons Inc., 1967.

3.   Segal, H.J. *Combined 10th and 11th Annual Survey of Community Pharmacy Operations.* Toronto: Eli Lilly Canada, 1992.

4.   Smith, H.A. *Principles and Methods of Pharmacy Management.* 3rd ed. Philadelphia: Lea & Febiger, 1986.

5. Huff, D.L. "Defining and Estimating a Trading Area." In R.D. Gist, ed. *Management Perspectives in Retailing.* New York: John Wiley and Sons Inc., 1967.

6. Haber, H.M. *Landlord's Rights and Remedies in a Commercial Lease—A Practice Guide.* Aurora, Ont.: Canada Law Book Inc., 1994.

7. Black, H.C. *Black's Law Dictionary.* West Publishing Co., 1968.

8. *The Statute of Frauds R.S.O. 1990* (Revised Statutes of Ontario).

APPENDIX 4A: SAMPLE OFFER TO LEASE

TO: _____ (Lessor)

I/We, _____ (Lessee)

having inspected the premises, hereby offer to lease, premises known as:

_____

Street West, _____ , comprising 6,600 square feet for a term of SIX (6) years commencing October 1, 1996 to September 30, 2002, yielding and paying therefore yearly and every year during the said term unto the said lessor RENTAL AS BELOW net of GST, in lawful money of Canada without any deduction, defalcation or abatement whatsoever to be payable monthly in the amount AS SET OUT BELOW.

   Cheque for *fourteen thousand and eight hundred fifty dollars* ($14,850) payable to your solicitor in trust and to be deposited into an interest bearing account, is attached hereto to apply as a deposit on rental and to be returned if this offer is not accepted. Deposit to be applied to the first and last month's net rent.

Electricity to be paid by: lessee
Heating costs to be paid by: lessee
Water rates to be paid by: lessee
Property taxes to be paid by: lessee
Business tax to be paid by: lessee

Net Rent and Rent Payment Commencement Date

The lessee shall commence its rental payments to the lessor on October 1, 1996. Years 1, 2, and 3 of the term the rent shall be calculated at $12 per square foot and the lessee shall pay yearly the sum of $79,200 payable monthly in the amount of $6,600 on the first day of each and every month.

Year 4 of the term the rent shall be calculated at $13 per square foot and the lessee shall pay yearly the sum of $85,800 payable monthly in the amount of $7,150 on the first day of each and every month.

Year 5 of the term the rent shall be calculated at $14 per square foot and the lessee shall pay yearly the sum of $92,400 payable monthly in the amount of $7,700 on the first day of each and every month.

Year 6 of the term the rent shall be calculated at $15 per square foot and the lessee shall pay yearly the sum of $99,000 payable monthly in the amount of $8,250 on the first day of each and every month.

Use of Premises

The lessee shall occupy the premises throughout the term and the tenant shall not cause, suffer, or permit the premises to be used for any other purpose than for FULL SERVICE DRUG STORE AND PHARMACEUTICAL DISPENSARY AND ANCILLARY USES in accordance with existing zoning bylaws and permitted uses.

Lease Renewal

Provided the lessee is not in default in any of its obligations under the terms of the lease, the lessee shall have the option to renew the lease for two further terms of FIVE (5) years each. The lessee will be required to give written notice to the lessor of its intention to renew at least three months prior to the expiration date of the lease for the first renewal and three months prior to the expiration of the first renewal term for the second renewal term.

The first renewal term shall be on the same terms and conditions at the sixth year of initial lease term except for rent which shall be the prevailing market rent and no greater than $15 per square foot.

The second renewal term shall be on the same terms and conditions as the first renewal term except for rent, which shall be set at the prevailing market rent for similar properties in size, use, and purpose. In the event the parties are unable to agree upon a market rent, a submission shall be jointly made to arbitration at the shared cost of the parties.

Assigning and Sub-leasing

The lessee may assign or sub-lease part or all of the leased premises at any time during the lease term and any renewal thereof for use as medical suites and postal station without the consent of the lessor and without having to notify the lessor.

Net Lease

The lessee acknowledges that the lease shall be an absolute net lease to the lessor and the lessee shall be responsible for all costs, charge, outlays, or other expenditures relating to the premises and the lessee's occupation thereof which may include any tax in the nature of the Goods and Services Tax or other taxes which are levied on the lessor as a result of the lessee's use and occupancy of the premises, and in respect of the use by the lessee of the common facilities and the lands.

Form of Lease Agreement

The undersigned lessee hereby acknowledges that on receipt of the lessor's standard form of lease agreement for the property, the lessee shall review same forthwith with its solicitor and if found to conform to this offer to lease shall execute and deliver same to the lessor. The lessee shall be reasonable in any changes it may require to the form of lease so to conform to this offer to lease.

Option to Purchase

The lessee shall at any time during the term have the option to purchase the property at the purchase price of _____ .

The lessee is also hereby granted a first right of refusal to purchase the property so that in the event the lessor receives a third-party offer for the property, the lessor shall notify the lessee in writing immediately who shall have seventy-two (72) hours from receipt of notice to enter into an acceptance agreement of purchase and sale with the lessor.

Warranty

Lessor warrants that the existing buildings, equipment and premises are in good repair and good working order at the time of occupancy by the lessee and that any and all environmental concerns have been addressed and that the lessee shall be permitted to operate its business upon occupancy without regard to such environmental controls as same are the responsibility of the lessor who shall indemnify and save the lessee harmless from all costs and business loss that may result from any non-compliance by the lessor.

Telecopier

The lessor and lessee agree that this offer/counter-offer when executed and/or the executed acceptance thereof may be communicated by telecopier and that such agreements shall be binding upon the parties hereto.

No Representation

It is understood and agreed that there are no covenants, representations, agreements, warranties, or conditions in any way relating to the subject matter of this offer, whether express or implied, collateral or otherwise, except those set forth in this offer and in the lease.

Time of the Essence

Time shall be of the essence in this offer to lease and with every particular thereof.

Irrevocable Offer

The offer shall be irrevocable by the lessee until 5:00 p.m. on the _____ day of September 1996 at which time, if not accepted, this offer shall be null and void and the lessee's deposit returned forthwith in full without interest or penalty.

Upon acceptance this offer shall constitute a binding agreement upon the parties hereto.

Dated at [city], [province], this _____ day of September, 1996.

Signed, Sealed and Delivered

in the presence of:

              per:

_____

        I have authority to bind the corporation/lessee

_____

I, the lessor, do hereby accept the above Offer and am bound by its terms.

_____

Dated at [city], [province], this _____ day of September, 1996.

Signed, Sealed and Delivered

in the presence of:

_____

_____

                            Lessor

5

STARTING OUT—CAPITAL REQUIREMENTS

INTRODUCTION

Financial information is the heart of any business enterprise—whether it be profit- or non-profit-oriented. In order to understand financial statements, it is helpful to appreciate where the information originates and how it becomes part of a financial statement. Once this is accomplished, the analysis of these statements can reveal a great deal about how the business is progressing.

There are three basic financial statements: a balance sheet, an income statement, and a statement of retained earnings. The balance sheet provides a picture, at a point in time—its date—of the balances in the asset, liabilities, and owner's equity accounts. The income statement indicates the change in retained earnings from one balance sheet date to the next, illustrating the amount of profit earned; in other words, it shows the contribution to owner's equity resulting from the operation of the business. The changes in the statement of retained earnings illustrates how the business' retained earnings changed during the accounting period or fiscal year. This may include dividend payments that will reduce retained earnings, and net income that will increase retained earnings.

The information necessary to prepare financial statements begins with transactions. These are events such as the purchase of inventory and supplies, sale of merchandise or services, and payment of expenses. As many transactions occur during a fiscal year, a system consisting of a "journal" and a "ledger" is required to keep track of them.

The basic element of this system is an "account" that exists for each asset, liability, owner's equity, revenue source, and expense. Each account acts as a place to deposit collected information about the on-going transactions of operating a business. As the transactions of operating a business occur continuously, they are entered on a daily basis in a journal. They are later posted to appropriate accounts in a ledger either weekly or monthly. The ledger captures the accounts' information in the same order as they appear in the financial statements. For example, the balance sheet ledger accounts begin with current assets and the accounts that constitute them: cash, accounts receivable, inventory, and prepaid expenses. For the income statement, the ledger would list the accounts in the same way starting with sales.

The balance sheet represents the basic accounting equation:

assets = liabilities + owner's equity.

In order for this equation to be constant, a system is required that can detect errors. The system that is used is called "double-entry bookkeeping" and consists of debits and credits. This results in each account having a debit side (the left-hand side) and a credit side (the right-hand side) that allows transactions to be recorded such that each double entry allows the account to balance.

The accounts in the ledger fall into two categories: permanent and temporary. The balance of the permanent accounts at the end of the fiscal year makes up the business' balance sheet. The balance in the temporary accounts, which are revenues or expenses, is used to construct the income statement. The income statement indicates the amount of profit earned as a result of operating the business. The profit is then transferred to the retained earnings account, closing the income statement with a balance of zero and allowing it to start over in the next fiscal year. The retained earnings account increases owner's equity after tax and dividends, if any, are paid.

In the double-entry bookkeeping system, each account has a debit and a credit. At any time, the sum of the debits must equal the sum of the credits. The rules of recording transactions are as follows.

- Each transaction must be recorded separately.

- The transaction must be recorded so that assets = liabilities + owner's equity.

- Each transaction will affect at least two accounts.

- Every transaction must be recorded such that debits equal credits.

Additional rules include:

- An increase in an asset is a debit.

- An increase in a liability or owner's equity is a credit.

- A decrease in an asset is a credit.

- A decrease in a liability or owner's equity is a debit.

- An expense decreases owner's equity and is a debit.

- A revenue increases owner's equity and is a credit.

When an accounting period ends—either weekly, monthly, or quarterly, etc.—and the journal entries have been posted to the ledger, a trial balance is taken. Essentially, the accounts are checked for errors by checking the entries and summing the debit and credit columns. They must balance. Once done, the information is used to prepare financial statements.

INCOME STATEMENT AND BALANCE SHEET

Financial statements provide a picture of the financial status of a business. Basically, they comprise an income statement (profit and loss statement) and a balance sheet. The financial statement reflects the pharmacy's income, expenses, profit, assets, and liabilities over a period of time—usually a fiscal year of 12 months. The progress of a business can be analyzed by comparing data in current-year financial statements with those in previous years' statements, as well as with published industry averages. Financial ratios can also be calculated from financial-statement data and are similarly compared with previous ratios of the business and with past industry averages to gauge progress. The basic formats of an income statement and of a balance sheet are shown in Figures 5.1 and 5.2 (p. 98). Both dollar figures and percentages (based on total sales in the income statement and on total assets in the balance sheet) are reported.

Figure 5.1   *Sample Income Statement*
            Average Canadian Pharmacy Limited
            December 31, 199y

	199x		199y	
	Dollars	*Percent of Total Sales*	*Dollars*	*Percent of Total Sales*
Sales				
Prescription sales	$1,206,871	55.3%	$1,173,543	54.2%
OTC sales	311,593	14.3	311,654	14.4
Cosmetic sales	79,257	3.6	102,411	4.7
Other sales	583,807	26.8	576,945	26.7
Total Sales	$2,181,528	100.0	$2,164,553	100.0
Cost of Goods Sold	$1,534,677	70.3	$1,524,897	70.4
Gross Margin	$ 646,851	29.7	$ 639,656	29.6
Expenses				
Owner/manager salary	$ 87,494	4.0	$ 80,920	3.7
Employee wages	249,704	11.4	244,862	11.3
Rent	48,025	2.2	51,311	2.4
Heat, light, power	8,106	0.4	12,542	0.6
Acct., legal, prof. fees	9,988	0.4	9,006	0.4
Taxes and licences	9,395	0.4	9,415	0.4
Insurance	5,620	0.3	5,478	0.3
Interest paid	10,365	0.5	8,708	0.4
Repairs	6,681	0.3	7,274	0.4
Delivery	5,465	0.3	4,741	0.2
Advertising	24,131	1.1	26,156	1.2
Depreciation for fixtures	19,522	0.9	16,947	0.8
Bad debts	1,854	0.1	1,367	0.1
Telephone	4,345	0.2	4,516	0.2
Miscellaneous	84,416	3.9	102,615	4.7
Total Expenses	$ 575,111	26.4%	$ 585,858	27.1%
Profit (or Net Income) before Tax	$ 71,740	3.3%	$ 53,798	2.5%
Other Income	$ 13,140	0.6%	$ 20,242	0.9%
Total Income (before Tax)	$ 84,880	3.9%	$ 74,040	3.4%

Figure 5.2   *Sample Balance Sheet Average*
                Canadian Pharmacy Limited
                December 31, 199y

	199x		199y	
	Dollars	*Percent of Total Sales*	*Dollars*	*Percent of Total Sales*
Current Assets				
Cash	$ 58,581	9.6%	$ 63,558	11.3%
Accounts receivable	118,374	19.4	100,806	17.9
Inventory	261,415	42.9	263,777	46.9
Prepaid expenses	15,613	2.6	9,234	1.6
Total Current Assets	$453,983	74.5%	$437,375	77.7%
Fixtures and equipment	$155,015	25.5%	$125,416	22.3%
Total Assets	$608,998	100.0%	$562,791	100.0%
Liabilities				
Accounts payable	$180,257	29.5%	$187,569	33.3%
Notes payable < 1 year	54,763	9.0	42,271	7.5
Accrued expenses	16,432	2.7	23,528	4.2
Total Current Liabilities	$251,452	41.2%	$253,368	45.0%
Long-term Liabilities (Notes payable > 1 year)	90,442	14.9%	50,991	9.1%
Total Liabilities	$341,894	56.1%	$304,359	54.1%
Net Worth	$267,104	43.9%	$258,432	45.9%
Total Liabilities & Net Worth	$608,998	100.0%	$562,791	100.0%

The income statement shown in Figure 5.1 (p. 97) shows sales by selected product categories. The cost of goods sold is calculated by adding the value of the beginning inventory to the cost of the pharmacy's purchases through the course of the year, then subtracting the ending inventory value. Hypothetical data are used for purchases in the following example (in practice, purchase data would normally come from suppliers' invoices):

Beginning Inventory	$ 261,415
+ Purchases	1,527,259
Total Value of Goods Available for Sale	1,788,674
– Ending Inventory	263,777
Cost of Goods Sold	$1,524,897

The difference between sales and the cost of goods sold is the gross margin (sometimes referred to as gross profit). Gross margin can also be expressed as the sum of expenses and profit. The point to note is that the gross margin must be sufficient to cover expenses and leave an amount for profit.

Expenses are normally listed as illustrated in Figure 5.1 (p. 97). It is interesting to recalculate the expense percentages using total expenses as a base, as shown in Figure 5.3 (p. 100). This serves to demonstrate the significance of several of the expense categories; specifically, salaries, rent, and "miscellaneous," and the need to monitor these carefully, as they account for 81.8 percent of total expenses.

Of the expenses listed, perhaps the least familiar to those who are inexperienced in accounting procedures is depreciation. Because fixed assets (including fixtures, equipment, and buildings) deteriorate or become obsolete over time, the owners of those assets may deduct a certain percentage of their original cost from annual income for a period of time, from acquisition of the asset to the time of its disposal or replacement.

Such deductions are represented as an expense on the income statement, and the declining value of the assets will be reflected accordingly in the annual balance sheets. It is important to remember that depreciation is a non-cash expense. Several methods of computing depreciation over the life of an asset exist; the pharmacy's accountant should determine the optimal method to be applied.

Figure 5.3   Expenses Calculated as a Percentage of Total Expenses for Fiscal Year 199y

Expense Item	Percent of Sales	Percent of Total Expenses
Owner/manager salary	3.7	13.8
Employee wages	11.3	41.8
Rent	2.4	8.7
Heat, light, power	0.6	2.1
Accounting, legal, professional fees	0.4	1.5
Taxes and licences	0.4	1.6
Insurance	0.3	0.9
Interest paid	0.4	1.5
Repairs	0.4	1.2
Delivery	0.2	0.8
Advertising	1.2	4.7
Depreciation for fixtures	0.8	2.9
Bad debts	0.1	0.2
Telephone	0.2	0.8
Miscellaneous	4.7	17.5
	27.1	100.0

"Other income" may be the income from investments held by the business (interest or dividends), sales generated from lottery tickets or a post office, or gains from the realization of extraordinary items, such as profits realized on the sale of fixed assets.

An expanded view of an income statement appears in Figure 5.4 and illustrates the four variables that affect profit:

1) unit price;

2) unit volume (i.e., number of units sold);

3) unit cost;

4) expenses.

Figure 5.4   Expanded Income Statement

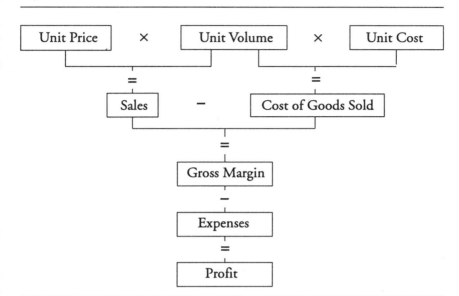

Source: Adapted from W.R. Davidson, D.J. Sweeney, and R.W. Stampfl, *Retailing Management,* 6th ed. © 1998. John Wiley and Sons, p. 169.

By manipulating one or more of these variables, profit performance can be affected. In addition, it is important to note that unit price, unit volume, and unit cost affect gross margin, thus providing three opportunities to improve profit, whereas expense control provides only one.

The balance sheet indicates the financial position of a firm as of the date that appears on it (see Figure 5.2, p. 98). Balance sheets, like income statements, are prepared periodically—at least annually—and contain comparative figures from the previous accounting period. Once again, it is important to keep in mind the basic accounting equation:

liabilities + owner's equity = assets.

Assets are those items that are owned by the business—in other words, all of the business's resources; liabilities (also called creditors' equity) are the debts of the business; and owner's equity is the personal capital contributed by the owners, together with accumulated earnings retained in the business, commonly known as retained earnings. All assets are attributed to claims of creditors or owners; conversely, the claims of creditors and owners must be balanced by total assets. Assets can be current, meaning that they can be converted into cash within a 12-month period, or non-current (fixed), meaning that they can be converted to cash but over a longer period of time. Included among non-current or fixed assets are fixtures, delivery vehicles, and buildings. The largest asset in a pharmacy practice is usually its inventory, which represents almost one-half of total assets.

Liabilities are also categorized as current or long-term, with similar constraints of payment: current liabilities will be paid within a year and long-term liabilities are paid over a longer period of time. Current liabilities include accounts payable, that is, the amount that the pharmacy owes on purchases obtained on credit from its suppliers. In addition, short-term notes payable are a current liability. These are loans provided by lending institutions for the purchase of seasonal merchandise and are expected to be repaid upon demand. Long-term liabilities include such items as a mortgage on the building and loans incurred in the purchase of the business, generally for the purchase of fixed assets.

Owner's (or shareholders') equity or net worth is the difference between total assets and total liabilities. It represents the owner's or shareholders' claim to the assets that remain after debts to creditors have been discharged; hence, the owner's interest is equal to the net assets of the business.

Finally, the profits of the firm (as a corporation) can be distributed to the shareholders as cash dividends or they can be reinvested in the business as retained earnings. Retained earnings are used for expansion of the business.

An expanded view of a balance sheet appears in Figure 5.5. The advantage of expressing a financial statement as a flow chart is that it can be a useful visual aid in presenting current data and speculating on future data by posing "what if" questions. Each rectangle can be split diagonally, with current data inserted in one section and forecast data in the other. In addition, while the usual method of reading the chart is from left to right, according to the usual flow, reading it from right to left (starting with anticipated financial outcomes) allows some insight into what the assets and liabilities must be in order to arrive at the expected outcomes. In this way, the flow chart can be used as a planning aid.

Figure 5.5   **Expanded Balance Sheet**

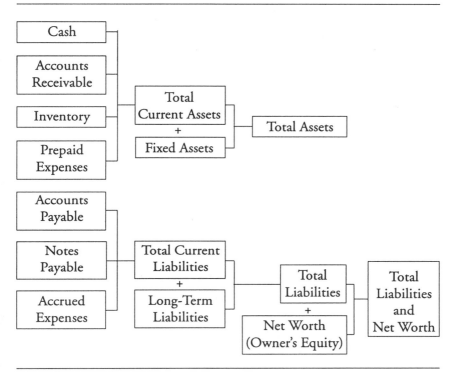

Source: Adapted from the NACA Bulletin, 1952 Conference Proceedings © 1952 by the National Association of Cost Accountants. As reprinted in C.A. Kline Jr., and Howard L. Hessler, "The DuPont Chart System for Appraising Operating Performance." In W.E. Thomas, Jr., ed. *Readings in Cost Accounting, Budgeting and Control.* 2nd ed. Florence, Kentucky: South-Western Publishing Co., 1960, p. 797.

ESTABLISHING A NEW PHARMACY PRACTICE
Estimating Start-Up Costs

To establish a new pharmacy, the prospective owner must first undertake to forecast its financial operations and viability and to determine the initial investment that will be required. This is accomplished by projecting the owner's anticipated sales and estimated expenses in earning those sales in the form of an income statement. In this process, industry averages can be used as a guideline for forecasting a working plan. Financial forecasting is critical throughout the life of the pharmacy practice, but, over time, the practice will have generated its own financial history from which projections can be made. Following is one approach to estimating start-up costs that can later be integrated as a step in operational planning.

Industry averages for Canadian pharmacies can be found in the Statistics Canada data. In the absence of historical financial data, the prospective owner can refer to the industry averages as an aid in his or her investigation of the costs involved in opening a new pharmacy. The data must, of course, be selected by the province or region that is most applicable to the site of the pharmacy under consideration. Forecasts of financial activity are known as projected statements, meaning that they are hypothetical or anticipatory. (They are also referred to as "proforma" or "forecast" statements.)

There are no rigid guidelines for preparing a projected income statement. On the other hand, common sense and judgment, together with thorough and astute research, are critical in making the estimates as reliable as possible. For example, if the pharmacy is to service an elderly population, the number of prescriptions dispensed is likely to be greater than if the predominant clientele were young and healthy. Having conducted the research necessary for location analysis, the prospective owner will have a good sense of the particular characteristics of the trading area that will call for adjustments to industry averages in the estimating process.

The projected income statement is constructed around an estimate of expected total sales for the period being planned, based on results of location analysis, comparison with industry averages, and the size and type of the proposed pharmacy. This figure then serves as a base and is taken as 100 percent. Other items on the income statement may be calculated as a percentage of this total sales figure. Examine Figure 5.6 to see how this principle is put into practice in our sample proforma income statement. Read the statement following the sequence of numbered annotations in the right-hand column. Notice that we have used the industry-average percentages from Figure 5.1 (p. 97) as our base.

Where known data exist or can be determined (rent or utilities, for example), they should always be used in lieu of estimates. Salaries and wages can be projected by determining the type and number of employees to be hired and researching current rates of pay. Current costs of utilities can also be researched and projected. As a check, the resulting percentages of total sales represented by these projections can be compared to the corresponding percentages in the industry averages.

Figure 5.6   *Average Pharmacy Limited*
Sample Projected Income Statement
December 31, 199y

Total Sales	$841,790	100.0%	2.	Based on prescriptions representing 54.2% of total sales
Prescription sales	456,250	54.2	1.	Based on dispensing 50 prescriptions daily at ave. price of $25—a conservative estimate, as sales in the first year are normally below average
Other	385,540	45.8	3.	Calculated difference between total sales and prescription sales
Cost of Goods Sold	592,620	70.4	4.	Based on discussions with suppliers and industry averages
Gross Margin	249,170	29.6	5.	Calculated difference between total sales and cost of goods sold; owner likely to strive to exceed industry-average gross margin percentage, which it is reasonable to assume may not occur in the first year
Expenses				
Salaries	126,269	15.0	6.	Based on estimates of salaries
Rent	20,203	2.4	7.	Based on landlord's lease
Utilities	5,051	0.6	8.	Based on estimate of utilities' costs
Other	76,603	9.1	9.	Based on industry averages
Total Expenses	228,126	27.1	10.	Calculated sum of expenses
Profit	21,044	2.5 *(before tax)*	11.	Calculated difference between gross margin and total expenses; over time, owner to expect profit in excess of industry average
Other Income	7,576	0.9	12.	Based on industry averages
Total Income	$ 28,620	3.4%	13.	Calculated sum of profit and other income

All expenses except salaries, rent, and utilities are grouped under the category "other." The projection is based on the percentage of total sales represented by these expense items in the industry averages. This is therefore a very rough estimate, and, in practice, should be adjusted and fine-tuned to reflect research into current costs for some of the items involved (e.g., licences and insurance). An important point to note is that one item included under "other" is interest payments. It is clear that this amount will require adjustment once projections have been completed and the amount of money that is actually needed to be borrowed to finance the pharmacy can be estimated. Of course, this requires reworking the projected statement to achieve desired financial outcomes.

Once a sense of the costs involved for an average year of the proposed pharmacy's operation has been gained, as well as the gross margin required to cover expenses and provide an acceptable level of profit has been estimated, it is necessary to consider the actual costs involved in the initial investment in the pharmacy. From the projected income statement, it will be necessary to develop proforma monthly income and cash-flow statements in order to estimate the amount of working capital that will be required for the first three months of operation. Working capital, in this context, refers to the funds needed to cover expenses in addition to interest payments or other financing costs, until the pharmacy becomes profitable and can meet these obligations out of its own revenues. Sufficient working capital for at least the first three-month period should be in hand at the outset of the venture.

Expenses for the initial period should be adjusted upward to reflect the cost of first and last months' rent deposits, possible required deposits on utilities, fees for licences and permits, initial legal and accounting fees, and higher advertising costs connected with the opening of the new business.

In addition to working capital, the prospective owner must plan for a large initial outlay of capital in the areas of: inventory, and fixtures and equipment. The financing costs (whether to financial institutions or suppliers) for funds borrowed to cover these investments will be added to the expenses in the income statement. The prospective owner must explore payment terms with suppliers of merchandise and of fixtures and equipment: down payments of a certain percentage of the costs will be required and repayment schedules for the balance will be negotiated. Such arrangements will affect the amount of funds that must be borrowed at the outset. It is also possible to lease, rather than buy, fixtures and equipment.

Suppliers of drugs and merchandise can offer invaluable assistance in determining the products and quantities to stock in the pharmacy in its first year of operation. The estimate for cost of goods sold for the projected income statement can be derived through discussions with suppliers, analysis of market demand in the trading area, and comparison with industry averages. Suppliers can also help with the critical selection of the initial inventory that will be required. The size of the investment in initial inventory will vary significantly with each operation. However, a useful way of checking that the estimated initial investment is reasonable is to divide the cost of goods sold figure from your projected income statement by a basic rate of inventory turnover of four (meaning that the store's entire inventory is expected to be sold and replenished four times in the course of the year). Using the amount for cost of goods sold from the sample statement in Figure 5.6 (p. 105), an estimated initial inventory value would be: $592,620 ÷ 4 = $148,155. To ensure that such estimates are not exceeded in actuality, new owners must select merchandise very carefully during the first year, focusing on product lines that are known to be salable, and making cautious investments into less proven lines. Suppliers can provide statistics on the rates of sale of the products they distribute and these should be investigated thoroughly by the new pharmacy owner. In addition, many suppliers will offer extended dating on items purchased for store openings.

Fixtures and equipment include all of the shelving (gondolas) needed for the store, special display fixtures, magazine and card racks, signs, carpeting, cash registers, computers, dispensary equipment, and reference library materials. The costs for these items will depend on their quality and on the prices that can be negotiated with various suppliers. It is wise to conduct extensive research into current market prices to arrive at a reliable estimate of these costs, balancing requirements for the desired image of the pharmacy with critical cost considerations.

Calculating the Break-Even Point

Another useful tool in financial planning is break-even analysis, a test that determines the degree of business volume at which total sales equal total expenses, or, in other words, at which sales equal fixed costs plus variable costs. A break-even analysis should be conducted before proceeding in any business venture. There are several approaches to calculating the break-even point: a rough calculation is presented here. In Chapter 7 (p. 148), a more sophisticated and detailed approach is introduced.

The rough estimate is calculated by dividing total estimated expenses by the estimated gross margin percentage. Hence, using the figures from the sample projected income statement in Figure 5.6 (p. 105), a break-even point of $770,696 is calculated. This means that the pharmacy must achieve sales of at least $770,696 to avoid a financial loss. Since it is estimated that the pharmacy's sales in the first year will exceed this amount, this encourages proceedings.

However, a second test that should be made is the calculation of the profit point to determine whether the proposed pharmacy can make a reasonable profit. For an established, thriving pharmacy operation, a rule of thumb is that a reasonable profit is 25 percent of the gross margin. The profit point is calculated by the same formula used to determine the break-even point, except that the gross margin percentage is reduced by 25 percent. Hence,

$$\frac{\$228,126}{0.296 - (0.25 \times 0.296)} = \frac{\$228,126}{0.222} = \$1,027,595.$$

The resulting profit point is thus in the area of a sales volume of $1,027,595. This sales volume will generate a profit equivalent to 25 percent of the gross margin, as can be seen from the following reconciliation:

Sales	$1,027,595
Gross Margin (29.6%)	304,168
– Total Expenses	228,126
Profit	$76,042, or 25% of estimated gross margin.

If it is feasible for sales to reach $1,027,595 within the first three to five years of the pharmacy's operation, the prospective owner is further assured that it is sensible to proceed with the new pharmacy practice. It can be argued that this goal is too ambitious, but many well-run pharmacies do achieve profits in excess of the guideline of 25 percent of gross margin. Note that industry averages might not reflect such profits because, as averages, they include statistics from pharmacies that are unprofitable, whether through poor management, detrimental shifts in their markets, or newness in business.

BUYING AN ESTABLISHED PHARMACY
Estimating the Value of a Pharmacy

If the prospective owner is planning to purchase an established pharmacy, the task at hand is to estimate the value of that pharmacy's operating assets in order to determine the price that he or she would be willing to pay. The operating assets consist of inventory, fixtures, and goodwill. Various methods are currently being used to assess the value of both the tangible and intangible assets of pharmacies. Formal valuations are comprehensive and may include, for example, physical counts of inventory by independent appraisers, as well as thorough financial analyses and projections. Following is an example of a valuation that calculates a theoretical or notional value for operating assets based on historical financial data. (Note that our discussion assumes that assets, rather than shares of the corporation, are being purchased).

Estimating the value of a pharmacy is a specialized area and the services of an accountant experienced in mergers and acquisitions or a business valuator should be engaged. Background in pharmacy valuation should be a prerequisite for the adviser selected. However, the prospective owner should also be able to make informed judgments, and an understanding of the following method, known as the capitalization of earnings method, would allow him or her to do so.

INDICATED EARNINGS

The two major factors involved in determining a reasonable value for any small business are: 1) indicated pre-tax earnings[a], and 2) the earnings multiplier. Indicated earnings are the pre-tax income that a purchaser can expect the pharmacy to achieve after reasonable wages (for both the owner and the staff) and all operating expenses have been paid. To determine indicated earnings, financial statements for the last three to five years of the pharmacy's operations (along with the forecast or budget for next year's expectations) must be reviewed. Expenses should be recalculated to eliminate any charges that would no longer apply under new ownership. Similarly, if the current owner was taking his or her remuneration by dividends rather than salary, a

[a] Another, more traditional, approach to the capitalization of earnings method uses net or after-tax income in calculating indicated earnings. The use of pre-tax earnings is an alternative approach that is also practised today. Once again, prospective owners should discuss their professional adviser's method of choice in detail and understand all its implications fully.

reasonable amount for owner remuneration would have to be added to the expenses. If, after such adjustments are made, the pre-tax earnings show an increase from year-to-year, and if there are prospects that this trend will continue, then the latest year's adjusted pre-tax earnings may in fact represent the indicating-earnings figure that is being sought.

It might be helpful to consider a hypothetical financial statement for a pharmacy that is being offered for sale, as shown in Figure 5.7. The figure shows the adjustments that have been made and the resulting indicated earnings.

Figure 5.7   Sample Financial Statement: Calculation of Indicated Earnings

	Per Financial Statement	%		Adjustments	Indicated Earnings	%
Sales	$1,300,000		$		$1,300,000	
Gross Margin	390,000	30*			390,000	
Expenses						
Wages	250,000	64**	–	75,000	175,000	45**
Occupancy (rent and utilities)	35,000	9**			35,000	9**
Other	100,000	26**	–	18,000	82,000	21**
Total Expenses	385,000	99**	–	93,000	292,000	75**
Pre-Tax Earnings	$ 5,000	1**	+	$93,000	$ 98,000	25**

*   percentage of total sales
**   percentage of gross margin

As can be seen, the annual pre-tax income in the original financial statement is $5,000. "Wages" and "other" expenses, at 64 percent and 26 percent of gross margin respectively, appear to be excessive. This would prompt a prospective purchaser to analyze the financial details further.

Assume that this analysis indicates that the owner took a bonus of $75,000 in excess of a reasonable salary; this would call for an adjustment to reduce the wage expense to $175,000, thus bringing it to a more acceptable 45 percent of gross margin. In addition, it is found that, among "other" expenses there is a $10,000 financing cost and an $8,000 automobile expense that will no longer apply once the pharmacy is sold. This results in an $18,000 reduction in "other" expenses from $100,000 to $82,000, or 21 percent of gross margin. The indicated pre-tax earnings are therefore $98,000, rather than $5,000 as suggested by the financial statement.

Although the adjustments in this example lead to improvements in the indicated earnings, this will certainly not always be the case. Also, the need for an adjustment may not always be apparent to one who is inexperienced in accounting procedures; hence, as suggested earlier, the assistance of a professional accountant is critical.

THE EARNINGS MULTIPLIER

To determine the theoretical value of the operating assets (i.e., inventory; fixed assets, excluding property; and goodwill), the capitalization of earnings method multiplies the indicated earnings of the pharmacy by a certain factor, or multiplier, which is related to return on investment (ROI). The earnings multiplier is in fact the reciprocal of the percentage return on investment that the business should be expected to bring to its owner.

The purchaser will be willing to pay, in part, for the security of the business' earning power. The return on investment in a small business is expected to be greater than the prime-rate return that would be received on a guaranteed investment with a bank, for the simple reason that the former is not as secure an investment as the latter and the investor expects compensation for taking on the greater risk. This higher return on small-business investment is commonly estimated to be about four times (or 400 percent of) the current prime rate. For purposes of illustration, if the prime rate is five percent, then the suggested return on investment is 5 × 4.0 = 20 percent. The reciprocal of 20 percent is 100 ÷ 20 = 5, which is our earnings multiplier. Hence, the academic value of the operating assets in this example would be as follows: $98,000 (indicated earnings) × 5 (earnings multiplier) = $490,000. While using the 20 percent ROI for the sake of our example, it should be emphasized that it is not an absolute, but a yardstick only. The multiplier used in actual valuations would be adjusted in recognition of various factors, including prospects for growth, efficiency of the business, the state of the economy, competition, and the demand for the particular type of business at the particular time.

What has been described is the basic return on investment expected in a normal small business. A pharmacy, however, is generally a much safer investment than most small businesses, and the prospect of future profits is more reasonably measurable. Because of this, the anticipated rate of return on investment in a pharmacy need not be as high as it is in a normal small business, as there is less risk of failure for which the investor might deserve compensation. The seller may feel justified in placing a higher value on a pharmacy, and the purchaser must determine whether the particular pharmacy is such a low risk that it justifies the higher price—by considering profits in the past, the location of the pharmacy, and the measurable prospects for increased sales in the future. The effects on profitability of current legislation in the province and the prevailing provincial drug plan should also be taken into consideration. If future prospects are encouraging, then a reasonable expectation for ROI might be as low as 15 percent. Applying the formula to a 15 percent ROI, a high-value earnings multiplier of $100 + 15 = 6.7$ is obtained with a resulting high value for the pharmacy of $98,000 × 6.7 = $656,600. Hence, under normal circumstances, this pharmacy should sell for between $490,000 and $656,600. The notional value of the operating assets would be somewhere in the middle—at approximately $573,000. These calculations are summarized in Figure 5.8.

It is useful to put this calculated value into perspective relative to the actual value of the physical assets of the pharmacy. If the final purchase price is set at $573,000, and the actual worth of the inventory and net fixed assets has been assessed at $250,000 and $35,000 respectively, then the balance of $288,000 is the amount being paid for the intangible asset of goodwill. Some sources suggest that goodwill should be valued at between two and three times the indicated pre-tax earnings. The $288,000 paid for goodwill in this example is 2.9 times the indicated earnings of $98,000. A purchase price of $573,000 is at the high end of a reasonable value.

STRUCTURING THE PURCHASE

Once the buyer and seller have agreed to a price for the pharmacy, the purchase must be "structured," which means that the question of purchasing assets versus shares of the corporation must be decided, terms of payment must be negotiated, and various other details of the transaction confirmed.

Figure 5.8   Notional Value of Operating Assets

Indicated earnings	$98,000
ROI expected from normal small business	5% × 4.0 = 20%
Earnings multiplier	100 ÷ 20 = 5
Value of normal small business	$98,000 × 5 = $490,000
ROI expected from pharmacy with measurable potential for high earning power	15%
High-value multiplier	100 ÷ 15 = 6.7
High value	$98,000 × 6.7 = $656,600
Selling price	$490,000 – $656,600

The income-tax implications in the purchase of any business, including a pharmacy, are extremely important and integral to the decision of whether to purchase the corporation (i.e., its shares) or the assets of the corporation only. Traditionally, the seller wishes to sell shares while the purchaser wishes to purchase assets. The advantage to the seller of selling shares has recently been enhanced in the Income Tax Act, since the seller is now eligible for a capital-gains exemption of up to $500,000 on shares of qualifying small business operations.[b] (Capital gains are gains that result from the disposition of capital property.) However, redundant assets—those that are not essential to operating the pharmacy, such as excess cash in bank accounts, marketable securities, or real estate holdings unrelated to the pharmacy—must be removed from the balance sheet before selling the shares of

[b] In order for the shares of the pharmacy to qualify for the $500,000 capital-gains exemption, the business must comply with a number of complex provisions of the recently enacted income-tax legislation, and most notably with the "90 percent rule": at least 90 percent of the fair market value of the underlying corporation must be represented by operating assets (such as accounts receivable, inventory, and fixed assets).

the corporation to any purchaser. Any income or expenses attributable to these redundant assets must also be removed. This can either result in a considerable increase in the seller's personal income tax, possibly offsetting any tax savings afforded by the $500,000 capital-gains exemption, or in increased costs related to professional advice sought in order to minimize any potential problems.

The situation is further complicated as follows: the purchaser will be at an extreme financial disadvantage when buying shares. First, in certain provinces, 51 percent of the shares must be held by the pharmacist personally. The pharmacist will undoubtedly have acquired a debt to purchase those shares, and will be repaying it out of the purchased company's earnings that will be paid to him in the form of salary, bonuses, or dividends. Of course, such funds are then part of the pharmacist's personal income, on which tax must be paid at personal income-tax rates. (In the case of dividends, the pharmacy will have paid tax on the earnings, and the pharmacist will pay tax at personal rates on the portion of income remaining after dividend tax credits are taken into account.) The amount remaining after tax will be used to pay the debt. This may be onerous and costly.

If the pharmacist purchases the assets of the corporation instead of its shares, the newly formed company can "write off" a portion of the goodwill purchased. A decreasing annual write-off applies until the balance is virtually eliminated.

In addition to the financial problems involved, the other major disadvantage of purchasing the corporation (by buying its shares) is that the purchaser is buying a legal entity. Any problems associated with that entity since the day of incorporation will be inherited by the new owner. This means that the purchaser's lawyer and accountant must be extremely careful in examining the corporate records to be certain that there are no skeletons in the closet. Although the purchase agreement will contain various warranties to guard against such problems, the purchaser should be aware that complications associated with income-tax irregularities or other contingent liabilities could nevertheless surface in the future.

Once the price and structure of the purchase have been determined, the next step is to prepare a simple letter of intent. To save on the costs involved in preparing a major contract, the buyer and seller should be in complete agreement about the basic elements of the purchase, such as price, terms of payment, and structure, before the lawyer is commissioned to draw up a formal purchase agreement. The letter of intent that precedes the formal agreement should include a sentence indicating that the closing will be subject to the purchaser obtaining the necessary financing to complete the purchase. When both parties have signed the letter of intent, the buyer may proceed with negotiating the necessary financing. This involves the preparation of a business plan.

Any pharmacist planning to enter into an independent business venture should assemble a reliable advisory board or management team, including an accountant with proven income-tax expertise, a lawyer, and a knowledgeable banker. The group may be supplemented by a financial consultant, an insurance broker, and, perhaps, a realtor.

BUYING VERSUS LEASING PREMISES

Many pharmacy owners believe that it is important to own the premises in which the pharmacy operates. However, an investment in the premises is not an investment in the pharmacy. As mentioned earlier, a reasonable return on the investment in the operating assets of a pharmacy is 15 to 20 percent. The return (before finance costs) in a real estate property will probably not exceed ten percent.

Independent pharmacists starting out on their own will normally find that cash is short. The safest approach may be to start as a tenant by taking over the existing lease, rather than to tie up funds in real estate. It is, however, to the buyer's advantage to include an option-to-buy clause in the purchase agreement, or, at least, to ensure a right of first refusal (known as a pre-emptive right). After five years in operation, the new pharmacy owner should be in a better cash position to consider purchasing the premises.

In the case of opening a new pharmacy, once the desired premises has been located, the next step is to have the real estate agent prepare an "offer to lease," which was covered in detail in Chapter 4 (p. 78).

A common mistake made by pharmacists is to lease too much space or agree to a lease that bases rent on a percentage of the pharmacy's sales. Too often that percentage is excessive. Before signing any offer to lease, the pharmacist should determine the proposed pharmacy's estimated sales and gross margin. Occupancy cost, which includes rent, utilities, maintenance, and property taxes, should not exceed ten percent of the gross margin. For example, in Figure 5.7 (p. 110), occupancy cost, at $35,000, is nine percent of the $390,000 gross margin. In an ambitious rental property, the occupancy cost may be 20 percent or more of the gross margin. Under such terms, the pharmacy owner is in effect entering into partnership with the landlord, as the extra ten percent will probably represent close to 50 percent of the anticipated profits of the pharmacy.

SUMMARY

Pharmacists who plan to own their own businesses must recognize the extent of the financial risks involved and protect themselves by investing the necessary time and energy in planning financial needs and expectations. The practical skills required at the outset of the venture, whether they involve estimating the costs of opening a new pharmacy or evaluating the worth of an existing pharmacy under consideration for purchase, are perhaps the most critical of all. A working knowledge of the basic principles of accounting and a familiarity with financial statements are essential prerequisites that will enable prospective pharmacy owners to apply the tools and methods presented in this chapter.

6

THE BUSINESS PLAN

UNDERSTANDING THE DOCUMENT

INTRODUCTION

An understanding of the business plan is critical for all entrepreneurs and owners of small businesses. The business plan is essential as a necessary document for loan applications and other forms of financing, and as a tool for setting, monitoring, and meeting business goals. In a sense, the business plan is a summary of all the pharmacist's knowledge about, and plans for, the business, whether starting up a new pharmacy or buying an established one.

Before beginning a business plan, it is useful to conceptualize what the business is about—the size of investment needed, where revenues are to come from, and what expenses are likely to be. Further, one must consider what proportion of revenues will result from cash or credit sales, as this may dictate the need for on-going financing.

A business plan focused on all aspects of the business forces the owner/manager to put into words and numbers what is to be done and how it is going to be accomplished. It is a blueprint or roadmap for the business which will clarify ideas about start-up costs, provide useful information for investors and lenders, and provide a standard against which managerial performance can be measured.[1]

As a management tool, a business plan is a means of communication between entrepreneurs and potential investors or lenders. As such, there are other reasons to have a business plan.[2] A business plan creates an opportunity to test the economic viability of the business concept. If the idea fails on paper, it is certainly less costly than failing in the marketplace. Because the business plan represents the main vehicle for the entrepreneur to create a case for potential lenders, it must include details of the amount of funds required, how they will be used, the type of funding (e.g., loan, line of credit), other funding sources, an exit strategy for the investors, and the expected repayment schedule. Lastly, the question of implementing the business plan must be addressed. This is answered by examining the operating and cash flow budgets—benchmarks with which to measure progress—, and provision of an assessment of whether goals are being met. The business plan generally has a life of one to five years and should be re-worked when necessary.

THE ESSENTIAL COMPONENTS: PEOPLE AND FUNDS

The two main components of a business plan are people and funds. The inclusion of people in the business plan should reflect two positions: 1) those inside the business, the employees; and 2) those outside the business, the professionals providing services and advice.

The Advisory Board

An advisory board or management team is not the same as a board of directors that is found in a publicly-owned company. The five key factors to consider when assembling an advisory board follow:[3]

1.   why outside advisors;

2.   role of an advisory board;

3.   where to find advisors;

4.   what is the cost;

5.   how to terminate the relationship.

All of these are important issues and should be considered carefully. As the marketplace evolves, opportunities for business will increase, as will risks. It is impossible for one person to be current on all of the changes important for operating a successful business. Appropriately related advisors can provide perspectives that allow more informed, better decisions to be made.

An advisory board for a pharmacy practice might include a banker, an accountant, a lawyer, a realtor, and an insurance professional, who will provide guidance and strategic direction. It is important, however, to establish the role of board members before inviting them to participate. What should not be forgotten is the possibility of conflicts of interest and not to place the board members in positions that would compromise their integrity and reputation.

In addition to defining the role of the board, thought must be given to the expected time commitment from the members. Decide on the number of formal meetings to be held, if any, or informal lunches with each, before inviting people to participate. The use of the board member's name in any business proposals should be discussed and clearly understood to avoid any potential embarrassment. The unique knowledge and personal contacts will enhance the contribution from each board member. The sense of working well together must also be taken into account.

Appropriate advisors can be found within the community in which the business is located. Having identified potential members, informal interviews may be useful to determine a level of interest, what the individual has to offer, and if their philosophy of business is compatible with yours.

The question of payment must be addressed. It can be formalized by a letter of appointment or a contract and should be consistent with the stature of the advisor as well as the time and commitment expected. On the other hand, the arrangement can be quite informal and remunerated by a token gift or stipend.

Lastly, there may be a need to terminate the relationship. This can come about after a specified time period or given the inability to participate because of time constraints. Usually, an agreed period of service followed by a review allows the board member and/or owner/manager a graceful way to continue or terminate the relationship.

Funding

Funding is the second essential component of the business plan. The most likely source of funding will be from a bank, as they are as interested in lending as entrepreneurs are to borrow. The key is to borrow intelligently. If banks refuse to fund a business, chances are the business is not "bankable." Banks, after all, are just another supplier to a business. Their product is capital and they, like other suppliers, want to deal with customers who are financially stable.

In order to prepare a loan proposal that a bank will look at positively, consider the soundness of your business plan, level of working capital, and "bankability" of your business.[4] The business must state clearly the objectives and strategies for creating a competitive advantage over the competition. Availability of working capital will determine when and how much money to request. Whether the business is a candidate for financing will be determined by its level of profitability, working capital, equity, expansion plans, and margins. All of these elements must be perceived to be under control and contributing to the success of the business. Lenders are not interested in providing financing to solve problems or correct flaws in strategy or management. They do, however, want to provide funds to make a business grow or become more successful.

Borrowing money is almost an art form in terms of the required negotiating skills. Some factors to include in your loan negotiations are:[5]

- involving multiple lenders;

- including non-lending bank products and services;

- obtaining fixed and floating-rate options;

- obtaining release of personal guarantors;

- avoiding restrictive covenants.

By not using these factors, lenders gain the upper hand, which can result in having to live with unfavorable loans, restricted terms, and higher costs. These, in turn, will raise the costs to service the loan and decrease the business' competitiveness in the market place.

By presenting the loan proposal to several lending institutions, a better sense of the availability of funds can be obtained. By having a choice of lenders available, you can negotiate the terms of the loans to be more favorable to you. Because financial institutions don't earn large amounts from loans to small businesses, they are anxious to provide additional financial services such as payroll, merchant credit card services, and employee Registered Retirement Savings Plans from which they can generate further revenue. These non-lending products can be used to entice the institution to provide a more flexible loan program.

When financing current assets, a floating rate is the one of choice. On the other hand, fixed assets should be funded with long-term, fixed rates. This mix allows short-term rates to rise and fall with the demand for funds, while long-term rates are locked in at the most favorable rate obtainable.

Small business owners almost always are asked to sign personal guarantees for loans thus negating the liability protection of a limited company. Personal guarantors are also used to assure the borrower's commitment to the business. If the lending institution insists on a guarantor, make sure it is limited in the amount and that a release can be achieved on specific performance criteria or balance sheet ratios. This must be part of the loan arrangement and signed before the deal closes.

Lastly, because performance criteria are based on the numbers provided in the financial statement forecasts, be certain they are realistic and achievable. Otherwise you will discover that you restricted yourself financially and also jeopardized your credibility.

Banks have begun to realize that small business represents an opportunity for their own growth. This has been evidenced recently by the increased competition for this market by US banks operating in Canada and by non-traditional lenders such as GE Capital and AT&T Capital, which offer loans at slightly higher rates but require less security. The federal government has also entered the fray attempting to persuade the big Canadian banks to be more accommodating to small business. This has resulted in the size of loans guaranteed under the Small Business Loans Act more than doubling in 1993.[6]

The importance of obtaining sufficient funding is the key to the successful operation of a business. It should not be forgotten that one's financial business strategy is derived from strategy. The way a business is financed determines how it will operate and pursue its goals. In turn, the business plan largely determines the source and amount of funds a business generates.

DEVELOPING THE BUSINESS PLAN

The business plan is an essential document and tool for the small-business owner from several perspectives. It cannot be emphasized enough that, in order to borrow money from the bank or any other financial institution, it is essential that a business plan be prepared. It is the document that the lender will use to determine if the applicant is worthy of a loan. Even if funds are not being borrowed, a business plan prepared at the outset of the venture, and at least once a year thereafter, will help the pharmacy owner focus on and attain personal and business goals.

The discussion in this chapter assumes planning for an established pharmacy with historical financial records. The prospective owner of a new pharmacy would base a business plan on research and projections from industry averages and on results of a location analysis.

The Business Plan

The business plan consists of four sections presented as concise narrative reports: 1) the business, 2) the market, 3) competition, and 4) finance. These sections are preceded by an executive summary, and concluded with an appendix. Figure 6.1, can serve as a template for a business plan. It is a step-wise progression that illustrates where a business is going, how it will get there, and how it might look when it is there.[a]

EXECUTIVE SUMMARY

This is probably the most important part of the business plan as it presents the key issues and distinctive competence of the company. It is a very brief overview of the plan intended to capture lender interest by answering all the questions about management, marketing, and finance. It should be two or three pages at most—the shorter the better. It is recommended that this summary be written first and used as an outline for the balance of the plan.

PART A: THE BUSINESS

This section provides a legal description of the business, its location, purpose, mission/vision statement, and strategy for growth. In addition, it describes the management and staff structure, including job responsibilities, experience, longevity of the business, and how they work together to the benefit of the business. This should be followed by a statement of the business' strengths and weaknesses.

As all businesses require the services of professionals such as lawyers and accountants to some degree, this is an appropriate place to identify them and the services provided. Furthermore, if an advisory board has been constituted, the members and the expertise they bring to the business can be described.

---

[a] For further reading on business plans, please see: "Your Guide to Business Planning", CIBC; "Outline for a Business Plan", Ernst & Young; "The Money Hunter/North Point IT Business Plan Template" (http://www.moneyhunter.com).

Figure 6.1   Suggested Outline for a Business Plan (Sample)

EXECUTIVE SUMMARY

PART A: THE BUSINESS

Company Profile
- legal business description, location
- purpose
- management and staff structure (strengths/weaknesses)
- advisors: accountant
              lawyer
- board of advisors
- succession plan (buy/sell agreement)

PART B: THE MARKET

Industry Outlook
- third-party payers: public insurance plans
                        private insurance plans
- demographics
- managed care as a cost-containment issue

Products and Services
- prescriptions
- over-the-counter products (non-prescription medications)
- other products and services (e.g., home health care)
- medication management services

PART C: COMPETITION
- independents/banner groups
- chains/franchise groups
- supermarkets
- mass merchandisers (market share and proximity)
- pricing

Figure 6.1 (cont'd)

PART D: FINANCE

Historical	• income statement
	• balance sheet (ratio analysis)
	• cash flow (ratio analysis)
Operational Plan	• projected income statement (ratio analysis)
	• projected cash-flow statement
Funds Required	• loan application
APPENDIX	
Résumés of managers	
Significant contracts	• leases
	• partnerships
	• long-term care facilities
	• life insurance

Lastly, a succession plan can be included in order to complete the planning cycle. In some instances, this succession plan might be as straightforward as a buy-sell agreement funded by life insurance, or might be a more comprehensive plan that sets out how management and assets are to be transferred once the owner/manager is no longer with the business.

PART B: THE MARKET

Industry Outlook. The market place in which the business operates needs to be described in concise detail. This includes an explanation of how the industry works: the proportion of prescription patients who are funded by third parties (private and public) as well as the proportion who pay cash. Of importance, also, are the changes occurring in the marketplace that will have an effect on the practice. These are the changes in the demographics of the population and the emphasis on the growing numbers of elderly. Another change is that of restricted payment for health products and services by managed care companies. The business plan must account for changes in the practice that reflect growth but may also reflect a possible downsizing.

Products and Services. Here, one is concerned about the contribution to sales, margins, and profits of each of the products and services supplied. Pharmacy practices traditionally offer prescriptions, over-the-counter (non-prescription) medications, and a myriad of related and non-related products and services. Some discussion about the switching from prescription to non-prescription status of specific products should be included, explaining the increased role of the pharmacist and its implications for growth of the practice.

A recent trend among community pharmacy practitioners is to de-emphasize the mechanical aspects of dispensing medication and to focus on the services that can be delivered to enhance the effectiveness of the medication being used. These fit under the umbrella of medication management services and utilize the pharmacist's education, knowledge, and experience. The business plan should describe the menu of services available and how these will create a competitive advantage for the practice, and how the revenue from these services will enhance profits and add to patient loyalty.

Part C: Competition

Competition among pharmacy practice types is becoming more intense and is being felt from non-pharmacy outlets also. It is important to illustrate an understanding of the competitive forces of the marketplace and how you plan to operate in such an environment. It is equally important to demonstrate an understanding of the distribution of market share among the various competitors and how you plan to attract and retain your fair share.

Related to market share and aggressive competition is the issue of how the competition's proximity to one's practice and the effect of advertising, promotion, and pricing will affect sales and profits. An explanation of the market niche that is targeted and a justification of why it can be attained is required to convince lenders that the practice is viable. This should be reinforced with a statement as to why these might be barriers for competitors to enter your niche as a result of the uniqueness of your services or your pricing strategy. This serves to consolidate your hold on an identified market and increase your chances of success.

Part D: Finance

The financial part of the business plan should include historical data, prospective data, and a clear request for funds. Historical data consist of the past three to five years of income statements, balance sheets, and cash flow statements (see Figures 5.1 and 5.2, p. 97 and 98 and Figure 6.5, p. 134). The level of personal involvement in preparing and interpreting these financial statements should be stated. It is critical that you understand these statements fully when presenting your business plan to a bank. Should questions about the data arise, it is expected that you are able to answer the routine ones and can defer to your accountant for the more complex ones.

An analysis of the financial statements should be included in your business plan, consisting of a trend analysis and a ratio analysis of your data, which are detailed in Chapter 7 (p. 148). Both of these analyses should be compared to appropriate industry averages where appropriate or available.

The prospective proforma or forecast financial statements should also provide a similar analysis (see Figure 5.6, p. 105). These statements contain data that demonstrate how the pharmacy owner's goals are going to be met. Four major issues must be addressed:

1.   profits: How much profit is desired;

2.   costs: Costs to be incurred in earning the profit;

3.   sales: Level of sales required to achieve this profit;

4.   required cash: Cash or size of loan required to finance the pharmacy.

In order to arrive at reasonable answers to these questions, some operational planning is needed. Once completed, the operational plan is summarized and becomes part of the business plan. To develop the operational plan for the practice, the pharmacy owner must undertake six essential steps, as follows:

1.   setting goals: Personal, financial, and business goals should be determined at the outset.

2.   assembling information: Adequate information is needed to prepare a realistic operational plan. Much of this information will come from the previous year's monthly financial statements—historical facts about sales, cost of goods sold, gross margin (by front store and dispensary), and various detailed expenses for wages, occupancy, and "other." In addition, current-year information should be gathered by the month.

Other information needed to draw up an operational plan includes current events in the pharmacy industry: e.g., what effect will the provincial government drug plan have on the future gross margin of your dispensary? If the gross margin of the dispensary is likely to be reduced by two to five percent in the following year as a result of changes in legislation, this information should be used in planning for the following year's operation. Remember that operational planning can be ongoing; it need not wait until the fiscal year-end is approaching.

3.   analyzing sales information: The entire operational plan revolves around sales projections. Review the sales history of each product category in the front store to determine upward or downward trends. Try to forecast what the current trends indicate for the coming year and decide which product groups will increase in sales.

4.   establishing action plans: Assess the direction of the pharmacy for the coming year: is growth indicated or rather a possible downturn in sales? Based on general trends among pharmacies in recent years, the likelihood is that sales will increase slightly in both the front store and dispensary. If, however, there has been a negative shift of the market in your area (involving, for example, numerous job losses due to the closing of a plant), yours may be one of the few, less fortunate, pharmacies that will experience a downturn in sales. In this case, plans should be made to reduce costs in order to optimize profits. On the other hand, if a significant growth cycle is apparent, you should try to estimate the extent of the growth and the number of additional staff that may be required to provide adequate service for your new customers. A growth cycle could easily be predicted if, for example, a new housing development was being planned in the vicinity of the pharmacy.

5.   detailing the operational plan: Consider all your operating expenses, including wages, occupancy costs, and general expenses. Personnel requirements must be determined and noted in the plan: list either by name or by position the employees required and their estimated annual incomes and benefits. Occupancy costs should include estimates for rent, utilities, maintenance, and property taxes for the year. All the other expenses should also be estimated. Do not assume that

this simply involves calculating set increases over last year's expenses, since factors that indicate the need either to increase or decrease certain of these expenses may become apparent on assembling your information.

6.   reviewing and summarizing the plan: The operational plan for the year should be summarized by listing the key results of step 5 in the manner set out in Operational Plan A (Figure 6.2). Note that the profit in Operational Plan A is $20,000. If this does not satisfy the personal and business goals identified in step 1, then all data must be reviewed "with a sharper pencil."

Figure 6.2   Operational Plan A

	Front Store	Dispensary	Total
Sales	$ 600,000	$ 400,000	$ 1,000,000
Cost of Goods Sold	450,000	280,000	730,000
Gross Margin	150,000	120,000	270,000
	25%	30%	27%
Wages			140,000
Occupancy			30,000
Other Expenses			80,000
Total Expenses			250,000
Net Profit			$ 20,000

Operational Plan B (Figure 6.3) sets out the results of this rethinking of the data from the original operational plan. Part of this revised plan may be to reduce the volume of sales of low-profit items, such as paper goods, in the front store. This may reduce sales by $50,000 per year, with a corresponding $5,000 reduction in gross margin. One might also take a harder

Figure 6.3   Operational Plan B

	Front Store	Dispensary	Total
Sales	$550,000	$400,000	$950,000
Cost of Goods Sold	405,000	260,000	635,000
Gross Margin	145,000	140,000	285,000
	26%	35%	30%
Wages			120,000
Occupancy			30,000
Other Expenses			70,000
Total Expenses			220,000
Net Profit			$ 65,000

look at purchasing of products for the dispensary. The revised plan may indicate that purchasing could be effected more wisely, which may increase the gross margin from 30 percent, as originally estimated, to 35 percent. The overall effect would be a $15,000 increase in gross margin.

On reviewing the pharmacy's personnel, it might be possible to cut back on part-time staff in the front store because of the reduced sales activity there, and hire pharmacy assistants rather than higher-priced pharmacists for the dispensary. This could result in a reduction in wages of $20,000 per year.

"Other" expenses may include the costs of financing. Part of the plan might involve reducing inventory and extending some of the accounts payable over time in order to first reduce the bank debt and the related cost of financing (interest payments). Cutbacks in some of the minor expenses might also be involved in the $10,000 reduction in "other" expenses.

As illustrated in Figures 6.2 and 6.3, the goal is to make $65,000 in your pharmacy after paying yourself a reasonable wage. Consequently, you should start by preparing an operational plan and then reworking that plan to achieve the desired result.

Your chartered accountant can review the details of your operational plan to see if it is realistic. If you feel comfortable with the plan, the next step is to prepare your projected monthly income statement.

PROJECTED MONTHLY INCOME STATEMENT

The projected monthly income statement allows you to review or monitor your plan throughout the upcoming year. Preparing this statement should be the task of the pharmacy owner: don't be too quick to delegate it to your accountant or bookkeeper. Although it is generally wise to delegate, keep this particular financial report for yourself, as it is the key to the success of your pharmacy, and provides first-hand details of your financial affairs. Remember, the owner is the chief financial officer of the pharmacy.

Forecasting your monthly income is not as difficult as it may seem. All you need is a sheet of 13-column paper and the figures from your operational plan, together with the details of information assembled by month in the current year. Head each column with the appropriate month of the year and use the last column for the total. Then, in accordance with the operational plan, determine the sales and expenses by month and record them in the appropriate columns (see Figure 6.4). Note that the fiscal year in our example is October 1 through September 30: the pharmacy owner may choose a different 12-month period, but it is not necessarily advisable to adopt the conventional December 31 year-end. This decision should be made taking into consideration an accountant's advice with respect to the tax advantages.

You will notice on reviewing the sales activity of your pharmacy over the past years that certain months have greater activity than others. For example, November and December will probably indicate higher front-store sales due to Christmas shopping. Similarly, dispensary sales may be higher in the months just before your senior-citizen clients go south for the winter. Whatever the case may be, you should attempt to take the $950,000 in sales (Figure 6.3, p. 129) and spread it across the various months between the front store and the dispensary. In other words, the forecast monthly income statement represents the pharmacy owner's best estimates, based on experience and previous accounting reports. The more often the pharmacy owner prepares projected income statements, the more accurate they will become and the more informed the owner will be about the operation.

Figure 6.4   Projected Monthly Income Statement (in thousands of dollars)

Month	(1) Oct.	(2) Nov.	(3) Dec.	(10) July	(11) Aug.	(12) Sept.	Total
Sales							
Front Store	40.0	45.0	50.0	35.0	40.0	40.0	500.0
Dispensary	35.0	35.0	40.0	30.0	35.0	35.0	450.0
Total	75.0	80.0	90.0	65.0	75.0	75.0	950.0
Cost of Goods Sold	49.9	53.6	60.2	43.2	49.9	49.9	635.0
Gross Margin	25.1	26.4	29.8	21.8	25.1	25.1	315.0
Expenses							
Wages	10.0	9.5	10.0	9.0	9.5	9.5	120.0
Occupancy	2.5	2.5	2.5	2.5	2.5	2.5	30.0
Other	6.0	6.5	5.5	6.0	5.5	6.5	70.0
Total	18.5	18.5	18.0	17.5	17.5	18.5	220.0
Net Profit for Period	6.6	7.9	11.8	4.3	7.6	6.6	95.0

Projected Monthly Cash-Flow Statement

The next step is to consider cash requirements for the pharmacy. The projected monthly income statement is prepared on an accrual-basis. In other words, sales are recorded once the products in the front store and dispensary are sold, and the corresponding cost of the merchandise sold is recorded at the same time. This obviously does not reflect the actual flow of cash in and out of the pharmacy. For example, prescription sales covered by third-party insurance programs may be recorded in month 5, but the cash may not be collected until month 7. Similarly, drugs sold will be recorded (at cost) as cost of goods sold in month 5, but they may have been purchased in month 2 and paid for only in month 4.

Your operational plan might involve purchasing two new cash registers for about $2,500 in the second month and paying for them in the third month. The plan might also include a $5,000 renovation of the shelving for the reduced inventory, to be incurred in month 1 and paid in month 2. You may be planning to reduce inventory by $24,000 for the year at the rate of about $2,000 per month: this will be reflected in a reduced payment for merchandise of $2,000 for the previous month.

The question, then, is "How much cash is required to finance the pharmacy?" To answer this, a forecast monthly cash-flow statement must be prepared. This, too, may sound like a lot of detailed paperwork best left to the accountant, but, remember, it's your money and the cash-flow statement is not as difficult to prepare as it may seem. In simple terms, a projected monthly cash-flow statement sets out the estimated amounts of cash receipts and cash disbursements by month for the following year. A 13-column sheet is used once again, heading up the columns with the respective months and leaving the 13th column to represent the total for the year.

Let us consider cash receipts. You must determine when the cash from projected sales will actually be received. From Figure 6.4 (p. 131), you will notice that in month 1, front-store sales total $40,000 and dispensary sales total $35,000. Unless there are customer credit accounts, we can assume that the $40,000 is cash received on front-store sales. If third-party drug plans represent about 50 percent of dispensary sales, then we can assume that $17,500 of the $35,000 was received in month 1. If we assume the third-party payments are received within 30 days, then the remaining $17,500 will be received in month 2. The cost of goods sold will no doubt have been expended one, two, or even three months prior to month 1. Assuming that the average payment time to suppliers is 30 days, then the purchases in month 1 will be paid in month 2. In some cases, it is fair to assume that the pharmacy's purchases in month 1 equal its cost of goods sold in the same month. For example, the cost of goods sold in month 1 was $49,900 and purchases are assumed to be the same amount less $2,000 for the reduction of inventory. The $47,900 is to be paid in month 2. Expenses for wages, occupancy, and "other" are normally recorded as being paid in the month incurred. So, from Figure 6.5 (p. 134), you will see that the actual cash receipts and disbursements are indeed different from the projected income statement in Figure 6.4 (p. 131).

(*Note:* We have assumed that the accounts receivable for the previous month total $15,000, and accounts payable, $45,000). Notice the entry for depreciation, wherein an amount is being deducted from the cash disbursements (in the projected monthly income statement, depreciation is included within "other" expenses). This is done because depreciation is an expense only in an accounting sense: it is not an actual cash disbursement, and must not be allowed to distort the picture of actual cash flow.

As you can see, our planning has resulted in eliminating the $75,000 bank loan that was outstanding at the beginning of the year and establishing a positive balance of $36,100 at year-end. Remember that the readers of your business plan are most interested in assessing the operation's potential for success. Stress positive points and display knowledge and organizational skills, but keep the report concise and to-the-point. It must be informative and persuasive, not overburdened with unessential details.

THE LOAN APPLICATION

An important part of the business plan is to set out clearly the funds required and how they are to be used. It cannot be overemphasized that financial strategy drives the business' strategy. In other words, the way in which the business is financed will dictate the way in which the business operates and pursues its goals. Sound financial controls and monitoring are essential in order to convince a potential lender to make the loan. Although there are no rules to follow in preparing a loan proposal, there are some suggestions that will help in preparing an effective loan proposal.[7]

Obtaining funding or capital is no different than obtaining the other required supplies (inventory, fixtures) to operate the business. The need for funds should be reviewed continually as it fluctuates with changes in the

Figure 6.5   Projected Cash-Flow Statement for a Twelve-Month Period (in thousands of dollars)

Month	(1) Oct.	(2) Nov.	(3) Dec.	(10) July	(11) Aug.	(12) Sept.	Total
Cash Receipts							
Cash Sales							
Front Store	40.0	45.0	50.0	35.0	40.0	40.0	500.0
Dispensary	17.5	17.5	20.0	15.0	17.5	17.5	
Accounts Receivable	15.0 †	17.5	17.5	20.0	15.0	17.5	445.0
Total	72.5	80.0	87.5	70.0	72.5	75.0	945.0
Cash Disbursements							
Merchandise	45.0 †	47.9	51.6	42.0	41.2	47.9	608.1
Wages	10.0	9.5	10.0	9.0	9.5	9.5	120.0
Occupancy Costs	2.5	2.5	2.5	2.5	2.5	2.5	30.0
Other	6.0	6.5	5.5	6.0	5.5	6.5	70.0
Capital Expenditures	—	5.0	2.5	—	—	—	7.5
Depreciation	(.1)	(.2)	(.1)	(.2)	(.1)	(.1)	(1.7)
Total	63.4	71.2	72.0	59.3	58.6	66.3	833.9
Net Change	9.1	8.8	15.5	10.7	13.9	9.7	111.1
Opening Balance	(75.0)						(75.0)
Cash Balance (Deficit) Cumulative	(65.9)	(57.1)	(41.6)	12.5	26.4	36.1	36.1

† Previous month

economy, or in the industry, growth or expansion of the practice, and personal tax planning. It is best to deal from a position of strength for the times when funding will be needed as opposed to attempting to manage a crisis when it occurs.

Basically, two types of loans will be required: 1) current loans or operating loans, and 2) long-term loans.[8] Each has a purpose. For example, operating loans from banks provide the funds required for day-to-day operation of the business. They are approved on an "asset value to loan ratio," are on a demand basis, and are secured by inventory and accounts receivable. They also fluctuate in amount regularly. Long-term loans are available from banks and other lenders and are secured by the business' fixed assets and repaid on a schedule that is related to the life of the asset.

Other issues of which to be aware in "shopping" for a loan are the requirements of the lender. For example:

- How much supporting data are required?

- How flexible is the lender in adjusting terms of the loan as the practice's needs change?

- How quickly can the lender react to a request for funds?

- What security or collateral is required?

- Are future loan requests possible or is it a one time loan?

- Are personal guarantees required?

The importance of a well-prepared loan application cannot be overstressed. Often, loan requests are turned down because they are presented poorly, are prepared inadequately, or the borrower is not precise in his requirements. Kyle suggests using the following outline when preparing a loan application.[9]

1.   Program:
     - use of the funds;
     - cost of the loan;
     - specific amount requested.

2.   Operations:
     - what the business does and its degree of success;
     - description of how the business operates;
     - suppliers, market, competition.

3.   Management:
    •   résumés of key people and shareholders;
    •   personal net worth statements.

4.   Ability to Repay:
    •   financial statements for two to three years.

5.   Financial Strength:
    •   debt to equity, working capital positions.

6.   Security:
    •   assets to be pledged as collateral.

Another approach to preparing a loan proposal has been suggested in *Inc.* magazine. It is claimed that this particular proposal outline "forces borrowers to think well before their meeting with lenders about what they want from a bank—how much money they need, for how long, at what price, by when, and, naturally, how they'll pay back the loan."[10] The proposal outline is as follows:

1.   Date.

2.   Borrower.

3.   Type of loan.

4.   a) Amount;
    b) Use of proceeds.

5.   Term (of loan).

6.   Closing date.

7.   Takedown at closing (amount needed immediately).

8.   Collateral.

9.   Rate (interest rate to be paid).

10.   Repayment schedule.

11.   Guarantees.

12.   Source of funds for repayment.

13.   Alternative source of funds for repayment.

APPENDIX

This is the place in the business plan where any additional information useful to the reader can be found. For example, résumés of the key people in the practice, relevant copies of leases, contracts with nursing homes, non-competition agreements from former employees, and insurance coverage of key people. As well, background information on advisory board members could be included in this section.

SUMMARY

Developing a well-written business plan serves two purposes: 1) it serves as a useful management tool by quantifying objectives and expectations, and 2) it is often required by lenders. A typical plan contains several sections: an executive summary, a description of the business, an analysis of the market-place, an understanding of the competition, a financial history and forecast, and an appendix. Each section is equally important to the total plan, except the executive summary which is the most important.

The business plan often provides the first impression of the business. This is followed by the background of the principals who are responsible to operate it successfully by using their own and borrowed capital.

References

1. Neyman, J. "How Business Plans Set a Point of Reference." *Toronto Star*, March 1992. "Creating a Blueprint for Action." *Toronto Star*, 16 March 1992.

2. Furlotte, M. "Why Business Plans Make Sense." *The Globe and Mail*, 25 March 1996.

3. Ginsberg, L. "How to Set Up an Advisory Board." *The Globe and Mail*, 14 April 1997.

4. Title, A. "How You Can Make Your Business Bankable." *Business Matters*, Toronto Dominion Bank, Winter, 1994.

5. Allard, B. "Don't Let Lenders Gain the Upper Hand." *The Globe and Mail*, 22 May 1995.

6. Church, E. "Do Banks Believe in Small Business?" *The Globe and Mail*, 28 April 1997.

7. Bank of Montreal. "The Financial Proposal." *Small Business Problem Solver No. 10.*

8. Kyle, A.A. "Keys to Business Financing." *The Pharmacist*. Pharmaceutical Association of Nova Scotia, February 1995.

9. Kyle, A.A. "Preparing a Business Loan Application." *The Pharmacist*. Pharmaceutical Association of Nova Scotia, October 1994.

10. Posner, B. "The 1 Page Loan Proposal." *Inc.*, (September 1991) p. 73.

7

FINANCIAL ASSESSMENT

INTRODUCTION

Once a pharmacy practice is in operation, it becomes necessary to monitor its financial progress—in other words, to assess the performance of the business. Regular performance assessment allows problems to be identified, and, once understood, those problems can be corrected through modifications that will ensure the continuing profitability of the practice.

Because it is possible to successfully increase sales, yet simultaneously run out of the cash necessary to replenish stock or pay wages, it is possible to be operating the pharmacy with a negative cash flow. The reason may be as simple as accepting credit sales and failing to collect on the accounts receivable in full or within an acceptable period of time.

In response to such situations, techniques have been developed to monitor factors such as:

- average length of time required to collect accounts receivable (commonly referred to as the "average collection period");

- average length of time taken to pay invoices (known as the "average payable period").

Comparing these two factors has been recognized to be an important measure, based on the simple premise that collected receivables will provide the funds needed to pay suppliers. If the average collection period exceeds the average payable period, there are clearly no funds available to pay all suppliers. If those funds are being borrowed, the pharmacy practice is incurring needless interest charges. The concept of "aging account"—that is, the calculation of the number of days that accounts receivable have been outstanding—represents an important area for regular monitoring by pharmacy owners or managers.

This technique is an example of financial ratio analysis, which is a systematic way to:

- determine how well the assets of a business are being managed;

- identify problem areas before they are out of control;

- separate profitable from unprofitable products or services;

- provide an objective insight into one's business from outside.

The results of financial ratio analysis do not explain why something occurred, only that it occurred. Therefore, when changes from the norm are detected through ratio analysis, the pharmacy owner is prompted to search out the causes. The implied comparison to norms involves two aspects:

1. comparison of current data with the pharmacy's own historical data (internal comparisons);

2. comparison with industry averages as reported in the professional literature (external comparisons).

The ratios that can be calculated are usually categorized into groups, reflecting liquidity, profitability, and solvency (and, indirectly, managerial efficiency). Liquidity is the ability to turn assets into cash quickly, in order to repay debt from short-term capitalization. The ratios frequently used to determine liquidity are known as the current ratio and the quick ratio. Profitability refers to the firm's ability to generate sufficient revenue not only to pay its expenses but also to reward its owner(s). Profitability is usually expressed as a percentage of sales and is calculated on the basis of income before tax is paid. Solvency is a measure of the firm's ability to repay debt from long-term capitalization.

The tables that appear in this chapter categorize the more frequently used financial ratios, illustrate the methods by which they are calculated, and use industry averages from the Annual Survey of Community Pharmacy Operations (Ontario pharmacies for 1994) in the sample calculations. You will notice that the industry averages often fail to meet the standards described as ideal or desirable in the financial ratios. In some cases this is due to certain unique characteristics of pharmacy as a business. In others, however, it is simply attributable to the fact that industry averages do not represent the ideal, but include businesses that are either newly established or inefficiently managed, together with those that are well established and distinctly profitable. Each individual pharmacy should, of course, strive to achieve the kind of ratios described in this chapter as attainable and desirable.

Read the tables along with the text, which elaborates on each of the ratios illustrated. Refer to Figures 5.1 and 5.2 (p. 97 and 98) for the complete financial statements on which the examples in this chapter are based.

Ratios Used to Assess Liquidity

Table 7.1 illustrates the liquidity ratios discussed in this section.

Table 7.1   Liquidity Ratios

Ratios	Formula	Calculation	
Current Ratio	$\dfrac{\text{Current assets}}{\text{Current liabilities}}$	$\dfrac{437,375}{253,368}$	= 1.7 times or 1.7:1
Quick Ratio or Acid Test	$\dfrac{\text{Current assets} - \text{Inventory}}{\text{Current liabilities}}$	$\dfrac{173,598}{253,368}$	= 0.7 times or 0.7:1
Average Collection Period	$\dfrac{\text{Ending accounts receivable}}{\text{Annual credit sales}} \times 365 \text{ days}$		data not available
Inventory to Net Working Capital	$\dfrac{\text{Inventory}}{\text{Current assets} - \text{Current liabilities}}$	$\dfrac{263,777}{184,007}$	= 1.43 or 143%
Net Sales to Net Working Capital	$\dfrac{\text{Sales}}{\text{Current assets} - \text{Current liabilities}}$	$\dfrac{2,164,553}{184,007}$	= 11.8 times or 11.8:1

CURRENT RATIO

The current ratio is "a measure of a firm's ability to meet its current obligations on time and to have funds readily available for current operations."[1] This ratio should have a value of 2:1, which allows current assets—the sum of cash, accounts receivable, inventory, marketable securities, and prepaid expenses—to shrink by 50 percent and still cover current obligations. Creditors like to see a high ratio, indicating a wide margin of safety for claims against the business. However, a very high ratio—greater than 3:1—may indicate that funds are not being used to greatest advantage and that inventory, receivables, and cash may be at levels that are higher than necessary. A ratio of less than 2:1 may occur during the early years of a new pharmacy's operations, or may indicate continuing unprofitability or insufficient capital.

QUICK RATIO OR ACID TEST

This is the ratio "between the liquid, or 'quick,' current assets, and the current liabilities. Quick current assets are cash, marketable securities, and receivables."[1] Because inventory is difficult to convert into cash readily, it is not included among quick current assets. The quick ratio is thus a more critical measure of liquidity than the current ratio, indicating the ability of readily available resources to meet current obligations. An appropriate value for this ratio is 1:1. If the current ratio is acceptable, but the quick ratio falls below 1:1, the size of the inventory relative to total current assets is probably too great, and requires the owner/manager's close attention. Pharmacies tend to have a proven quick ratio lower than desirable because of their dependence on large-dollar values of inventory, particularly in the dispensary. This is why efficient inventory-control systems are so critical in pharmacy practice.

AVERAGE COLLECTION PERIOD

Since most pharmacies grant credit, either personally to individual patrons, to drug-insurance programs on behalf of their patrons, or through credit-card acceptance, this is a useful ratio to calculate. Unfortunately, industry averages for annual credit sales are unavailable and we are therefore unable to calculate the ratio for the industry. This, of course, in no way diminishes its importance for individual pharmacies, and it should be calculated periodically in order to determine the number of days accounts receivable are outstanding.

The pharmacy owner or manager can establish parameters for the pharmacy's collection period and monitor deviations from those parameters. The average collection period is ideally 30 days or less—and this goal is frequently achieved by pharmacies that submit accounts to third-party payers promptly, train staff to complete billings properly, transmit billings electronically, and disallow personal credit accounts (or employ rigorous credit policies and collection procedures where they do not exist).

Accepting credit cards as opposed to personal credit accounts in pharmacies is one way to control the collection of receivables. It must be remembered, however, that there is a cost charged to the business by the financial institution that issues the card, and that staff will have to be trained in the proper use and validation of credit cards. There is also a cost in processing privately held charge accounts: a bookkeeper, record books, statement preparation, and postage. Overall, credit cards cost the merchant less and the risk of bad debts is eliminated.

INVENTORY TO NET WORKING CAPITAL

This is another measure of liquidity and inventory balance, and is usually expressed as a percentage. As explained previously, when a large proportion of the pharmacy's assets is represented by inventory, it may be difficult to meet current obligations. An appropriate value for this ratio is 90 to 100 percent. A higher ratio, however, is not uncommon in newer pharmacies. A value over 100 percent may indicate that inventory is too high and that the cash position could be improved by liquidating some portion of it.

NET SALES TO NET WORKING CAPITAL

This ratio illustrates how many dollars of sales are supported by each dollar of working capital. Thus, it provides some indication of the amount of working capital that would be needed if sales volume were to be increased. An appropriate ratio is 5:1. If the ratio is too high, the business may be operating on scarce resources and the pharmacy may not have sufficient funds to meet any new liabilities that could be incurred in the near future. New pharmacies, or those relying heavily on supplier credit, tend to have higher ratios. A low ratio indicates that more working capital is being used to generate existing sales than should be necessary.

Ratios Used to Assess Profitability

Table 7.2 illustrates the profitability ratios discussed in this section. Note that profitability ratios are normally expressed as percentages.

PROFIT ON SALES

This is a measure of managerial effectiveness in increasing owner's (or shareholders') equity. Although this value may vary greatly among pharmacies, the average profit on sales in the industry over the years has been approximately five percent. This value will rise as the sales of departments that earn

Table 7.2   Profitability Ratios

Ratios	Formula	Calculation
Profit on Sales	$\dfrac{\text{Profit}}{\text{Annual sales}}$	$\dfrac{53,798}{2,164,553} \times 100 = 2.5\%$
Return on Investment	$\dfrac{\text{Profit}}{\text{Net worth (equity)}}$	$\dfrac{53,798}{258,432} \times 100 = 20.8\%$
Return on Total Investment	$\dfrac{\text{Profit}}{\text{Equity + Long-term liabilities}}$	$\dfrac{53,798}{309,423} \times 100 = 17.4\%$
Return on Asset Investment	$\dfrac{\text{Profit}}{\text{Sales}} \quad \dfrac{\text{Sales}}{\text{Total assets}} \quad \dfrac{53,798}{2,164,553}$	$\dfrac{2,164,553}{562,791} \times 100 = 9.6\%$
Profit on Net Working Capital	$\dfrac{\text{Profits}}{\text{Current assets} - \text{Current liabilities}}$	$\dfrac{53,798}{184,007} \times 100 = 29.2\%$

*Profit before tax is assumed with each use of the term profit in this table.

high gross margins assume a greater proportion of total sales. Yearly internal and external comparisons are useful in assessing the appropriateness of the profit-on-sales percentage.

RETURN ON INVESTMENT

This ratio evaluates how productively the owner's funds are being used. A valid return-on-investment figure can be derived only if a reasonable owner's salary and a fair rent value (if the premises are owned by the pharmacist) are included in the operating expenses. If this is not done, profit will be over-stated, as will the return on investment value. At today's interest rates, an appropriate value is 15 percent or higher. This ratio can be increased by increasing the debt-to-equity ratio—if assets can earn more than the cost of borrowing, then financing through fixed- or long-term debt is useful.

RETURN ON TOTAL INVESTMENT

This ratio evaluates income relative to total funds invested in the business, making no distinction between owner's equity and long-term liabilities. It measures how effectively the total funds invested in the business have been managed.

RETURN ON ASSET INVESTMENT

This ratio measures the productivity of total assets, making no distinction between owner's capital and borrowed capital. This ratio improves if sales increase while assets remain constant or if the rate of profit increases.

PROFIT ON NET WORKING CAPITAL

This ratio finds use in measuring profitability when a large portion of the operating funds is provided through long-term borrowing and when permanent capital is unusually low relative to sales.

Ratios Used to Assess Solvency

Table 7.3 illustrates the solvency ratios discussed in this section.

Table 7.3   **Solvency Ratios**

Ratios	*Formula*	*Calculation*	
Debt to Equity	$\dfrac{\text{Total liabilities}}{\text{Net worth}}$	$\dfrac{304,359}{258,432}$	$\times \quad 100 = 117.8\%$
Current Debt to Net Worth	$\dfrac{\text{Current liabilities}}{\text{Net worth}}$	$\dfrac{253,368}{258,432}$	$\times \quad 100 = 98.0\%$
Sales to Net Worth	$\dfrac{\text{Sales}}{\text{Net worth}}$	$\dfrac{2,164,553}{258,432}$	$\times \quad 8.4$ times or 8.4:1
Funded Debt to Working Capital	$\dfrac{\text{Long-term liabilities}}{\text{Working capital}}$	$\dfrac{50,991}{184,007}$	$\times \quad 100 = 27.7\%$
Fixed Assets to Net Worth	$\dfrac{\text{Fixed assets}}{\text{Net worth}}$	$\dfrac{125,416}{258,432}$	$\times \quad 100 = 48.5\%$
Average Payable Period	$\dfrac{\text{Outstanding accounts payable}}{\text{Annual purchases}}$	$\times \quad 365$ days	data not available
Degree of Newness of Fixed Assets	$100\% \quad - \quad \dfrac{\text{Accumulated depreciation}}{\text{Fixed asset cost}}$		data not available

Debt to Equity

This ratio compares the total debt of the practice to its total equity and is expressed as a percentage. When total debt exceeds owner's equity, the practice will be in a precarious position should a dramatic change occur in the operation, such as a sudden or prolonged drop in sales or an increase in expenses. A pharmacy with a low debt-to-equity ratio compared to that of other, similar pharmacies may not be using its borrowed funds effectively. Values of this ratio vary depending on the age of the pharmacy and its borrowing policy, but they are ideally in the area of 50 percent and should not exceed 100 percent.

The industry-average ratio is calculated as 117.8 percent, indicating that many reporting pharmacies either are new establishments with a sizable debt load or are highly dependent on borrowed capital.

Current Debt to Net Worth

This ratio, also expressed as a percentage, illustrates the extent to which the new capital of the practice is dependent on short-term debt. It may also be interpreted as indicating the pharmacy's ability to meet its current obligations from its net worth or equity capital. The ratio is usually higher in new pharmacies. If this ratio is high (over 80 percent), severe undercapitalization will occur in the event that a debt is recalled. Again, newly established pharmacies may constitute a high proportion of the pharmacies reporting to the survey, as the ratio here is 98 percent, which indicates a relatively poor credit position. Pharmacy owners should be aware that undercapitalization is one of the main causes of business failure, and should take measures to avoid this pitfall.

Sales to Net Worth

This ratio assesses the productivity of owner's equity in terms of the sales generated by the firm. A high ratio warns of inadequate capitalization by the owner and excessive debt financing, which results in what is known as a highly leveraged practice. A low ratio indicates that the practice is not utilizing its funds fully and the owner's equity is stagnating.

Funded Debt to Working Capital

This ratio examines long-term financial obligations and provides information on the practice's ability to borrow. A low ratio indicates little reliance on funded debt for working capital and therefore places the practice in a good position to borrow.

Fixed Assets to Net Worth

This ratio shows the percentage of net worth that is tied up in fixed assets such as fixtures and equipment. A higher ratio, for example 75 percent, suggests that too much capital is tied up in fixed assets and reduces the flexibility of current operations. A low ratio may indicate that fixtures are obsolete and require replacement, or that they have been depreciated to such a point that there should be sufficient funds in the depreciation account to replace them.

Average Payable Period

The average payable period, as mentioned earlier, indicates the number of days accounts payable are outstanding. The rationale behind increasing the average payable period, where possible, is to improve the pharmacy's cash position. If this strategy is selected, one should evaluate carefully whether benefits to the pharmacy are greater by extending the payable period or by taking advantage of cash discounts for prompt payment. This evaluation is critical for pharmacies that are reliant on debt capital. Regardless of the actual payable period, it should certainly be greater than its companion ratio for the collection of accounts receivable (average collection period).

Degree of Newness of Fixed Assets

The value of this ratio is that it provides some insight into the remaining "useful life" of the pharmacy's fixed assets. A ratio of under 50 percent might encourage the pharmacy to renovate or replace existing fixtures. The implications of this ratio should be discussed with the pharmacy's accountant, as they are largely relevant to the methods of depreciation employed.

The Profitability Equation

Some of the more critical ratios we have discussed are closely interrelated. One way to look at them is through a profitability equation that consists of a financial objective and a financial program.[2] The financial objective considers return on investment and the financial program considers profit, rate of asset turnover, and leverage. Two additional ratios are therefore involved, as follows:

1)   Asset turnover $=$ $\dfrac{\text{Sales}}{\text{Total assets}}$

2)   Leverage $=$ $\dfrac{\text{Total assets}}{\text{Net worth (equity)}}$

Asset turnover is a measure of the sales dollars generated by each dollar invested in the firm's total assets. Leverage measures the dollar value in total assets that is being acquired for each dollar of net worth or equity. By borrowing funds from banks or obtaining trade credit from suppliers, the pharmacy owner acquires assets that are worth more than the amount of capital invested in the business by the owner(s), thereby obtaining leverage for the firm.

With these ratios, we can proceed to the profitability equation, which is as follows:

$$\text{Return on investment} = \text{Profit} \times \text{Asset turnover} \times \text{Leverage}$$

or

$$\frac{\text{Profit}}{\text{Net worth}} = \frac{\text{Profit}}{\text{Sales}} \times \frac{\text{Sales}}{\text{Total assets}} \times \frac{\text{Total assets}}{\text{Net worth}}$$

or

$$\frac{\text{Profit}}{\text{Net worth}} = \frac{\text{Profit}}{\text{Sales}} \times \text{Asset turnover} \times \frac{\text{Total liabilities and Net worth}}{\text{Net worth.}}$$

If this equation were expanded to take into account the income statement and balance sheet, it would appear as illustrated in Figure 7.1 (p. 150).

Managerial Information

In assessing, over time, the operational performance of a pharmacy, some measures[a] may be useful in guiding day-to-day management. Some of the measures used on a once-a-month or once-a-quarter basis are:

- gross margin (gross profit);
- gross margin return on inventory;
- inventory turnover;
- sales per dollar of employee wages;
- sales per square foot.

ANTICIPATING PERFORMANCE: BREAK-EVEN ANALYSIS

Break-even analysis is an important tool in financial planning, used to assess the relationship between sales and expenses. It anticipates future performance by predicting the effect that manipulating retail prices, cost of merchandise, expenses, and gross margin will have on profits. The calculation of a break-even point—the level of sales volume at which total revenue equals total costs—is a straightforward procedure consisting of five steps:

1.   Categorize the expense items as fixed or variable expenses. Some expenses may be difficult to assign and a mix of common sense and good judgment is required.

---

[a] See chapters 12 (p. 260), 13 (p. 279), and 14 (p. 303) for more detailed discussion of merchandise management (inventory, purchasing and pricing), chapter 8 (p. 156) for discussion of human resources management, and chapters 9 (p. 194) and 10 (p. 229) for discussion of space allocation and layout.

Figure 7.1   Planning for Profits

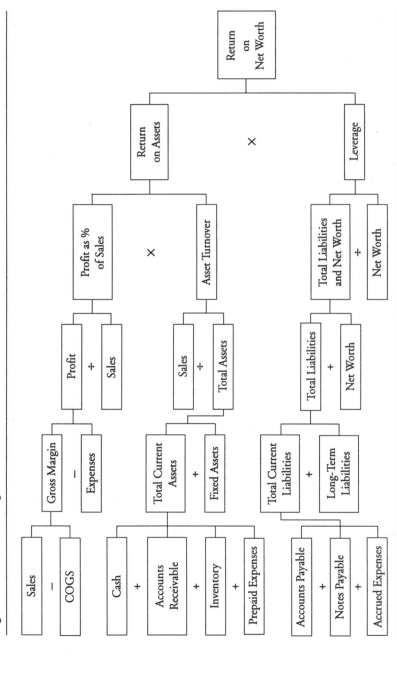

Source: C.A. Kline Jr. and Howard L. Hessler, "The DuPont Chart System for Appraising Operating Performance," in W.E. Thomas, Jr., ed., *Readings in Cost Accounting, Budgeting, and Control,* 2nd ed. Florence, Kentucky: South-Western Publishing Company, 1960, p. 799.

2.   Calculate the variable-expense ratio. This is simply the sum of the variable expenses expressed as a percentage of sales.

3.   Calculate the gross-margin ratio. The income statement will provide the gross margin as a percentage of sales.

4.   Calculate the marginal-income ratio. This is determined by subtracting the variable-expense ratio from the gross-margin ratio. The marginal-income ratio is the percentage of sales dollars left to cover the fixed expenses and profit (if any).

5.   Calculate the break-even point. This is determined by dividing the fixed expenses by the marginal-income ratio. The answer is the sales volume required for the business to break even.

Expense items can be categorized as shown in Table 7.4. Once again, the figures used in our example are drawn from the financial statements of 199y. Table 7.5 (p. 152) illustrates the break-even analysis calculations described above.

Table 7.4   Fixed and Variable Expenses

Fixed Expenses		Variable Expenses	
Owner/manager salary	$ 80,920	Employee wages	$244,862
Rent	51,311	Taxes and licences	9,415
Light, heat, power	12,542	Advertising	26,156
Acct., legal, professional fees	9,006	Bad debts	1,367
Insurance	5,478	Miscellaneous	102,615
Interest paid	8,708		
Repairs	7,274	TOTAL	$384,415
Delivery	4,741		
Depreciation	16,947		
Telephone	4,516		
TOTAL	$201,443		

Table 7.5   *Break-Even Analysis Calculations*

Variable-Expense Ratio	$\dfrac{384,415}{2,164,553} \times 100 = 17.8\%$	
Gross-Margin Ratio	$\dfrac{639,656}{2,164,553} \times 100 = 29.6\%$	
Marginal-Income Ratio	Gross-margin ratio 29.6 − Variable-expense ratio 17.8% = 11.8%	
Break-even Point	$\dfrac{201,443}{11.8\%} = \$1,707,144$ in sales	
Break-even Point in Days	$\dfrac{\$1,707,144}{\$2,164,553 \div 365 \text{ days}} = \dfrac{1,707,144}{5,930} = 288$ days or appr. 9.5 months	

The break-even point is interpreted as meaning that at a sales volume of $1,707,144 (as shown in Table 7.5) the marginal-income ratio of 11.8 percent produces a marginal income of $201,443 (.118 × 1,707,144) and that this amount is equal to the fixed expenses of the business. Sales above this volume begin to contribute to the profit at a rate of $0.118 for each dollar of sales beyond the break-even point.

The break-even point has other applications. It can be used as a basis for decisions on expansion, reducing margins through price discounting, or forecasting required sales volume for a predetermined profit.

Expansion plans must take into consideration any additional expenses incurred and determine whether these are fixed or variable expenses. For example, if additional space is obtained in order to store home health-care products, rent is going to increase by, let us say, $6,000. Refer to Table 7.5 and follow the steps below to calculate the volume of sales required to break even.

1.   Variable expenses are the same.

2.   Fixed expenses increase to $207,443 ($6,000 + 201,443).

3.   The variable-expense ratio remains the same.

4.   The gross-margin ratio remains the same.

5.   The marginal-income ratio would be the same.

6.   Therefore, the break-even point would now be:

$$\frac{\text{Fixed expenses}}{\text{Marginal-income ratio}} = \frac{207,443}{11.8\%} = \$1,757,992$$

Plans to discount prices and become more aggressive in promoting products could reduce the gross margin from 29.6 percent to 26 percent. If all other factors remained the same, what would be the effect on the break-even point? Refer to Table 7.5 and follow the steps below to calculate the new break-even point.

1.   Fixed expenses are constant.

2.   The variable-expense ratio is the same.

3.   The gross-margin ratio is now 26 percent.

4.   The marginal-income ratio becomes 26 – 17.8 = 8.2 percent.

5.   The break-even point is now:

$$\frac{\text{Fixed expenses}}{\text{Marginal-income ratio}} = \frac{201{,}443}{8.2\%} = \$2{,}456{,}622$$

If a predetermined profit of $65,000 is desired, what sales volume would be required under the existing circumstances? Here, profit can be considered a fixed amount that must be covered by the pharmacy's revenues to break even and is therefore added to fixed expenses. Refer to Table 7.5 (p. 152) and follow the steps below to calculate the required sales volume.

1.   Fixed expenses increase to $266,443 (201,443 + 65,000).

2.   Variable expenses are constant.

3.   The gross-margin ratio is still 29.6 percent.

4.   The marginal-income ratio remains 11.8 percent.

5.   The sales volume required to break even would be:

$$\frac{\text{Fixed expenses}}{\text{Marginal-income ratio}} = \frac{266{,}443}{11.8\%} = \$2{,}257{,}992$$

Break-even analysis is only a tool and must be used with care, as it has limitations. For example, the analysis uses forecasts of sales, margins, and expenses that are somewhat arbitrarily assigned into fixed and variable categories. If increased sales volume is achieved through price reductions and a corresponding gross-margin reduction, the projected profit relationship will also change.

Remember that the usefulness of this technique is limited: it can be applied without overall adjustments only in cases where a small increase in sales volume relative to forecasted expenses is under consideration. This is so because increasing sales beyond a certain level will also entail increases in fixed expenses to accommodate the greater sales volume—in terms of space (rent), labor (managerial salaries), and fixtures. Therefore, in such cases new estimates must be made and a new break-even point calculated.

Hence, it is important to be wary of the faulty assumption that once the break-even point is passed, profit can be increased with consideration only for increasing variable expenses, because fixed expenses are presumed to have already been met. If sales increase substantially, fixed expenses will indeed grow and result in changing the cost structure relative to profit.

SUMMARY

Professional services cannot be provided successfully or securely, for any length of time, from a practice that is not financially sound. It is the pharmacist-owner's responsibility to predict and promptly correct any problems in the operation that could jeopardize its financial stability and growth. The analytic tools presented in this chapter will assist the pharmacist in effectively monitoring and assessing the health of the practice on an ongoing basis.

References

1. Walgenbach, P. H., et al. *Principles of Accounting.* 1st Canadian ed. Toronto: Harcourt Brace Jovanovich Canada, 1988.

2. Davidson, W.R., Sweeney, D.J., and Stampfl, R.W. *Retailing Management.* 6th ed. Toronto: John Wiley and Sons, 1988.

8

HUMAN RESOURCE MANAGEMENT

INTRODUCTION

Human resources management is an area that many pharmacists tended to neglect in the past. Today, more pharmacy owners are recognizing the need to invest time and energy in this most crucial—and costly—aspect of their business. The impact of human resources is important as the consumers' interest in personal contact grows, particularly in professional services. It has been shown that a consumer's choice of pharmacy is strongly influenced by the quality of service offered, especially the time taken by a pharmacist to explain the medication.[1]

Pharmacy owners must also recognize the importance of their financial investment in human resources. Hiring a pharmacist today involves an investment of approximately $350,000 over five years, and perhaps $150,000 for a pharmacy assistant. It therefore makes sense to invest wisely by spending as much time and effort as necessary to locate, hire, and keep the best people for the positions.

The proper selection of staff is important from other perspectives as well. New employees must be considered in light of their compatibility with the existing team of pharmacy personnel. If such criteria are ignored, the harmonious atmosphere that is necessary for the successful operation of the pharmacy may be jeopardized, leading to morale problems and possible resignations by existing staff. Similarly, since pharmacy staff interact with outside suppliers and prescribers, the choice of personnel can affect the nature of the pharmacy's critical business and professional relationships.

Because human beings are complex, managing human resources is difficult. Although the human element can create unique problems for management, it can also bring tremendous benefits if managed properly. By respecting human elements and trying to understand the needs of staff members, pharmacy managers can increase productivity, while at the same time providing staff with greater job satisfaction.

There is no universal prescription for the successful management of human resources, partly because every relationship with staff members is in some way unique, and partly because the size and nature of the pharmacy will demand a particular policy and approach to communications with staff.

STAFFING REQUIREMENTS

The objective in assessing staff requirements is to relate the number of personnel employed to the amount of work that has to be done; this is another application of the principles of supply and demand. It is relatively straightforward in an established store with accumulated information about workload cycles, but more difficult in the case of a new pharmacy, where projections must be compatible with the distribution of work, which is accomplished by constantly monitoring for necessary adjustments in staff levels.

Three steps are involved in the assessment of staff requirements: job analysis, position description, and detailed job description.

1.   Job analysis is a concise and factual study of the pharmacy's staffing needs. The scope of each job must be delineated, anticipated problems outlined, and the hierarchy of positions established. A thorough job analysis will encompass all areas of the work to be done and will alert the pharmacy owner to any grey areas or duplication of functions. In the longer run, it will determine the responsibilities of each employee and help prevent potential interpersonal conflicts.

2.   The position description outlines the main components of each position. A good position description should be relatively short (no more than two pages), providing a general description of the job, the nature and the scope of the position, the main areas of responsibility, the positions which the incumbent will supervise, and those to which he or she will be accountable. (Three sample position descriptions appear in the appendix to this chapter.) Whenever possible, it is advisable to evaluate how much time is to be spent on each of the activities listed. In creating the position description, the employer should also consider the qualifications that will be required of the incumbent, in terms of educational level, type of degree (where applicable), length and nature of experience, and special skills.

3.   The detailed job description should list, all the tasks to be accomplished, in order of importance and describe each in detail. This is useful in establishing the priorities of job functions within each position.

The job analysis, position description, and detailed job description, together with subsequent study of the combined information, should result in a reasonably accurate assessment of staffing needs.

To ensure that all tasks will be accomplished by the optimal number of people, it is still necessary to estimate the actual volume of work in the pharmacy. In a larger store with a greater volume of work, it may be necessary to hire two or three employees to fill the same position. The daily and hourly fluctuations in workload must also be considered. In some pharmacies, weekdays might be much busier than weekends, and fewer employees would be required on a Sunday than on a Thursday or Friday. A store that dispenses up to 150 prescriptions in a day would normally require only one pharmacist; if, however, those 150 prescriptions occur in a four-hour span, one pharmacist will clearly be unable to cope with the rate of work. Or, if a pharmacy dispenses 400 prescriptions per day, with a rush hour between 4 p.m. and 6 p.m., a bottleneck situation will develop if only one pharmacist is on duty during that period, even if additional dispensary assistants are employed. A second pharmacist added during those hours would double productivity and increase production, resulting in more customer satisfaction by minimizing the waiting time and making more time available for consultation. This solution may not even involve a much greater cost for the pharmacy owner, because the second pharmacist's salary can be paid out of the savings from one less pharmacy assistant and eliminate overtime payments to the initial pharmacist.

Changes in patterns of work flow are always possible, and it is advisable to monitor operations regularly in order to react to them promptly. If one is familiar with spreadsheet software, one can design an operational supply and demand program that will provide pertinent information for staffing purposes.

The pharmacy manager will, of course, be concerned with the financial ability of the pharmacy to support its payroll. The literature suggests that total salary expenses (including the owner's) should not exceed 12 to 15 percent of sales.[2] Pharmacy owners should try keep abreast of provincial salary-to-sales ratios for pharmacies of comparable size and compare the ratios for their own operations. With properly planned staffing, a pharmacy should compare favorably against provincial industry averages.

STAFFING THE DISPENSARY

If the volume of business is high, a pharmacy will employ other staff in addition to at least one pharmacist in the dispensary. Some provincial regulations dictate the ratio of pharmacy assistants to each pharmacist (e.g., "one on one plus one," that is, one pharmacist to two assistants, two pharmacists to three assistants, and so on); other provinces set no limits on the number of assistants that a pharmacist may supervise. All provinces require that each prescription be dispensed under the authority of a pharmacist, and as discussed earlier, proper workloads should be maintained through discussion with the pharmacists and the delegation of responsibility to other staff. It is wise to investigate the possibility of automating the pharmacy's dispensing operations.

STAFFING SPECIALIZED AREAS

Some specialized areas of a pharmacy, such as the cosmetics department and the home health-care department, will require specialized personnel. Depending on the particular pharmacy, these staff members may not need to be on duty at all times during store hours. The cosmetician may only be needed in the latter part of the day, if that is when potential consumers of cosmetics tend to shop. Knowing the shopping habits of the pharmacy's clientele is essential to the proper planning of staffing requirements in specialized service areas.

OTHER PERSONNEL

The pharmacy owner must assemble a support staff of salesclerks, cashiers, stock clerks, and receivers. Some of the support-staff members may be hired on a full-time basis, while others will be part-time or temporary employees. Some pharmacies have chosen to employ mainly part-time support staff, because this allows for readily available replacement personnel, and greater flexibility during holidays or in the event of illness among staff members. The drawbacks to such an arrangement are that customers are less able to develop the sort of personal relationship with employees that can create loyalty to the pharmacy, and part-time staff take longer to learn as much or develop skills as thoroughly as full-time staff. The pharmacy owner must arrive at an arrangement that both enhances customer satisfaction and ensures the availability of backup staff. Part-time staff are most commonly used during rush-hour periods, while temporary replacements are generally used during vacation times and exceptionally busy seasonal periods. Students, and preferably pharmacy students, are a good source of part-time and temporary staff, especially since pharmacies often experience staffing shortages during the summer months. Pharmacy students are a valuable investment as well: upon graduation, they may return as replacement pharmacists, already familiar with the methods of the pharmacy.

It is important to avoid overstaffing, since it is not only financially burdensome, but can also have a negative effect on customer service and on the pharmacy's image. Employees who are not fully occupied will naturally tend to socialize with other employees, thereby distracting them from their work. This can create motivational problems among the busier employees, in addition to jeopardizing ideal service levels to customers.

Conversely, if the pharmacy is understaffed, service problems will arise because personnel are overworked and service is slower. Employee dissatisfaction is likely to develop, and possibly result in a high turnover of staff. This can lead to a poor reputation for the pharmacy as an employer, cause frustration among the store's customers, and prevent the development of a team spirit among the employees. It is therefore important that one develops some productivity criteria such as prescriptions per wage hour or sales per wage hour so that one can monitor performance in various departments and allocation of wage hours.

Managerial Staff and the Principle of Delegation

In a larger operation, it is impossible for the pharmacy owner to supervise all the employees directly. An organizational structure must therefore be established that will allow for the delegation of certain supervisory responsibilities. Depending on the size of the pharmacy, this structure might include a store manager; an assistant manager; a head cashier (if there is a team of cashiers); and a head cosmetician (if there is a team of cosmeticians).

Delegation is a particular problem for independent pharmacies, which are started by a pharmacist then grow beyond the managerial scope of one person. This is a crucial phase in the growth of an organization and demands that the pharmacy owner learn to delegate responsibility effectively, moving from the role of the entrepreneur who handles all problems to that of the manager who supervises, controls, and motivates a management team. While all this may seem obvious, it is frequently a major source of difficulty for pharmacy owners, who find that they are unable to "let go."

The principle of delegation consists of three components: responsibility, authority, and accountability. If, for instance, one owns two pharmacies, each of the managers should be fully responsible for the operation of his or her store and must be given the requisite authority. At the same time, both managers will be accountable for the decisions they make, and for the consequences of these decisions. The same principles would apply within each store, where, for example, the manager might assign direct responsibility for three employees to an assistant manager. The three employees might include a stock clerk responsible for receiving, a store clerk responsible for price ticketing, and a head cashier who in turn supervises three other cashiers. Each employee in this chain of responsibility would be accountable to his or her direct supervisor (in this example, head cashier, assistant manager, and manager). All organization structures are based on the principles of delegation.

Failure to observe these principles will result in a loss of one's own and the staff's time, as well as potential loss of money. It will also create dissatisfaction among the people promoted to positions of responsibility and confusion among the rest of the staff.

RECRUITMENT AND HIRING

Policies regarding recruitment and hiring should address the various issues and specifically answer such questions as the following: Will family members, spouses, or co-habitants of existing employees be eligible for hire? Who will be responsible for the hiring, the immediate supervisor for the job position, a designated manager, or the pharmacy owner? For more senior positions, does the store wish to adopt a policy of hiring from within? How are drop-in applicants to be handled? Does the pharmacy wish to use standardized application forms? Should there be a specific recruitment program directed toward high schools, trade schools, or universities?

Once a staff-requirement assessment is complete, the pharmacy owner will know exactly what positions are to be filled and how many employees hired. The first principle of effective recruiting is to hire the candidate best qualified for the job available. Before exploring the process that will best enable the pharmacy owner to realize that principle, however, we must stress the importance of avoiding any sort of discrimination in hiring. It is unethical, as well as unlawful, for an employer to refuse to hire a person on the basis of race, sex, or religion. Before engaging in active recruiting, the pharmacy owner or manager should become familiar with the Canadian Human Rights Commission's published guidelines and the pertinent provincial labor legislation. Observing the tenets of these documents will not only protect the owner as an employer, they will also help to increase managerial effectiveness in the task of recruitment.

Seeking Job Candidates

In initiating recruitment, one needs to outline the qualifications required for the position in a job specification. It sets out the education, experience, and skills that are being sought, and is used for advertising the position.

PHARMACISTS

The first eligibility requirement for new pharmacists is, of course, that they be eligible for licensure in the province where the pharmacy is located. Other qualifications may also be specified: knowledge of more than one language might be required; knowledge of the pharmacy's computer system may be essential; a number of years of experience or specific kinds of experience; skill in pharmaceutical care processes; or the flexibility to work evenings and weekends could be a prerequisite.

The recruitment of a pharmacist can be approached in several ways. In larger organizations, it is normal to begin with internal advertising and search. Next, one may seek referrals from staff and colleagues and review any unsolicited résumés, or applications on hand from prior competitions. Larger organizations often run an ad in a national trade journal, such as *Pharmacy Post* or the *Canadian Pharmaceutical Journal*, as well as in a regional journal or newsletter. A drawback here is that the ad may not appear for six to eight weeks after submission. Hence, this is not the ideal approach if the new pharmacist is needed in a hurry.

Another approach is to seek assistance from pharmacy faculties, professional associations, and provincial licensing bodies, which at times have placement agencies, and keep records of graduating or unemployed pharmacists. Such referral services can be very helpful and are a reliable source of information. Local newspaper advertisements can also be used, but usually as a last resort.

A pharmacy owner may not wish to have the pharmacy's needs known by competitors, especially if, for some reason, there is a high turnover of staff. This is an understandable concern, since the pharmacy community might speculate that working conditions are not satisfactory in the pharmacy, and this could indeed make the recruiting process more difficult. To avoid the problem, it is possible to use a post office box or reference number in the advertisement, and thereby remain anonymous.

MANAGEMENT STAFF

If the pharmacy is large enough to warrant hiring management staff, candidates must be evaluated carefully for their potential to meet the demands of the position description. The recruiting process is similar to that used for locating pharmacists, with the exception that, because this is not a closed professional community, the daily newspaper is the best advertising vehicle. Group advertising (e.g., seeking a pharmacist, cosmetician, head cashier, and supervisors through a single ad) should be avoided when seeking management personnel. Generally, preference is given to hiring from within the organization if suitable applicants are available.

OTHER STAFF

In the case of support staff, an anonymous ad in the district newspaper is probably the most efficient approach. Candidates should be advised to send their résumés or applications to a post office box number. Support staff should be recruited from the local area in order to avoid traveling problems during the winter season. It is quite likely that there will be store customers among the candidates for support staff positions; these situations should be handled with diplomacy and tact if the applicant is not qualified or suitable for the position. Help-wanted signs are often posted in pharmacies.

OUTSIDE AGENCIES

As mentioned earlier, the pharmacy owner might choose to use the services of a private agency or a government service, such as Employment and Immigration Canada, for assistance in fulfilling staffing requirements. All agencies, whether private or public, screen candidates and send only those who are considered qualified for the job. It is important to select a reliable agency, supply them with the position description for the job opening, and explain as precisely as possible the kind of employee being sought. The agency will then arrive at a short list of candidates from which the employer can select. Agency candidates are normally "guaranteed," meaning that if they do not perform to the employer's satisfaction within a specified probationary period, the agency will locate a replacement at no extra charge. Private agencies can be expensive and should probably be used only if the pharmacy owner is unskilled as a recruiter and interviewer, or simply cannot spare the requisite time. To avoid agency candidates altogether, it is wise to specify "personal applications only" in the advertisement for the job.

To summarize, this part of the recruiting process is not dissimilar to advertising. The product advertised is the job opportunity, which should be made attractive to its target market, and directed to that target population by the most economical and productive means.

Evaluating Applications

Applications for potential candidates will begin to arrive soon after ads have been placed. Depending on the level of candidate being sought, a certain quality in the presentation of the résumé or application form can be expected. Applying for employment should be one of the most important things a person does, which should be reflected in a job application.

The applicants will be screened on the basis of their applications. First, those that do not have the required skills and experience are eliminated. From the rest, it is possible to perceive a great deal about an applicant's character and attitude from his or her résumé and covering letter, and to eliminate the applications that do not reflect sufficient care, interest, and effort. It is quite appropriate to adopt a selective attitude from the outset: if an application is full of spelling errors, it is fair to assume that the applicant would bring the same carelessness to the job.

The résumé will describe an applicant's career evolution. For a senior position, the pharmacy manager would look for indications of progress and commitment in the candidate's achievements of the past years. The applicant's stability as an employee will be reflected in the absence of erratic employment patterns. Someone who changes position regularly every six months, and has done so for several years, may be incapable of staying in the same place for a long period of time. Any employer who has invested time and money in the search for an appropriate candidate should be wary of one who could leave the organization in six months' time.

The receipt of all résumés or applications should be acknowledged by letter, even if the applicant is not selected for an interview.

The Interview

The interview is the next stage in the selection process. If at all possible, the pharmacy manager should try to interview several candidates—ideally between five and ten, since the interview process is invariably based on a comparison of applicants. Fewer than five candidates may not afford a broad enough view of what the market has to offer. If the pre-selection of applications has been successful, everyone interviewed will be essentially qualified for the position offered. The purpose is less to determine if they are qualified, than to determine how they will fit in with the staff and what contribution they will make.

The interview process should occur within a limited time frame: if it is spread over too long a period, the candidates seen initially may recede from memory by the time the last interviews are conducted, giving the later candidates an unfair advantage. Ideally, the interview process should take place over a period of not more than one week.

The interview itself is perhaps analogous to pre-contract negotiations. The interviewer is attempting to determine whether the candidate is best qualified for the job and is someone who will contribute to the value of the organization. At the same time, the interviewer must ascertain whether the candidate understands what exactly is being offered, and whether the candidate would be happy in the position. If either side in the "negotiation" is not satisfied, the relationship is not likely to survive over time. It is therefore important that all the rules of the game are clear to both parties at the time of the interview. This is not an easy process, since the two people involved in the interview are usually strangers, and the interviewer must try to establish a climate conducive to communication. To facilitate the process, the interview should be conducted in a relaxed atmosphere and without interruptions. Most pharmacies do not have an area appropriate for conducting interviews; if this is the case, it would be advisable to rent or borrow an office somewhere outside the pharmacy.

The opening conversation should be aimed at establishing a rapport between the two parties. Sometimes the manager may have another person sit in on the interview to get an additional perspective on the candidate, and to train staff in interviewing and participating in hiring staff that they will have to work with. The pharmacy manager should start by asking candidates how they see the position offered, to ensure that they do not have an unrealistic idea of the nature of the job. If a candidate seems to be knowledgeable about the position, it is likely that he or she has done some research to become familiar with the pharmacy—a positive sign, indicating a high level of interest. The next step would be to clearly establish what the job entails, perhaps providing a job description, and what is expected of the candidate. At this point, some candidates may decide that the job is not exactly what they are looking for—a disappointing development, but one best discovered at the interview stage.

Once both parties are clear on the position, the interviewer should work through the résumé or application form with the candidate to clarify and validate the information. Query the applicant about empty periods evident in the résumé and discuss the general trend of his or her career. Try to pose open-ended questions starting with a "why" or a "how," that require some explanation in the response by the candidate. Avoid leading questions, such as "We have an elderly population; do you like to work with older people?" The candidate can simply answer yes or no without having to think or explain, so these types of questions should be avoided. If it seems that the candidate is avoiding certain topics or being indirect, or that more information relating to the topic under discussion would be desirable, do not hesitate to remain silent after the candidate has finished answering. In an effort to end the slightly uncomfortable silence, the candidate may provide some information that could be of interest to the interviewer.

In interviewing a candidate, the pharmacy manager should be aware of a phenomenon known as the "halo effect." Every person is influenced by a particular personality or physical trait, an attitude factor, or a style of clothing that can cause them to react more favorably toward another person. As an interviewer, one must be aware of one's own bias and of the type of candidate that is likely to make a stronger impression, so that one's decision is not swayed by the halo effect. This is a bias that has no relevance to the position; it simply hides other factors that may be of greater importance. It is helpful, in this regard, to have a standard list of questions that will be asked of all candidates. The responses can then be compared. This approach also provides evidence that discrimination has not been a factor.

The interviewer's role is to orient discussion and draw out answers, encouraging the person being interviewed to do most of the talking. If the interview is conducted properly, one will find out if the candidate is capable of following a logical train of thought and expressing him/herself clearly and easily. This may be a feature one looks for in a pharmacist who will have to communicate effectively in counseling patients. Other aspects that will be of interest to the pharmacy manager, depending on the size of the company, are the candidate's future career plans and ambitions. If an employee is being sought for a large organization, it would be important to discover whether the person has the potential to move up in the organization and possibly occupy managerial positions. As a general rule, good people should be sought. It is not a good idea to avoid persons who will look for better positions later due to their ability. Hire them and get their contribution, even if for a shorter period.

The interviewer is best advised, even when very favorably impressed with a candidate, to avoid making premature promises, either about a job offer or possible promotion within a short time. Without having seen the person at work, any such suggestion is out of place; furthermore, the employee will be dissatisfied and lose trust in an employer who has made false promises.

If a candidate's personality and career progression are appropriate for the job, technical competence must then be determined. The criteria for this will differ with the type of position being filled. Where possible, try to give candidates an aptitude test or place them in a situation where one can see them perform. It is also important to consider whether the candidate will fit in well with the other employees and the customers. A candidate with the necessary technical skills may have a way of communicating that may antagonize the customers. If this is the case, and if it is felt that the candidate cannot change, he or she is probably not the best person for the job.

The questions asked in an interview must be related to the job exclusively. The personal life of the candidate, including age, marital status, or number of children, religion, race, and sexual preference are not to be raised as they do not apply to the job. These matters are covered by the Canadian Human Rights legislation in order to prevent discrimination against potential employees. These restrictions do not apply to the candidate's questions, however, and they may wish to raise some of these matters. Outside interests of the candidate should be explored during the interview. What candidates do in their spare time may have some relevance to the business, and may also give some indication of their capacity to work in a team, if not of their potential for leadership.

Do not hesitate to ask for references, as references are the most accurate way of finding out a candidate's level of work performance. The references provided should be work-related, not personal. Since references provided by the candidate will most likely be positive, one must try to ascertain their credibility and, if need be, contact other people who may know the applicant. It is advisable to make the employment of a candidate conditional to the verification of references. The length of a candidate's working life should be taken into consideration: a new graduate will obviously not be able to supply as many references as a person with ten years' work experience.

Toward the end of the interview, questions of salary, work schedule, and benefits should be discussed. The salary policy and benefits package of the organization should always be explained clearly. The candidate should understand that employees have the opportunity to move up in salary within a given range for the particular position. The salary range and work schedule might be raised initially to ensure that the candidate's expectations are not too divergent from one's offer; otherwise, the interview itself might be a waste of time for both parties. The best policy is to ask candidates what their salary expectations are, and proceed (or not) from there. Remember that the time for detailed discussion of salary is when one offers the applicant the job, not during the interview. Coming out of the interview, the pharmacy manager should know whether the candidate has the requisite technical competence and will be compatible with the clientele and other employees, and whether there is some potential for moving up in the organization. The candidate should know exactly what the job entails, what kind of organization he or she is joining, and have a good idea of the working conditions. It may be appropriate in some cases to take the applicant on a tour of the store/department to familiarize them with the organization.

For the successful candidate, one makes a written offer setting out the salary, benefits, hours, starting date, and the job title or description, and asks for a reply by a certain date. In this process, one should keep in mind that time may be requested to consider the offer—24 to 48 hours is normal —and other job negotiations may be underway that could take time. If the offer is turned down, one can then offer it to the next best-qualified applicant. Only when this process is complete are letters of rejection sent out.

Once the position has been filled, a file should be established for the new employee. It is important that all the other candidates interviewed be notified in writing as soon as possible that they have not been selected. A brief letter is sufficient, thanking the candidate for the interview, and advising with regret that the position has been filled. Lengthy and non-essential explanations should be avoided. However, thorough notes on the candidates, based on the interviews, should be kept in a file for future reference—you may want to return to these candidates when a new opening arises.

PERSONNEL AND PAYROLL RECORDS

Policy should define who will maintain the personnel records. In a large and diversified company, there may be a personnel department, but in an independent community pharmacy, the owner or manager will likely keep all records, or delegate the responsibility to a bookkeeper or secretary. As well as designating who will keep the records, specify where the files should be kept, who will have access to them, and what type of information at what intervals will be included. Remember that in most provinces, information in the employee file is strictly confidential, and cannot be divulged without employee authorization or a court order. Also be aware that employees have the right to see their own file. This should be set out in the policy and procedures manual of the pharmacy or collective agreement. Letters of reference or complaints from other employees not to be seen by the employee may be kept in a separate file (under "complaints" or "correspondence").

Employee files generally include hiring information, such as a copy of the résumé or job application form, reference checks, and all other relevant documents and correspondence. Since it is generally required, a policy statement might state that wage and salary information be included in an employee's file, including starting rate and rate adjustments, holidays and vacations used, attendance and punctuality records, sick leave taken, and any accidents or injuries that may have occurred.

Businesses are legally required to keep separate payroll records for each employee, not only during, but for a period of time after, his or her employment with the firm. Payroll records include such information as gross pay, legal deductions, training expenses, other deductions (and the reasons for them), net pay, holiday and vacation pay, and amounts paid during illness.

ORIENTATION, TRAINING, AND DEVELOPMENT

Policies regarding orientation, training, and employee development should reflect the pharmacy's philosophy toward its employees. During the orientation procedure, a new employee should be advised of policy regarding individual responsibility to the store, from observing regulations concerning parking, storing personal belongings, dress codes, and logging work hours to following the rules that govern personal behavior.

Issues surrounding training, development, and continuing education include assigning responsibility for the training; making the time available, place and materials needed; addressing the training expectations; and evaluating results. Consideration should be given to cross-training of personnel to facilitate coverage during illness and vacations. Policy should outline the pharmacy's position on outside training or education, including any payment employees would receive during the time they were absent from work for a course or training program, as well as subsidization of incidental costs, such as travel, meals, and materials. It is recommended that the pharmacy owner meets once more with a newly hired employee before work begins to review the position description and detailed job description, as well as compensation and work policies. Most positions have a probationary period of 60 to 90 days during which the performance of the employee is assessed. Several meetings should be held to discuss the employee's progress during that period. If problems are apparent, the employee should be warned, preferably in writing, and given an opportunity to improve. At the end of the probationary period, a meeting should take place with an employee to review job performance; if it has been satisfactory and both parties are in agreement, a permanent offer of employment should be made.

The first few days of the probationary period are usually an orientation period, preferably with a formal program.[3] Store philosophy and goals should be emphasized initially so that the new employee has the proper mental framework within which to learn about the operation of the business. The pharmacy manager or an immediate supervisor should give the newcomer an orientation tour of the store to meet fellow employees, learn who does what, and where everything is located. Give the new employee a copy of the relevant portion of the pharmacy's policy and procedures manual (or training manual, if one exists), and review it together a few days later. A senior employee should be appointed to train the newcomer and explain store policies and to answer questions and help with problem situations. A list of objectives is useful so that they can be signed off as the relevant tasks are learned. Documentation of progress is important as the process is designed to enable the new staff member to handle the job at the end of the training period, at which point the staff member will be given regular shifts, and be expected to function at a reasonable level.

MOTIVATION AND EMPLOYEE RELATIONS

Policy and procedure questions to consider in this area include the following: How much authority and responsibility will be delegated to whom? Once one has hired one's team one must establish and maintain a motivating climate. A highly motivated staff will be dedicated to the organization and to the customers. Furthermore, it will help to prevent discipline problems in the future.

Much has been written on motivation, but Maslow's "hierarchy of needs" theory is still the best known.[4] Maslow suggests that every person has five basic levels of needs, ordered from lowest to highest as follows: physiological, safety and security, social, esteem, and self-actualization needs. The theory holds that only upon satisfying one level of need, can people move on to satisfy the next. Hence, if a primary level is not being satisfied, people will revert back to that level, then work their way up again. For instance, if one of the employees is highly motivated and works on satisfying self-esteem needs, but in the process a physiological need ceases to be satisfied, the employee will revert to the satisfaction of that need before pursuing the search for self-esteem. Elements of all levels are in play simultaneously in an employee.

PHYSIOLOGICAL NEEDS

This is the most basic level, representing the need for warmth, nourishment, and rest. This level is therefore satisfied through good working conditions. The pharmacy must be properly lit, well-ventilated, and adequately heated or cooled. Employees must have reasonable breaks during the day (for coffee and lunch), as well as an area in which they can relax during break periods. Work schedules can also affect the satisfaction of employees' physiological needs. When possible, it is wise to be flexible, accommodating employees' stated preferences for working on a particular day rather than another, because of family obligations or other important factors in their lives. In general, try to make work schedules meet employees' needs as closely as possible, while being fair to the other employees. This area should be given serious thought, especially since recent surveys have shown that dissatisfaction among pharmacists stems largely from the working conditions imposed on them.[5] Never forget that the market is competitive and that your employees will certainly consider working for different employers if better working conditions are offered; that is, they are more respectful of their employees' physiological needs.

Security Needs

Especially at the beginning of their employment, employees will experience a measure of uncertainty, not knowing exactly what is expected of them, and being unfamiliar with the overall functioning of the store. After the orientation period, the new employee will need frequent feedback, either from the pharmacy owner or manager, or an immediate supervisor, depending on the size of the store. An absence of feedback could lead to a feeling of insecurity, and consequently to a lessening of initiative, as the employee tries to avoid making mistakes and works defensively rather than confidently, in the interest of the operation. The need for security is also satisfied through work performance reviews at regular intervals after the orientation period.

Social Needs

Every employee wants to become part of the group. It is up to the pharmacy owner or manager to ensure that new employees are encouraged to participate in employee activities. Department or general staff meetings should be held at fairly regular intervals. Such meetings will develop a team spirit by allowing employees to express themselves, and including them in plans for the pharmacy. Employees may be encouraged in this way to offer suggestions for improving the efficiency and productivity of the operation. Various employee get-togethers will also ease the integration of new staff; the pharmacy owner does not necessarily have to subsidize such events, but should encourage, facilitate, and participate in them.

An employer may ask the following questions: What degree of sharing of information about the business and its goals will there be? Will the pharmacy sponsor get-togethers occur during leisure time? Will there be an employee suggestion system? Is it feasible to have a staff sports team or a one-day tournament to foster cohesiveness? Will the pharmacy have an "employee-of-the-month" program, and how and by whom will it be conducted?

ESTEEM NEEDS

If the first three levels of needs are satisfied, employees will become interested in addressing the higher levels, through recognition by the group as leaders or experts in their particular areas. The manager must attempt to identify the emergence of these ego needs in individuals and facilitate their satisfaction. The employees that seek recognition by their peers are the potential future managers of the store, and the people who can be relied on to advance the interests of the organization. Recognition can come in various forms; responsibilities might be increased as a consequence of excellent performance; the employee might be given an opportunity to address a particular topic before the other employees at a staff meeting; an employee-of-the-month award might be introduced; or bonuses based on achievement, or a speedier progression on the salary scale could be considered. Smaller operations may not be able to extend as many opportunities for recognition; nonetheless, the pharmacy owner must find ways to let employees know that their efforts and expertise are recognized and appreciated.

SELF-ACTUALIZATION NEEDS

This is the highest level of needs, wherein employees will strive toward greater accomplishment and responsibility in their work because it gives them personal satisfaction. At this level, employees work for the benefit of self-fulfillment, and it is at this level that the best results are achieved. Do not forget, however, that if store policies or working conditions act to reduce the satisfaction derived in one of the lower-level needs, even the achiever will revert to a preoccupation with satisfying that lower level. It is thus important to constantly monitor the satisfaction of all the five levels of needs among pharmacy staff.

Under ideal conditions, the first three levels will be satisfied for the employee group as a whole. The pharmacy owner will also have given those employees who have the potential a chance to position themselves as higher levels of motivation. Their leadership will help to draw the rest of the staff in the right direction.

There are a number of motivation theories and concepts. One that is often referred to is that developed by Frederick Herzberg, who conducted extensive research into what satisfies and motivates employees. The elements of his conclusions and their relationship to those of Maslow show that they are similar in many ways.[6,7] He concluded that only factors directly related to the content of the job can increase motivation by being satisfied. They include the work itself, responsibility, achievement, chances of advancement, and recognition for achievement. On the other hand, factors not directly related to the job, such as company policies, working conditions, salaries, and interpersonal relations, will not effectively motivate employees. These are referred to as "maintenance factors." Although these maintenance factors can be a source of dissatisfaction leading to problems such as high staff turnover, satisfying them will not serve to motivate an employee. Herzberg's theory also holds that, overall, the duration of an employee's positive response is more prolonged when a motivating factor is satisfied than when one of the maintenance factors is satisfied.

PERFORMANCE REVIEW

It is essential that regularly, at least annually, the pharmacy manager and supervisors of departments conduct performance reviews with each of the employees for whom they are responsible. Performance reviews can be scheduled for the anniversary date of the person's employment, or at the same time of the year for all the employees. (When salary reviews are also involved, the latter option will simplify accounting procedures, but it may place too great a burden on the pharmacy's cash flow and the owner's time.) Evaluation criteria should be known to the employee and be pertinent to the job. Figure 8.1 lists the kinds of criteria that can be used for evaluation. It can be very productive to have employees evaluate their own performance and to base the discussion on a comparison of their perceptions and those of the supervisor or manager.

Whenever possible, performance evaluation should be based on the achievement of established performance standards that are known to the employee. In addition, mutually agreed-upon objectives can be used to upgrade the knowledge and skills of the employee in achieving the goals of the pharmacy (known as "management by objectives"). It is thus essential for the objectives to be discussed, understood, and mutually accepted by the employer and employee. Objectives should be quantifiable and not left open

Figure 8.1   Criteria for Employee Evaluation

Work-Related
Theoretical knowledge
Practical knowledge
Quantity of work
Quality of work

Employee-Related
Attitude
Initiative
Autonomy
Punctuality
Dress

Social
Relationship with other employees
Cooperation

Growth
Potential
Ambition

---

to interpretation. For instance, improving the staff morale is not a quantifiable objective, but increasing sales by five percent over last year is easily measured. Make sure that the method used is compatible with the employee's level of responsibility, and always apply the same method. Agreed-upon objectives should be recorded; one copy is given to the employee and one is kept in the employee file. This system enables continually higher objectives to be set, with resulting employee competence and knowledge.

As with the hiring interview, the performance review should be conducted without interruption in a relaxed atmosphere. To overcome certain psychological barriers, it is also wise to sit next to the employee rather than behind a desk. Employees tend to approach evaluations with some apprehension, especially the first time, fearing that their work will be criticized.

The manager should try to dispel such fears by explaining that the exercise has a constructive purpose: to examine the employee's strong features, as well as the areas of work that may require improvement. Clarity and directness are important: employees should leave the review knowing exactly what they are good at, and what they must work on during the forthcoming period. Always relate the evaluation to the employee's position and job description, be as specific and as quantitative as possible, and provide some tangible objectives that the employee should try to achieve by specified target dates—this makes it much easier for employees to monitor their own progress. Under no circumstances should comparisons be drawn between one employee and another: they are irrelevant and decidedly unproductive.

For most employees, the performance evaluation can take place during any time of the day or week. If, however, your evaluation is somewhat negative, or you suspect that an employee may react to the review in a negative way, schedule the review early in the week and at the beginning of the employee's shift. That way, if the employee does not respond well to what has been said, or feels discouraged, there is time left in the day to follow up—either to encourage the employee or clarify any points that may continue to cause concern. The employee should have goals developed for the coming period, and management should determine what help the employee might need to achieve those goals.

The performance review also provides a good opportunity to assess your employee's level of satisfaction in his or her work, as well as to explore his or her potential for increased responsibility.

SALARY POLICIES

When establishing wage policy, check minimum-wage laws in the area of operation, union wage agreements, professional association guidelines, and competitive factors. Wage policy generally stipulates the starting wage per job category, a specified probationary period, and a time frame for wage increments, with a particular grid or system for establishing what they will be. It also specifies the length of the pay period and answers questions regarding paid hours, such as the following: Should the particular employee or job position be paid on a salaried or hourly basis? How will overtime be handled? What is the shortest paid shift? If there is a changing schedule, how much advance notice of work hours will the employee receive? Will time for meals or breaks be paid? What are the maximum hours per day, or per week, an employee will be required to work?

The performance evaluation can be used as a guide to determine employees' salary progression. While performance reviews can be undertaken several times a year, salaries are usually adjusted annually, with the possible exception of new employees' salaries. New employees' salaries may be adjusted after a three-month probationary period, with a performance and/or salary review during the initial year of employment.

A sound salary policy is based strictly on the employee's performance in the job. Whenever an increase is given, it should be related to an improvement in performance. It is important that owners and managers adhere carefully to a merit-increase policy. Salary policy should also respect internal equilibrium and external equilibrium. Internal equilibrium means that, within a given organization, two people doing equivalent jobs should earn the same amount of money. External equilibrium means paying a fair market value for the services your employees provide. Overpayment is an unnecessary cost to your operation; underpayment will, sooner or later, result in high staff turnover.

Ideally, every job in the pharmacy will have a dollar value, which should be revised annually according to market conditions and, of course, the pharmacy's ability to pay. The factors that influence a job's value include cost of living, and the supply and demand for the particular service at the particular time. Employees believe wage increases to be related primarily to the cost of living, but this principle does not necessarily hold, since some jobs increase in value faster than the cost of living, while others may not increase at all.

The value of a position should be a target for the employee to reach within a certain period of time. New employees should be hired at 80 to 90 percent of the value of the job, allowing them to acquire experience and expertise over the course of several years, before they can qualify for a salary that represents the full value of the job. The level at which an employee is hired is related to previous experience in a similar job, and to the person's technical abilities. Hiring at more than 90 percent of the value of the job will create a problem in the next year, since the new employee will presumably have made some progress, but there will be no room in the pay scale to reward them. The steps of progression over time between the hiring point and the target point should be determined in advance so that all employees could theoretically advance at the same rate. Adjustments can be made more frequently in the case of employees who show a higher-than-average potential.

The performance of employees is said to follow a bell distribution curve. One can expect approximately two-thirds of one's employees, after a reasonable period of time, to perform within the target zone. In some cases, however, employees will be unable to reach this level and, if their performance cannot be improved, the manager must face the possibility of terminating their employment. Conversely, the performance of especially high achievers must be recognized in monetary terms: the manager might allow their salaries to exceed the top of the range by up to 10 to 12 percent. Anything more than this would wreak havoc with the pharmacy's pay scales, and is probably a sign that an employee has outgrown the position. Whenever possible, it is best to relocate these high achievers in more senior positions that allow them greater self-fulfillment.

Contrary to popular belief, salary adjustments and higher salaries are not a source of motivation. Referring back to Herzberg's theory of motivation, salary falls into the group of factors not directly related to the job—an increase will provide satisfaction for a relatively short duration, but not effectively motivate the employee.

BENEFITS AND INCENTIVES

If the pharmacy offers bonuses or incentive plans, policy should stipulate the positions that are eligible for such plans, the eligibility criteria, and the manner in which the total amount will be calculated and paid. Regarding vacations and holidays, policy must comply with provincial legislation and should once again be competitive. Questions include:

- If the store is open on statutory holidays, who will be required to work and how will they be reimbursed?

- How will vacation time be arranged or allocated?

- What length of vacation will be offered after what length of service (for full-time and part-time employees, and for different job categories)?

Some of the questions to be addressed regarding employee benefit programs are as follows: Who will be eligible for employee benefits? What benefits will be offered? Will some be mandatory and some optional? Which benefits will be entirely employer-sponsored and which shared by the employer and employee? Which will be paid entirely by the employee, but administered by the pharmacy?

Benefits can include sick leave, group life insurance, long-term disability, maternity and paternity leave, compassionate leave, dental plans, provincial health care plans, extended health care plans, pension plans or group RRSPs, retirement programs, jury duty, provision of uniforms, shopping privileges or discounts, and payment or leave for further education. Many community pharmacies today are in a position to provide employees with a full-benefits package. The range of positions and salary levels in the pharmacy should be considered in establishing a benefits policy. Benefits for managerial staff are usually different from those offered to other staff. Information on the kind of compensation and benefits offered to different classes of employees is available from management firms or business consultants. It is also advisable to monitor market trends in order to position your firm relative to others.

Incentive policies should aim at rewarding excellence according to the basic principles of management by objectives, as outlined in the discussion of the performance review on p. 174. A bonus plan to reward employees who significantly surpass the expectations of their jobs is a valuable incentive. (It is worth mentioning, as well, that bonuses have the added advantage for employers of not raising the salary base or increasing cumulative salary paid.) The criteria employed, however, must be clearly understood by management and staff and must be objectively quantifiable. Subjective interpretation may lead to more dissatisfaction than positive incentives among personnel. A bonus plan for pharmacists could, for example, recognize achievement in terms of the profitability of the dispensary, or involvement in continuing education, professional conferences, or other professional commitments outside the pharmacy.

Managers should be aware of the employment standards legislation that exists in each province. This legislation sets out the minimum provisions that apply to employees and employers. It sets out minimun wage rates, hours of work and overtime, overtime pay, hours of rest, vacation and vacation pay, general holidays, termination of employment (notice period), and special situations (maternity leave).

SUPERVISION, DISCIPLINE, AND DISMISSAL

Managing human resources will also involve certain unique difficulties, and communication is the key to minimizing the occurrence of such difficulties. One's management staff should be seen not as a disciplinary team, but as a supportive resource for employees, assisting them in their efforts to become more proficient in their work. Educate the managers to be consistent in the decisions they make and to avoid showing favoritism. One's management team must understand the need to be approachable enough for employees to seek their help if they have a problem, but distant enough that their authority is not undermined. Detailed policy regarding disciplinary action and termination procedures is also extremely important. Policy should outline a specific disciplinary procedure that requires the supervisor to discuss performance problems. Documentation of all such meetings should be mandatory.

Termination policy should specify exit-interview procedures, final work day determination, calculation of termination pay, severance arrangements, resignation options, and follow-up support, such as references the store would be willing to provide. Termination procedure should also ensure that all store property, such as uniforms and keys, is returned, that outstanding staff charges are fully paid, and that locks be changed if necessary.

If a supervisor encounters a disciplinary difficulty with an employee, the first step is to communicate verbally with the person to inform the employee of the nature of the infraction and to have the employee indicate what will be done to correct it (a note on the incident should be placed in the personnel file setting out the details). A target date for resolving the identified problem should be set and monitored closely. If the supervisor cannot detect any improvement in the situation by that date, a second meeting is necessary wherein the details of the problem are recorded and the expectations of management are clearly documented in writing. This is known as a letter of reprimand which clearly states the situation, the policy being violated, the previous verbal warnings, the action required of the employee, and the possible consequences of the continuation of the situation. This letter should be factual and correct, as it may be used in a legal suit later. The employee must at this point be made to understand that failure to resolve the problem—again, within a specified period of time—could result in the termination of their employment. The employee should acknowledge receipt of this performance-evaluation update in writing. All documentation of such proceedings, from the outset, should be kept in the employee's file.

In the ladder of events, mediators often look for escalating sanctions as proof that the employee was really aware of the severity of the situation; whenever possible, it would thus be recommended to suspend an employee without pay for a day, then a week, before the final dismissal. In the case of alcohol or drug abuse, these are not cause for termination in themselves but result in poor performance. If the employee acknowledges the problem and agrees to therapy, termination may not be necessary, as the problem is one of illness.

If an employee must be let go, the separation should be effective immediately. Most of the staff in a pharmacy is in direct contact with customers, and a disgruntled employee might well be tempted to vent resentful feelings on customers or suppliers. If possible, try to sustain good relations with the terminated employee. Explain that although his or her relationship with your organization has not been successful, another company that functions differently in terms of work and requirements may well be interested in the employee's services. The pharmacy owner or manager must not lose sight of the human element involved in such situations, and must try to make this difficult transition as smooth as possible for the employee by exercising tact, discretion, and a supportive attitude.

NEPOTISM

Nepotism refers to people who are related to one another—often to a supervisor or owner—working in the same organization. Disciplining could be a problem in a subordinate-superior relationship within the family. As a result, staff may see the related person getting away with things and getting preferential treatment. Obviously this is not good for employee morale. In family-owned businesses, the manager should have a policy in place to cover related persons working in the same pharmacy before a problem occurs.

A side issue is romantic involvement between staff. Some places try to prevent romantic liaison between staff members. If two people are linked romantically they may be required to notify their manager so that one of them can be moved to another job. This is easier in a large corporation than in a pharmacy.

INDUSTRIAL RELATIONS AND COLLECTIVE BARGAINING

As a community pharmacy moves from a collection of small businesses to a mixture of large and small firms, it is likely that the pharmacy manager will come into contact with collective bargaining. Currently, most of the institutional-practice pharmacists in Canada are under collective agreements.

The federal and provincial governments have encouraged the growth of unions in Canada. The underlying assumption is that collective bargaining is good. Current legislation makes it relatively easy for a union (a bargaining unit) to be formed in a company or industrial sector. To be formally recognized as a bargaining unit for a group of employees, the union must acquire the right to bargain by acquiring a certificate (certification process) from the provincial government agency, which sets out the rules to be followed.

To become certified, a union first sells memberships in the union. If they sign up a substantial proportion of the employees, they can apply for certification. The labor relations unit in the government will then arrange for a vote by the employees. If a majority vote in favor of a union collective agreement, then a firm must bargain with the union on behalf of the employees and develop a contract (collective agreement). In this process, a firm must not try to intimidate the employees to stop them from joining the union.

Employees join a union for improved compensation, improved working conditions, and, most importantly, protection from unilateral decisions. The purpose of unions is to engage in collective bargaining on behalf of its members as the bargaining power of the individual worker is weak. It is possible for individuals to negotiate better compensation or working conditions, but if refused, they must accept the decision or resign. Both of these alternatives are unsatisfactory. On the other hand, employees acting as a group have more power and can bargain on behalf of all the workers. The union is an organization of employees that has collectively agreed to have its conditions of employment determined by negotiation by the firm and union representatives. This means that the individual can no longer go to management and get a special arrangement, nor can the manager take action in pay and benefits without going to the union. This constrains the manager and makes changes more bureaucratic and subject to negotiation.

Firms that do not want to have a union could create a high-quality work environment with trust and communication with superiors. Even this, however, may not prevent the certification of a union. In Vancouver, the move to a union at Starbucks—a company with progressive employee relations—was initiated by an employee who was increasingly upset with several unpopular actions by management.[8] A union spokesman stated that when communications in a firm break down, the unions, not management, get the first call.

Many organizations, including hospitals, have collective agreements which set out the respective obligations, and rights of management and employees. When an employee believes that they are not being managed in accordance with the terms of the agreement, they have the right to file a grievance. This is a statement of the circumstances of the alleged contract violation.

Grievances are handled in a step-by-step graduated system. Attempts are made to solve the matter at the first (supervisor) level. If this is not possible, it goes to middle management. Should the matter be contentious or have policy implications, it will go to senior management. There is normally an arbitration process using outside experts in important cases where the two sides cannot agree. While this is an impartial and formal way of dealing with problems under the agreement, it is bureaucratic, expensive, and time consuming. In organizations with morale problems, grievances are often filed out of frustration. The sheer weight of the greivance load imposes an administrative burden on managers, to the delight of the employees. One of the indicators of staff morale in an organization is the number of grievances filed.

INTELLECTUAL PROPERTY AND COPYRIGHT

There are three forms of property recognized in law: 1) real property consisting of land and interests in land; 2) personal property consisting of cars, clothes, jewelery and similar posessions; and 3) intellectual property.

Intellectual property is becoming more important in pharmacy as the knowledge base and marketing aspects of pharmacy practice become more important. Managers should be aware that legal suits over intellectual property can be expensive, and the pharmacy may lose access to valuable assets in the form of an identity for the firm and its products. Managers should make sure that employees know the policies of the pharmacy with regard to intellectual property. Rights to some intellectual property may be lost if steps to protect it are not in place. In larger firms, legal assistance will be available for this purpose. In independent pharmacies, the manager needs to seek out the necessary legal advice.

A particular problem is the rights of the employees in developing intellectual property. Many problems occur if employees feel that they were not treated fairly in terms of the development and sale of intellectual property. The contract of employment for any staff that develop intellectual property should include a clear statement that the intellectual property developed as part of the employee's job is owned by the employer. While this is generally the case, it may be less clear where the usual job of the employee is different from that involved in creation of the intellectual property.

Forms of Intellectual Property

People involved with intellectual property should understand the terms explained below.

- *Patents*: Patents are a lawful monopoly to make, use, and sell an invention, which provides protection of the research investment allowing the inventor to profit from the research. There are few patents by community pharmacists, although some pharmacists have developed topical products and sought patents for them and others have developed pharmacy software or dispensing gadgets.

- *Trademarks*: Trademarks consist of a word or words used to identify the origin of wares or services in order to distinguish them from wares made or services offered by other enterprises. Its importance is to have consumers link a particular product or service to its manufacturer or supplier. For example, Life brand products are from Shoppers Drug Mart and Tylenol is made by McNeil Consumer Products Ltd.

    Under the Trademarks Act, a "trade-name" is a name under which a business is conducted. It can be the name of a corporation, a partnership, or an individual. A trade-name identifies the whole of an enterprise.[9] Examples would be London Drugs, PharmaScience, Medis, and Broadmoor Pharmacy.

- *Industrial design*: Industrial design is the exclusive right to commercialize the ornamentation or shape of a useful object, such as a cutlery pattern, a medicine container, etc. The classic example is that of the Coke bottle shape.

- *Copyright.* Copyright is the authors' "right to protect the form of expression of a literary, musical, artisic or dramatic work." In a pharmacy, it might be a newsletter or other communication form that is used (HealthWatch), or patient form that has been designed for monitoring patients' progress. To secure copyright is fairly simple and inexpensive, and worth the effort of having legal advice. It is likely that pharmacies will be developing more specialized documents and systems in the future, and these may be worth protecting so that they are not copied and used by competitors.

SUMMARY

Personnel policies and procedures can be implemented to improve the efficiency of, and to ensure that the overall direction of, a pharmacy. The extent to which such policies and procedures are formalized, and the manner in which they are communicated to staff, will depend on the size and nature of the organization, and on the management approach preferred by the pharmacy manager. A policy and procedures manual, brochure, or handbook can be invaluable in both fostering a clear understanding between management and staff, and ensuring order and continuity in the way the pharmacy's business is conducted over time.

Effective human resources management is an integral aspect of effective business management. Productivity and profitability can be improved by recognizing the importance of accurately assessing staffing requirements, hiring the right candidate for the job, and effectively providing a motivating climate for staff members. Consistent and progressive policies in the areas of performance evaluation, salary policy, and staff supervision will create a positive image for the pharmacy as an employer, and attract valuable additions to its staff. It is perhaps most important to remember that, simply, a high level of job satisfaction among the employees will result in a high quality of service to the pharmacy's customers.

References

1.   Anon. *The AltiMed CFP Report on Pharmacy Services 1997.* Toronto: AltiMed Canada, 1998.

2.   Segal, H.J. *Combined 10ᵗʰ and 11ᵗʰ Annual Survey of Community Pharmacy Operations.* Toronto: Eli Lilly Canada, 1992.

3.   Jerris, L.A. *Effective Employee Orientation.* New York: American Management Association, 1993.

4.   Maslow, A.H. "A Theory of Human Motivation." In H.M. Strange, ed. *Milestones in Management.* Oxford: Blackwell Business, 1992.

5.   Anon. *Inside Pharmacy: The Anatomy of a Profession.* Kenilworth, NJ: Schering Laboratories, 1986.

6.   Herzberg, F. *Work and the Nature of Man.* Cleveland: World Publishing Co., 1966.

7.   Donnelly, J.H., Gibson, J.L., and Ivancevich, J.M. *Fundamentals of Management.* 5ᵗʰ ed. Plano, TX: Business Publications Inc., 1984.

8.   Damsell, K. "Service with No Smile." *The Financial Post*, 23 August 1997.

9.   Anon. "Trade-Marks and Trade Names: Registration Issues." Intellectual Property Law Update, *Milner Fenerty Bulletin*, April 1997.

APPENDIX 8A: SAMPLE POSITION DESCRIPTIONS

JOB TITLE: PHARMACY MANAGER/HEAD PHARMACIST

PRIMARY FUNCTION: To manage the resources (human, physical, financial) of the dispensary, to interface with other store departments, and to ensure achievement of store objectives.

REPORTS TO: Associate

SUPERVISES: All dispensary Department Personnel.

DUTIES:
HUMAN RESOURCES
- may interview and recommend to Associate final candidates for hiring in Dispensary;

- ensures that subordinates comply with all store policies, operating procedures, and professional/legal requirements;

- schedules staff hours, days off, and vacations withing established guidelines;

- trains employees in job functions;

- gives on-going guidance and instruction;

- completes performance reviews of subordinates in consultation with Associate;

- recommends performance pay increments for subordinates to Associate.

CUSTOMER SERVICE
- ensures that efficient and pleasant customer service is provided;

- ensures that subordinates present proper image to the public according to policy, e.g., clean appearance, approved uniform and name badge, etc;

- provides professional and friendly patient counseling;
- answers inquiries, e.g., location of products, rain checks, etc;
- ensures that applicable professional programs are implemented;
- resolves customer complaints according to established guidelines.

OPERATIONS

- maintains balanced dispensary inventory;
- maintains projected dollar inventory for assigned product categories;
- ensures that narcotic products are properly received and recorded at the dispensary;
- ensures that pricing of all merchandise is current, including Actual Acquisition Cost.

MARKETING AND MERCHANDISING

- may participate in setting up and implementing local community service programs.

FINANCE

- assists in setting and achieving financial objectives for the Dispensary;
- ensures timely and accurate completion of all documentation for third-party plans, e.g., processing, billing, resubmissions.

GENERAL

- ensures that the standards of housekeeping and image are maintained;
- performs other duties as assigned.

The above reflects the general details considered necessary to describe the principal functions and duties and shall not be construed as a detailed description of all the work requirements that may be inherent in the job.

JOB TITLE: PHARMACIST

PRIMARY FUNCTION: To deliver pharmaceutical care and to ensure that all prescriptions are dispensed in accordance with regulations and store policies.

REPORTS TO: Pharmacist Manager (Associate)

SUPERVISES: Dispensary Assistants/Pharmacy Technicians

DUTIES:

PHARMACEUTICAL CARE

- ensures professional pharmacist responsibilities are fulfilled including:
    - entry of current and accurate patient medication history into the pharmacy's computer;
    - intervention by contacting physician when prescription accuracy is questionable;
    - documentation of course of action if a pharmaceutical intervention occurs;
    - patient counseling;
    - review of printed medication information with patients;
    - monitors compliance and helps patients maintain or improve quality of life;
    - ensures that technical responsibilities of pharmacy assistants are fulfilled, therefore allowing the pharmacists time to practise pharmaceutical care.

HUMAN RESOURCES

- interviews and recommends to associate final candidates for hiring in dispensary;
- ensures that subordinates comply with all store policies, operating procedures, and professional/legal requirements including the pharmacy's standards of practice;

- recommends disciplinary measures to associate up to and including termination;

- schedules staff hours, days off, and vacations within established guidelines;

- trains employees in job functions;

- gives on-going guidance and instruction;

- completes performance reviews of subordinates in consultation with the pharmacy manager;

- recommends performance pay increments for subordinates to associate.

LOSS PREVENTION
- ensures all loss prevention systems and procedures are performed according to established guidelines.

CUSTOMER SERVICE
- ensures that superior customer service is provided;

- ensures that subordinates present proper professional image to the public, according to policy (e.g., clean appearance, approved uniform and name badge, etc.);

- provides professional and friendly patient counseling;

- answers inquiries (e.g., location of products, rainchecks, etc.);

- ensures that applicable professional programs are implemented;

- resolves customer complaints according to established guidelines.

OPERATIONS
- maintains balanced dispensary inventory;

- maintains projected dollar inventory for assigned product categories;

- ensures that narcotic products are properly received and recorded at the dispensary;

- ensures that pricing of all merchandise is current, including actual acquisition cost.

MARKETING AND MERCHANDISING
- participates, as appropriate, in setting up and implementing local community service programs;
- ensures pharmacy marketing/POP materials maximize department potential and comply with company policy.

FINANCE
- assists in setting and achieving financial objectives for the dispensary;
- ensures timely and accurate completion of all documentation for third party plans, (e.g., processing, billing, resubmissions);
- ensures timely and accurate completion of daily reports for electronically-submitted third-party plans.

GENERAL
- ensures that standards of housekeeping and professional image are maintained;
- performs all responsibilities of pharmacist;
- performs other duties as assigned;
- complies with all health and safety requirements.

PHYSICAL DEMANDS
The incumbent will be required to spend most of the shift standing. There is an occasional need to lift boxes and equipment weighing up to 20 kg. There is also a requirement to drive to pick up supplies or deliver medication at least weekly.

The above reflects the general details that describe the principal functions and duties and shall not be construed as a detailed description of all the work requirements that may be inherent in the job.

JOB TITLE: DISPENSARY ASSISTANT/PHARMACY TECHNICIAN/PHARMACY ASSISTANT

PRIMARY FUNCTION: To perform the dispensing functions of filling prescriptions and to assist in the related administration under the direct supervision of a pharmacist.

REPORTS TO: Pharmacist/Pharmacist Manager/Head Pharmacist

SUPERVISES: None

DUTIES:

OPERATIONS

- performs all technical functions related to the filling of prescriptions, allowing pharmacist time to practise pharmaceutical care;

- assists the pharmacist in the preparation of prescriptions;

- may complete documentation (e.g., third party prescriptions, filing, invoices, etc);

- maintains and controls the cash register in the dispensing area in accordance with cash-handling policies and procedures;

- merchandises and maintains the stock in the dispensary;

- assists in the merchandising of other areas as requested.

LOSS PREVENTION

- ensures that all loss prevention systems and procedures are performed according to established guidelines.

CUSTOMER SERVICE

- ensures that any and all patient inquiries regarding prescriptions and non-prescription medications, uses, treatments, and recommendations are referred to the pharmacist;

- ensures that customers are referred to the pharmacist for direct involvement in the sale of restricted access OTC products;

- ensures that efficient and pleasant customer service is provided;
- answers inquiries (e.g., location of products, rainchecks, etc.);
- answers and places telephone calls in an efficient and friendly manner;
- ensures that applicable marketing programs are implemented;
- resolves customer complaints according to established guidelines;
- ensures that concerns regarding prescriptions, OTC, BTC products, professional fee, etc., are referred to the pharmacist;
- presents proper professional image to the public according to policy (e.g., clean appearance, approved uniform and name badge etc.).

GENERAL
- ensures that standards of housekeeping and professional image are maintained;
- performs other related duties as assigned;
- complies with all health and safety requirements.

The above reflects the general details that describe the principal functions and duties and shall not be construed as a detailed description of all the work requirements that may be inherent in the job.

APPENDIX 8B: POLICIES

Personnel and Human Resource Development Policy

Policies covering personnel and human resource development ensure compliance with government employment standards and regulations, facilitate fair employment practices by reducing favoritism and discrimination, and ensure uniform standards and practices, within the firm. When developing or reviewing personnel policies, it is useful to consider provincial labor laws, competitors' employment and personnel practices and any union contracts. One could also reflect on the problems or experience that you have had with employees. All of these factors could affect the store and its operation. Also, take a longer-term perspective and consider the pharmacy's business strategy, particularly with respect to growth and diversification, which will affect the type and number of employees required.

9

MARKETING AND MERCHANDISING

INTRODUCTION

Marketing is the process by which the demands of the public for goods or services are not only satisfied, but also predicted and enhanced. Marketing enables goods and services to be made available for sale to the public at appropriate prices. Retailing is part of the marketing process; it involves the provision of the physical environment in which the exchange of goods and services for a price is accomplished—in our case, the community pharmacy.

There is an increasing tendency among business experts to define the marketing approach as consumer-oriented; anticipating and meeting the needs of the public, rather than as a selling or merchandising approach. The consumer-oriented marketing approach has proved successful in providing consumers with what they want and generating profits for the businesses that perform best.

Changes in Retailing

Over the past 25 years, there have been enormous changes in retailing, which have evolved partly in response to societal changes in culture, education, technology, and patterns of trade, and partly as a result of the competitive nature of the retail marketplace. Many of these changes are reflected in the ways in which pharmaceutical products and services are currently sold.

Shopping has become a recreational pursuit in its own right. Stores have become larger as a greater array of products flows onto the market. In most of the categories of goods sold at retail, there has been a marked increase in the variety and kinds of products available. This is certainly true for pharmacies, where there are many new types of non-prescription drugs, home-care products, giftware, paper goods and cards, sunglasses, watches and clocks, confectionery, health and beauty aids, and cosmetics. As Canadian consumers became more affluent and sought a wider variety of products, pharmacies grew in size from approximately 2,000 square feet in the 1960s to an average of approximately 3,100 square feet by 1995. The average franchise pharmacy was 5,430 square feet, versus 3,187 for chains and 2,492 for independents.[1]

Major changes have taken place in the design of metal shelving and pegboard and display islands, which now allow for mass displays of leading non-prescription drugs and other products. These new fixtures are part of an overall change in decor, involving new methods of layout, more emphasis on signs, and an attempt to make the customer feel comfortable at all times while in the pharmacy. The initial emphasis on well-lit, clean, and orderly pharmacies has evolved into a demand for convenience, a wide variety of products, a pleasant shopping atmosphere, and a high level of professional service.

A market demand for services is prevalent today, and pharmacies, particularly chain stores, advertise and promote a service-oriented image. The concept of "image" in advertising refers to the promotion of a type of store or service, rather than the specific goods and services it provides. In response to the perceived needs of their customers, pharmacies now promote a professional service image, which is reflected in the appearance of the pharmacy and the provision of fast and efficient service and convenience.

THE CONSUMER ENVIRONMENT

In marketing, consumer desires and needs must be anticipated. In pharmacy, successful marketing depends on an accurate interpretation of societal trends that relate, directly and indirectly, to health and health care.

Understanding the Contemporary Consumer

Health has always had a high value in human society, but perhaps never more than today. This is reflected in current trends toward health and fitness, preventive health care, self-care and self-treatment, and holistic medicine and "natural" products. With this interest comes a general increase in consumer demand for a full range of pharmaceuticals and health-care products, from basic hygiene products, health and beauty aids, and non-prescription drugs, to natural-source vitamins and self-diagnostic equipment.

Each year, firms market new, more effective products for self-care and self-diagnosis. The growing proportion of the elderly in our society contributes to the increased demand for home health-care products. With these changes, today's consumer is predisposed to rely more heavily on the products offered by pharmacies and the information, assistance, and counseling services that pharmacists can provide. Recent surveys have documented that the pharmacist enjoys high regard in the community as a health-care provider.[2]

Generally speaking, the contemporary consumer aspires to a high quality of life, attempts to avoid or minimize stress, and seeks pleasure and relaxation. This is reflected in the kinds of products that people desire. Products that enable them to relax, make them feel and look healthy, and in some way make life easier are in greatest demand. Younger families tend to try to achieve a high standard of living in a relatively short period of time, not only to satisfy desires as soon as possible, but also to ensure that their children are well looked after and have opportunities for personal growth. To achieve the objective of a moderate, enjoyable standard of living, people turn to the accessibility of funds using credit or long-term borrowing. Credit has thus become a major force in retailing.

Although the object of perhaps the greatest thrust in North American marketing and advertising today is the aging generation of baby boomers—people born between 1946 and 1965 and tagged with various labels, such as "yuppie," to describe their characteristics—there is a growing focus on people over the age of 50 who are affluent and now have the time and inclination to spend money in various ways. Because these people place great value on their health, they tend to be a group to whom a wide variety of pharmacy-related products can be sold. Of course, the pharmacy owner cannot ignore young people, among whom fads change rapidly and can cause sizable shifts in the market for a wide range of goods. The marketer must try to anticipate and utilize such apparent shifts in the pharmacy's marketing strategy.

The pharmacist-manager may or may not agree with, or understand, the preferences of consumers, whether they be related to popular trends or cultural differences, but is obliged to observe them in order to properly meet the demands of the public. For example, the pharmacist may doubt the scientific validity of the current trend that favors natural-source vitamins and herbal medicines, but will nonetheless purchase and promote these products. (The ethics involved in their sale must of course be kept in mind so that the patient is not taken advantage of through lack of knowledge.) Another example involves cultural or religious groups whose beliefs might prevent them from using certain product groups, such as birth control products. An awareness of this will enable the pharmacist to provide alternative products to help the patient control conception.

Consumer Behavior

In marketing, demographic analysis is commonly used to understand the purchasing preferences and habits of consumers. Demographic analysis focuses on factors such as age, sex, income, family structure, education, ethnic background, socio-economic class, residence, religion, and politics. More and more, however, marketing of consumer products has come to draw heavily on psychological analyses of human behavior to determine how decisions are made by consumers. A variety of models of consumer behavior has been proposed, which can be found in the literature on the subject.

Individuals have a particular psychological make-up based on their perception of themselves and of their role in society. In other words, the personality of the individual and his or her general pattern of behavior is what distinguishes one individual from another. One approach based on psychological factors is called psychographics. It combines personality theory with lifestyle analysis, paying attention to an individual's activities, interests, opinions, and ambitions. A similar tool, called psychometrics, has also been advocated. Psychometrics differs from psychographics in that it focuses more exclusively on personality and an individual's need to structure experience, and less on lifestyle.

The usefulness of this type of information depends partly on the size of the organization. These methods are used largely by national manufacturers or distributors, whereas a small market area would not justify such a complex research procedure. Also, the results of such studies must be weighted critically against possible compensating factors, such as differences in the nature and quality of services offered by the different pharmacies that members of the survey group patronize. Such differences could clearly affect the participants' attitudes to pharmacies in general. Finally, the results of such a study might be called into question because of the relatively small size of the survey group. Nonetheless, pharmacy managers should be aware of current research into consumer behavior, which may contribute valuable new ideas to their marketing plans.

A MARKETING APPROACH

The pharmacy manager must determine what the customer needs or wants and try to provide the kinds of activities or products that would satisfy these needs. However, the effort to meet the consumer's needs and the amount the consumer is willing to pay for the goods and services offered must be balanced.

This means that a pharmacist should first assess the need for particular goods and services that are to be provided in the given geographical area. The results of such an assessment will be reflected in the types of product lines carried and the depth in which they are stocked, the number of staff and nature of their training, and the availability of delivery services and credit accounts.

In a study of the features of a pharmacy that influence where consumers obtain prescription medication, it was found that the most important attribute was that the pharmacist takes the time to explain how the medication works and any possible side effects. Other important features in selecting a pharmacy are outlined in Table 9.1.

A pharmacy manager would want to give such stated preferences appropriate attention in planning and marketing pharmacy services.

Consumer Market

The manager of a pharmacy must determine the size of the market that will be served—that is, define the trading area of the pharmacy. The "consumer market" is defined as the potential of a selected group of consumers to purchase the goods or services offered to them; for a pharmacy, this will be determined by the number of people in the trading area, and the amount of money they are prepared to spend on health care and related products.

Assessment of the consumer market should be a dynamic process that defines the current number and the characteristics of the customer population, and also considers apparent trends and their potential impact on future business. The pharmacist can examine the demographic characteristics of the trading area's constituent neighborhoods to determine the kinds of families that live there and their potential needs. This information is available from the census that is conducted every ten years by Statistics Canada. More timely data are usually available from the municipal government, which has economic and social information on each area.

Table 9.1   *Importance of Features in Deciding Where to Fill a Prescription*

Feature	Importance (Percent Reporting)			
	Very	*Somewhat*	*Not*	*Not at all*
Pharmacist explains	76	22	2	1
Complete Rx record	68	26	5	1
Stock to dispense	67	29	3	1
Close to home/work	54	35	10	2
Professional appearance	47	42	9	1
Rapport with pharmacist	42	41	13	4
Waiting time	39	48	9	3
Free delivery	33	35	22	9
Pharmacist's fee	32	37	22	8
Variety of goods and services	31	47	17	5
Other health-care services	30	47	18	5
Confidential counseling area	23	46	25	7

The market may be changing from established families to younger families with less income, which would significantly influence the pharmacy's planning and marketing strategy. Similarly, it would be obvious that in an affluent neighborhood people will likely spend more on personal products than in a neighborhood with a lower income level. The relative affluence of a neighborhood can be determined by looking at census data that give average incomes by census tract.

The consumer market can be segmented into various groups. For example, the proportion of elderly in an area represents a potential demand for certain types of goods and products, whereas a neighborhood with a large number of infants and young children represents a very different kind of demand. One of the determinants of the kind of market one is dealing with would be the nature of family composition in the area. Meeting the needs of these different populations calls for a different product mix, services tailored to the needs, and having the pharmacy organized and designed to provide these services.

The pharmacy manager may choose not to try to build sales by marketing to all the identified consumer groups, but to focus on one or two predominant groups. In other words, services might be targeted to specific market segments. If there is an even demographic mix, marketing experts suggest that you identify who your competition is targeting, and pursue the remaining market segments. Such choices are commonly referred to as "positioning the business in the marketplace."

Assessment of market need should be balanced against the estimated cost of operating the pharmacy over a period of years. A pharmacy offering a high level of service, with high rental costs and a low sales volume, could not effectively compete with low-priced, high-volume competitors if the customers in the trading area were price sensitive.

Marketing Information Systems

While the initial planning for a pharmacy is complex, subjective, and filled with risk, once a pharmacy is in operation there is a wealth of marketing information that can be used to refine marketing activities.

INTERNAL DATA

From sales data, accounts receivable, and prescription records, pharmacies can collect information such as customer names and addresses, the amount purchased per visit or per year, and fluctuations and trends in sales.

Sales information from the cash register can be recorded by product or product line. The rate of purchase and sale of an individual item is referred to as its sales velocity; reports on sales velocity are often available from wholesalers. This shows the number of units of each item or the dollar sales of a product line. The pharmacy point-of-sale (POS) system (scanners) enables one to assess velocity by different groups of products or by department. The effectiveness of special promotions and sales can also be assessed by regularly monitoring quantities sold over the period of the sale. Profitability should also be assessed periodically by product and product line, by groups of customers, and by the sales and special efforts undertaken in each department.

Linking of sales to specific customers (target marketing) is now becoming more common as retailers use loyalty programs. In these programs, the specific purchases and total purchases of each customer in the program are recorded and are available for marketing purposes. For example, if a patient purchases diabetic supplies, they could be placed on a mailing list for the promotion of a new diabetic product or service. Use of patient information from prescriptions can only be used in a professional context due to the confidentiality of these data. This form of direct marketing is selective and can be used to build closer ties with the patient.

Monitoring based on internal data will provide the pharmacy owner or manager with information essential to formulating a marketing plan, in that it reflects the degree to which customer needs are being met. Failure to meet consumer needs can also be monitored more directly, by putting a system in place to record and deal with returned goods and customer complaints. Information technology is a useful tool for managers but is currently underutilized.[3]

MARKET RESEARCH

Market research is the study of the attitudes and beliefs that shape the consumer's response to a product or service. Market research can be initiated in a pharmacy as an informal system, based on verbal comments and suggestions from customers, and written comments obtained by request— for example, in a suggestion box. This is a common approach among community pharmacies. Through their close relationships with customers and other staff members, pharmacy staff can develop a good idea of the issues and problems facing the pharmacy, but they must be sensitive and alert to these issues and must have a means of using the information they gain to improve service.

To evaluate the image of one's pharmacy, one should try to see it through the eyes of a customer and mentally compare it to other pharmacies. What is the visual impact and image conveyed? Has a professional atmosphere been achieved, through cleanliness, orderliness, and comfort? Is the pharmacy well stocked and are products well displayed and uniformly marked with prices? Observe competitive pharmacies in the same way to derive a sense of the different approaches used and how they might influence a customer's choice of pharmacy.

Regular analysis, or environmental scanning, of the advertising of competitors should be conducted in order to stay abreast of activities in the competitive market, and be able to respond to them quickly and effectively. Regularly checking of competitive prices is now standard practice in community-pharmacy market research. Such information will show competitors' reactions to market changes and will provide insight into the overall strategy of the competing pharmacy. Newspapers, newsletters, and advertising flyers should be read with an eye to both institutional and product advertising.

A more formal method of market research involves the systematic collection of information that is of specific interest to the pharmacy manager. Companies such as A.C. Nielsen specialize in market research, generating data on product movement and trends in market shares for various industries, including the pharmaceutical industry. While larger pharmacy organizations can hire market research firms to address specific problem areas, smaller firms will probably have to conduct their own research. Newer software packages can be integrated to support a company's merchandising, accounting, and purchasing systems. For example, one system enables the head office to analyze "what products are selling, in what volumes, and in what stores."[4]

Questionnaires are a usual form of market research and are easy to use, although it can be difficult to design a good questionnaire that gives accurate, unbiased results. An open-ended format can be used, eliciting customers' views on the services or products they would like to see in the pharmacy. Another, simpler questionnaire format is the checklist, on which people indicate their preferences for services. Figures 9.1 and 9.2 (p. 204) show a sample of the open-ended questionnaire and the checklist.

Figure 9.1   *Open-Ended Format Questionnaire*

SHOPPERS DRUG MART
HELP US TO HELP YOU!

What did you like about our store?

_____
_____
_____

What didn't you like about our store?

_____
_____
_____

Are there any products or services that you would like to see in our store?

_____
_____
_____

Any additional comments?

_____
_____
_____

OPTIONAL:

NAME   _____

ADDRESS   _____
                                          PLEASE DEPOSIT IN OUR CUSTOMER
            _____   COMMENT BOX. THANK-YOU! WE
PHONE   _____   APPRECIATE YOUR INTEREST.

Source: Courtesy of Shoppers Drug Mart.

Figure 9.2   Checklist Format Questionnaire

YOUR OPINION COUNTS

In order to better serve you, we would like you to complete this brief questionnaire. Please take a few minutes to answer the following questions. We will use the information you provide to serve you better.

Please use a lead pencil to fill out the form, do not use a pen. Completely fill in the circles of your choices. Do not mark outside of the circles.

Thank you for your assistance.

Fill in the one circle which best represents
your **agreement/disagreement** to each statement.

① = Strongly Disagree   ② = Disagree   ③   = Undecided/Don't Know

④ = Agree   ⑤ = Strongly Agree

1. The pharmacist(s) at this pharmacy provides excellent information about how to properly use each prescription.
   ①   ②   ③   ④   ⑤

2. The employees at this pharmacy always make an extra effort to help me find what I need.
   ①   ②   ③   ④   ⑤

3. The merchandise displays in this pharmacy are always attractive.
   ①   ②   ③   ④   ⑤

4. The hours this pharmacy is open are convenient for me.
   ①   ②   ③   ④   ⑤

5. The pharmacist(s) at this pharmacy provides me with useful information in selecting non-prescription medication.
   ①   ②   ③   ④   ⑤

6. This pharmacy's prescription medication prices are competitive.
   ①   ②   ③   ④   ⑤

7. The pharmacist(s) at this pharmacy is always available to answer my questions about non-prescription and prescription medication.
   ①   ②   ③   ④   ⑤

8. The pharmacist(s) at this pharmacy always reviews my prescription medication with me to explain possible side effects or problems.
   ①   ②   ③   ④   ⑤

9. The employees at this pharmacy are always friendly to customers.
   ①   ②   ③   ④   ⑤

10. This pharmacy's non-prescription medication prices are competitive.
    ①   ②   ③   ④   ⑤

11. This pharmacy always looks very neat and clean.
    ①   ②   ③   ④   ⑤

12. This pharmacy carries the non-prescription medication I need.
    ①   ②   ③   ④   ⑤

Figure 9.2   (cont'd)

Overall, how satisfied are you with this pharmacy?

① Not at all satisfied   ② Somewhat satisfied   ③ Satisfied   ④ Very satisfied

Please darken the circle that best represents the **importance** of these factors to you.

① = Not Important ② = Slightly Important

③ = Important ④ = Very Important

Convenient Pharmacy Hours	①	②	③	④
Clean and Attractive Pharmacy	①	②	③	④
Wide Merchandise Selection	①	②	③	④
Friendly and Helpful Service	①	②	③	④
Competitive Prescription Prices	①	②	③	④
Competitive Non-Prescription Prices	①	②	③	④
Useful Prescription Information	①	②	③	④
Useful Non-Prescription Information	①	②	③	④
Concern for My Health	①	②	③	④
Convenient Parking	①	②	③	④
Convenient Location	①	②	③	④

Please rate this pharmacy on each of the following factors
compared to other pharmacies available to you.

① = Much Worse   ② = Somewhat Worse   ③ = Similar

④ = Somewhat Better   ⑤ = Much Better

Convenient Pharmacy Hours	①	②	③	④	⑤
Clean and Attractive Pharmacy	①	②	③	④	⑤
Wide Merchandise Selection	①	②	③	④	⑤
Friendly and Helpful Service	①	②	③	④	⑤
Competitive Prescription Prices	①	②	③	④	⑤
Competitive Non-Prescription Prices	①	②	③	④	⑤
Useful Prescription Information	①	②	③	④	⑤
Useful Non-Prescription Information	①	②	③	④	⑤
Concern for My Health	①	②	③	④	⑤
Convenient Parking	①	②	③	④	⑤
Convenient Location	①	②	③	④	⑤

Figure 9.2   (cont'd)

Where do you primarily buy your non-prescription medication?	About how often do you shop here?
o This pharmacy o Another pharmacy o Grocery store o Department store	o First visit here o 1 or 2 times a month o More than 2 times a month
How frequently do you purchase your prescription medication from this pharmacy? o Always o Some of the time o Never	In which age group are you? o Less than 21 years o 21–40 years o 41–60 years o Over 60 years
Are you: o Male o Female	In which income group is your family? o Under $15,000 annually o $15,000 to $25,000 annually o $25,000 to $35,000 annually o Over $35,000 annually

Source: Sandoz Consumer Health Care Group, 1987.

Information on competitors can be obtained through competitive pricing studies that are conducted by chain pharmacies and wholesale-based or co-operative groups. Regular information on the relative position of prices enables the managers to set competitive prices on selected items.

One method of collecting information that may be appropriate for pharmacies is the ongoing questionnaire—one that the same group of customers would be asked to complete periodically over time. This approach gives continuous feedback as to customers' perceptions of service levels, product offerings, and general image, and enables the pharmacy to keep in touch with a client base and to adapt to better meet their needs. Questionnaires should be mailed out regularly—say, three times per year—and should include general questions that are repeated each time as well as questions that address specific issues of interest to the pharmacy owner or manager at the particular time. As an incentive to participate, randomly chosen customers might be offered a prize or preferential treatment such as prior announcement of sales. As customers drop out of the survey, new ones should be recruited. While this approach is used by some national firms, it has not been extensively used by pharmacies.

THE MARKETING PLAN

From Strategic Plan to Marketing Plan

The strategic plan is the overall direction or goal that is set for the pharmacy. It outlines the philosophy by which the pharmacy will operate. For example, a strategic plan defines the image that is to be created, the pricing approach taken, and the levels of service offered. A small pharmacy in a clinic would have a very different philosophy from a large merchandising pharmacy in a shopping mall.

The operational plan (on which the business plan is based) flows from the strategic plan and sets out objectives in terms of sales, profits, gross margins, and market share. Based on the general directional guidelines of the strategic and operational plans, the pharmacy establishes a specific objective, or set of objectives, toward which to work, say, over the next five years. The operational plan is reviewed and revised annually in the context of the original projection of objectives. Each year, a marketing plan is also devised to implement those objectives (see Figure 9.3).

Figure 9.3   Strategic Plan to Annual Marketing Plan

Strategic Plan (Philosophy and Direction) Operational (Business) Plan (Financial Plan, Marketing Plan, Operations and Staffing Plan) Annual Marketing Plan (Merchandising, Advertising)

In establishing the annual marketing plan, it will be necessary to review outside sources of data (consisting of international and national surveys and statistics) in order to gain a sense of general trends and new products, and to conduct one's own marketing research from internal sources. Some of the various factors involved and their influence on the marketing plan are described in the following sections.

To start, however, the manager should determine the average transaction sale of the pharmacy from cash register data on total sales and total number of transactions. (This figure should be higher during sales due to the increased activity resulting from special promotions.) Examining such data by department will provide valuable insight into what is actually taking place in the store. Similarly, internal data on the pharmacy's customers should be reviewed. As mentioned earlier, prescription files and informal surveys will supply information on customer characteristics such as age, number of prescriptions purchased, non-prescription drug purchases, and patterns of repeat prescriptions.

The marketing plan may be guided by an objective either to increase the average sale per customer or to attract more customers to the pharmacy, or both. To increase the average sale per customer, the pharmacy must encourage the customer to buy more while in the store; that is, it must strive to increase impulse purchasing, for example, by expanding or varying the product mix, or making the existing product mix more attractive to the customer. Revamping the merchandising will renew the customer's interest in the store.

Merchandising and image can be supplemented by promoting existing or new professional services (such as blood pressure measurement or home visits) through a mailing, or in direct conversation with customers. Attracting more customers to the pharmacy would call for increased advertising and special promotions geared to the needs of potential customers (as determined through your market research) encouraging them to come to the store.

Customer loyalty programs and other methods of encouraging customers to deal with a pharmacy are becoming a standard marketing approach. The value of a customer should not be taken for granted, and continuing efforts to keep their business is a key to success.

Competition

A pharmacy faces competition not only from other pharmacies, but also from grocery stores, specialty shops, health and beauty shops, and natural food stores. For pharmacies with a wider array of products, the list of competitors would be longer.

In drawing up the marketing plan, a manager would look at the different types of competition that exist within the trading area and analyze the competitors in terms of their prices, services, merchandise mix, and advertising. From this analysis the manager might determine to strengthen some product lines, perhaps discontinue others, and possibly reduce (or raise) prices of certain items.

The question to be asked in analyzing the competitive situation in the trading area is whether the pharmacy is getting an appropriate share of the market. From estimates of total retail sales of pharmacy-related products in the area, the pharmacist could estimate the pharmacy's market share and judge whether it is reasonable. Another simple approach is to count the number of families served by the pharmacy and compare that figure to the actual number of families listed in the Canada Census for the census tract(s) for the trading area. In addition, various local agencies, such as the Chamber of Commerce, can provide data indicating retail growth in the area over the year; the percentage growth in sales for pharmaceuticals should be comparable to, or greater than, overall retail growth. If the pharmacy's sales increase is less than the average for the region, it is reasonable to assume that there has been a loss of market share. The pharmaceutical press publishes average rates of growth for pharmacies in Canada and the US Comparisons against these averages—taking into account, of course, any mitigating local circumstances—will also indicate whether the pharmacy's marketing plan has been effective or is in need of revision.

Performance in a particular trading area will depend on the overall strategy adopted. The community pharmacy that carries a large number of product lines and competes in such a way as to reach a large number of market segments would adopt a very different strategy from one specializing in health-care products and placing a greater emphasis on service. In the first instance, the manager would focus on communication with a large number of current and potential customers in the trading area, notifying them throughout the year of promotions of selected products. The emphasis would be on merchandise mix and merchandising. In contrast, a pharmacy featuring only professional products would search out ways of providing better service to existing customers and look for closely related products to add to the store.

Attracting Customers

The strategic plan adopted by a pharmacy should result in a particular image that is apparent to the public. Various segments within the population look for a particular kind of pharmacy to suit their needs. If the image matches what they are looking for, they are likely to patronize the pharmacy. A knowledge of the characteristics of the customers in one's trading area will help determine the sort of image one will want to adopt for one's store. The range of goods and services provided will also have a major impact on the kinds of customers that are attracted. Generally speaking, a pharmacy that specializes in home-care supplies, and has a good deal of interaction with older or disabled people, will have a very specific orientation and attract a particular type of clientele. Conversely, large pharmacies with low prices, and a large volume of merchandise on display, will usually attract price-conscious shoppers who like to take their time exploring the various bargains. Stores on busy streets likely attract people who do not have time to browse but want to buy a particular item quickly (usually a commonly purchased item) and leave.

Attracting customers will depend in large part on the accessibility of the store. Location has an enormous impact on the sales of a pharmacy, and will also influence merchandising to some extent. For example, in suburban areas rents are lower and pharmacies therefore tend to be larger, allowing for a wider range of products to be stocked. Also, since virtually everyone in the suburbs travels by car, people are able to transport more purchases (including bulky products) in a single trip than the downtown shopper can. Consequently, the suburban pharmacy is likely to stock not only a wider selection of merchandise than the inner-city store, but also a higher percentage of bulk products, such as disposable diapers and beverages. The opportunity also exists to handle products that fit into a lifestyle in which travel and automobiles play a major role (e.g., certain automotive products, coolers, picnic items, and maps). This would clearly not be appropriate for a store in a densely populated area where people tend to walk or use public transit.

ADVERTISING

The primary means by which people are attracted to pharmacies is advertising. One form is the institutional advertisement, which promotes the pharmacy and its services, rather than specific products. An institutional ad might focus on the fact that the pharmacy specializes in prescriptions and provides a delivery service. If such an advertisement is run in a local newspaper on a repeated basis, people will come to remember the pharmacy for the advertised services. To be effective, however, institutional advertising must be repeated frequently over a long period so that its message remains fresh in the minds of the public.

The more common form of advertising is the product or promotional ad, which tells the public that products are available at the pharmacy at an attractive price. Although product ads are often run in local newspapers, they are most commonly distributed as printed flyers, mailed out by the pharmacy or by a bulk-mailing service. Flyers are normally used by pharmacies that are organized into groups, whether through ownership (chains such as London Drugs), franchises (Shoppers Drug Mart, Jean Coutu, Medicine Shoppe), wholesalers (Guardian, IDA), or co-operative buying groups (Value Drug Mart, Price Watchers, Pharmasave).

The use of coupons in product ads in newspapers and flyers, calendars, or other promotional pieces is an effective tool in promotional campaigns. By redeeming the coupons at the store, customers receive special prices or discounts on advertised products. And, by counting the number of coupons redeemed, the pharmacy manager can evaluate how successful the promotion has been in attracting the attention of consumers.

MARKETING PLAN TO ADVERTISING PLAN

The annual marketing plan would set out the number of advertising promotions to occur during the year, the dates for which they are scheduled, and the overall annual advertising budget. For each promotion, an advertising plan and budget would be drawn up, specifying the media to be used (flyer, newspaper advertisement, radio or television advertisement, neighborhood publication), the duration of the campaign, and the link to in-store merchandising (see Figure 9.4, p. 212). Based on the expected sales, the promotion's contribution to profits would also be estimated.

It is important to note the advantages with regard to promotional campaigns, advertising plans, and budgets that come with involvement in a centralized group, be it a franchise or a wholesale-sponsored or co-operative buying group. Member pharmacies are provided with annual schedules of special promotions and sales—normally about 20 throughout the year, including the seasonal promotions, such as Easter, Christmas, and "back to school," and various other events such as Valentine's Day, Mother's Day and Father's Day.

Figure 9.4   *Advertising Plan Worksheet*

1. Name or theme of promotion (e.g., Easter Sale): _____
2. Dates of sale: _____
   Dates that advertising is to run: _____
3. Budget allocated for promotion: _____
4. Media to be used and cost: _____
   Flyer _____
   Newspaper _____
   Radio _____
   Other _____
5. Products to be promoted:

   _____
   _____
   _____
   _____
   _____

Estimates of anticipated increases in sales for featured products or product lines may also be provided, assisting member pharmacies in their purchasing and merchandising for special promotions, and in their own sales and profitability projections. In addition, advertising costs are naturally lower for participating pharmacies than they would be for pharmacies purchasing advertising independently. Finally, groups are often able to mount well co-ordinated advertising campaigns that make use of all available media. For example, flyer promotions are usually supported by newspaper, radio, and TV advertising. When advertising budgets are prepared, an analysis may be made of the impact of each of the media on the advertising programs of the organization, relative costs examined, and appropriate amounts allocated to each of the media.

Synthesis of Information for a Marketing Plan

Figure 9.5 (p. 214) shows examples of some of the objectives that might underlie an operational plan and drive the annual marketing plan. To prepare the marketing plan, a pharmacy manager would start by examining the store's business records for the past year or two. Ongoing environmental scanning would provide an idea of general business conditions and sales prospects. This information, together with changes in prices, the introduction on the market of any new product lines, and changes in the competitive situation, would determine the kinds of products to be purchased. The emphasis would be given to the pharmacy's different departments and the gross margin and sales to be expected for each department. These projections in turn would involve an assessment of the various target groups within the community and the prospects for penetrating them. This would also be the time to explore the possibility of offering new services in the pharmacy or to seek an outside service contract: a tender to provide services to a nursing home could be drawn up, for example, and, if it had potential, pursued with vigor. Non-professional service opportunities, such as a post office subunit, could be investigated. The selling of lottery tickets has also become common in pharmacies and represents not only new revenues, but also a mechanism to attract customers into the pharmacy who might also buy other products.

Allocation of Resources and Responsibility

An essential part of the marketing plan involves preparing a detailed list of responsibilities and duties in order to meet the objectives set. For the advertising program that is to be initiated, someone must design an institutional advertisement, negotiate space for it in a newspaper, and ensure that it is circulated on a regular basis as has been planned. For the promotional advertising, design of the flyer and arrangements for printing and distribution must be delegated or linked to a buying group. A budget should be established for the advertising program and monitored throughout the year.

Control Procedures

For each of the objectives, progress should be analyzed and reviewed periodically, and, where necessary, corrective action taken. For example, if sales of infant supplies are much lower than anticipated, possible causes would have to be identified and addressed. By going through each of the product areas that contribute to the total operation and assessing their performance, corrective action the manager can take in a timely way. Analyzing the reasons for the discrepancies offers insight into market forces and serves as the base for a revised plan. It might prove necessary to draw on other budgets and resources in developing such a plan.

Figure 9.5   Examples of Objectives for an Annual Marketing Plan

Sales	• Increase in sales of 8.5 percent (recognizing that a major part of this, about 5 percent, represents inflation).
Market Share	• Loss of market in toiletries and confections expected due to grocery store competition, but will increase share in infant supplies in response to increased birth rate in trading area by establishing infant-supplies department (see below).
Pharmacy Image	• Strengthen the image of the pharmacy as a family pharmacy with a wide range of products and everyday low (but not lowest) prices through a series of institutional ads.
Promotional Advertising	• Group promotions or independent instore promotions to families in trading area, featuring new infant-supplies department and special sales of infant supplies.
Profit	• Increase in net profit from 4.2 percent to 4.5 percent; decrease in gross margin from 32.5 percent to 30.8 percent. (Increase inventory turnover rate; improve inventory-management system; reduce expenses; to maintain margins in face of increasing competition, consider eliminating products with less than 30 percent gross margin and turnover rate under 3.)
Staff	• Decrease complaints on service by 50 percent by introducing an orientation program for new employees, quarterly staff meetings to discuss customer complaints, and customer surveys via questionnaires.
Product Mix	• Establish a department featuring infant supplies and generating sales of $11,000 in the first year. (Assess space for best location; relocate other products and/or departments. Assess overall traffic flow; tie in with new family-pharmacy orientation.)

MERCHANDISING

Merchandising is part of the marketing process; it is often referred to as the "art of visual selling," and it consists of having "the right product, at the right price, at the right time, and in the right place." It consists of activities that induce the customer to try your products and services. Such activities include purchasing products that will meet the consumer's specific needs, promoting them to the consumer at attractive prices, and displaying them in ways that will encourage their sale. Merchandising involves consideration of the target customers, competition, marketing objectives, and related financial objectives of the marketing plan.

Satisfied customers are the key to success in pharmacy, and customer satisfaction is achieved through the products offered, the service provided, and the customer's perception of comfort while in the store. Competition also plays an important role in merchandising. The degree of a pharmacy's competitive success is largely determined by the products carried, their presentation, and their price.

Merchandising has five facets that must be considered.[5] They are as follows:

1.   administrative procedures;

2.   suitable space, layout, and display;

3.   publicity about the products;

4.   purchasing suitable products;

5.   selling activities.

Merchandise Display

In the display of merchandise, visual impact is extremely important—in fact, it is an essential sales tool. Products must be clearly visible to the customer, attractively arranged in good lighting, and placed in proximity to related products. Although the techniques of merchandise display are essentially straightforward, it requires a good deal of effort to maintain a tidy, well-displayed stock of merchandise at all times. The importance of visual impact in selling may be illustrated by the fact that the visual appeal of product packaging alone is responsible for most impulse sales, which account for approximately 60 percent of all pharmacy sales.[6]

The principles of merchandise display combine aesthetic appeal with other known determinants of consumer behavior to direct shoppers' attention to particular products, and to expose them to different product areas in the store. Effective stock placement, manipulation of traffic flow, and the use of promotional displays are all important elements of merchandise display.

The effect of such efforts is the creation of a positive image in the mind of the consumer—one that is in keeping with the overall image intended for the pharmacy.

VISUAL BALANCE

Visual balance refers to the appealing arrangement of products on shelves by size or color. For example, larger items should be placed on the lower shelves and smaller items on the upper shelves. Similarly, color gradations should run from dark to light, with bright colors at the ends of the aisles. Mass displays of shampoos and other hair products, for example, can be structured vertically or horizontally, achieving symmetry and striking blocks of color. Vertical grouping refers to the placement of different sizes of the same product above and below one another on different shelves; horizontal grouping involves placing them side by side on the same shelf, with smaller sizes to the left and larger sizes to the right. Varying the approach can result in more aesthetically pleasing visual effects from the combinations of colors, sizes, and arrangements of product packages.

Although visual balance is important, it should not take precedence over other essential selling criteria: top-selling products must be at eye level, with related products appearing nearby, even if this detracts somewhat from visual balance.

PRODUCT FACINGS

An important aspect of the relationship between merchandise display and sales activity is the role of product facings. A facing is simply a product package on the shelf, facing out to the consumer, with stock of the product lined up behind the front package. A rule of thumb in merchandising is that "a product will generate 36 percent more sales when its facings are increased from two to four."[7] Hence, to a point, the number of facings of a stock item should be proportional to its sales. A slower-selling item might have a single facing, but if an item sells very well it should be given four or more facings, as sales have been shown to increase when up to four facings are used. Similarly, increasing the number of facings is useful in promoting the sale of new products by giving them prominence and having them stand out. Suppliers, especially wholesalers, can provide data on the relative sales of the products they distribute, but in-store data should also be used to track fluctuations in sales and adjust product facings accordingly. The purpose in this is to make most effective use of the space available for the display and sale of merchandise.

Consistent placement of price tickets improves the visual quality of displays and encourages customers to buy. The placement of price stickers should be done within a set of guidelines by trained staff. Price tickets must be placed on product packages where they will be in clear view, without obstructing printed information that the consumer may need to read about the product (e.g., the strength of a vitamin or instructions for use). Tickets are normally placed in the upper right-hand corner on the front of the package, although in the case of very small containers they may have to be placed on top. On containers with removable tops, such as aerosol containers, price tickets are normally priced on the body of the container. Uniformity in the placement of price stickers will not only improve the appearance of the display, but also help sales clerks when they ring up purchases.

Increasingly, price tickets are being eliminated and a scanning system used to price products at the checkout. This requires shelf price tags with the product that clearly identify the product and price. It also requires regular checking of the tags against the scanner to ensure scanning accuracy. This is particularly important for sales items and where price changes occur fairly frequently.

PLANOGRAMS

Another factor influencing stock placement is the relative effect on sales of various locations in a gondola. The highest sales are associated with products placed in the center of the gondola (which comes in uniform four-foot segments), sometimes referred to as the "hot-spot cross" or "bulls eye" because the consumer's eye travels from left to right at eye level, then up and down at the center of the gondola, as shown in Figure 9.6, (p. 218). Note the numbering from 1 through 6 that indicates most to least desirable locations for products on the gondola.

Figure 9.6   *The Hot-Spot Cross Merchandise Display Principle*

4	3	2	2	2	2	3	4
4	3	2	1	1	2	3	4

(consumer eye level)

4	3	2	2	2	2	3	4
5	4	3	3	3	3	4	5
6	5	4	4	4	4	5	6

Source: Courtesy of H.J. Segal.

Products with the highest sales velocity should be placed in the hot-spot cross area and should have the greatest number of facings (normally three to five). Translating this scheme into stocked shelves with the thousands of items found in a pharmacy is a formidable task. The tool used for this task is called a planogram.

A planogram is a precise, detailed scheme for merchandise display within given product categories. It specifies stock levels and the optimal number of facings for each product, as well as the optimal positioning of products in relation to one another on the shelves. A planogram is based on a space management analysis that measures velocity and profitability by unit sales. Planograms are often designed and supplied to pharmacies by the headquarters of chains or by the wholesalers of co-operative groups, in the form of photographs of ideally stocked gondolas (see Figure 9.7). Pharmacy staff then follow the photographs closely in stocking shelves. In a planogram, the positioning of each product's sales velocity and profitability (per linear foot) is combined with factors such as historical sales patterns, current trends and expectations for the future. Planograms can also be drawn up by the pharmacy on the basis of its inventory and its purchasing and sales records, together with data on item performance that are available from wholesalers and manufacturers. Today, POS systems record sales by item to give pharmacy managers instant access to sales velocity data and other relevant information. In addition, computer programs have now been developed to design merchandising plans for pharmacies.

Figure 9.7   Sample Planogram (Pain-Relief Products: Eight-Foot Island)

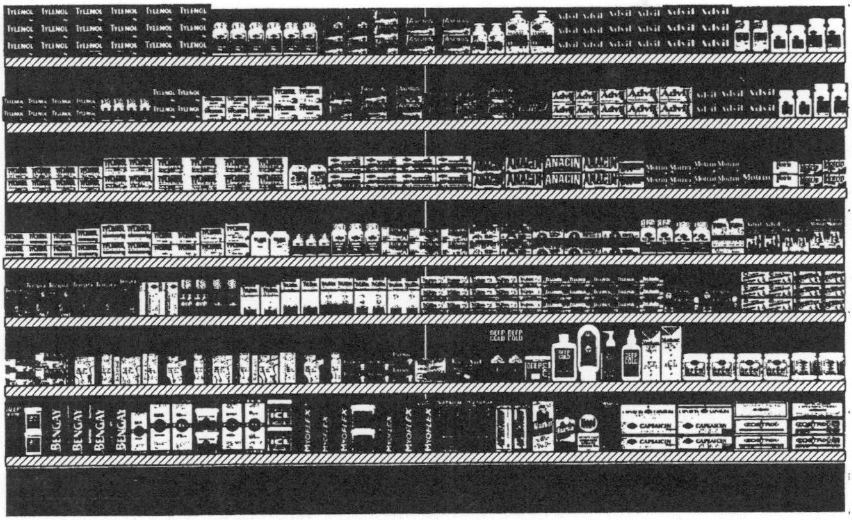

Source: Courtesy of Drug Trading Company Limited.

Merchandise Philosophy

Every pharmacy needs a merchandise philosophy that sets guidelines for the kind of merchandise to be stocked. Areas normally considered in this context are variety, price and quality, brands, turnover, gross margin, and inventory balance. In a pharmacy, the merchandise reflects the health-oriented professional nature of the organization.

VARIETY

The variety of products stocked in a pharmacy can vary enormously. Some pharmacies are very specialized in the range of products they handle (e.g., prescription drugs only). Others carry health and beauty aids, OTC products, and home health-care supplies, in addition to prescription drugs. Recently the potential variety of products in a pharmacy has been increased by the inclusion of foods (particularly convenience foods), infant apparel, computers and electronic merchandise, and lottery tickets. In each product category, the number of different items stocked (breadth), and the depth in which they are stocked (i.e., the quantity in stock), will reflect the merchandise philosophy adopted by the pharmacy manager. As pointed out earlier, the marketing plan, customer needs, and competition will determine the eventual variety that is to be stocked.

PRICE AND QUALITY

The kind of merchandise carried will depend partly on the area that the pharmacy serves. In lower-income neighborhoods, pharmacies tend to carry more lower-priced convenience items, such as cigarettes, magazines, confectionery, and audio- and videotapes. In more affluent neighborhoods, they might carry health equipment, electronic equipment, a wider variety of better-quality health and beauty supplies, and high-quality giftware. One exception to this is ethical pharmaceuticals (i.e., products purchased on the advice of a professional rather than those advertised to the public), which tend not to vary significantly in quality and price.

BRANDS

The brand name is the manufacturer's registered trademark on a product, such as Tylenol®. The success of a brand and the customer loyalty it can generate make brand-name products valuable in the retail marketplace.[8] Customers are more comfortable and feel safer with products they know, and often they know them through advertising. Traditionally, pharmacies have been more receptive than supermarkets to introducing new brands—especially in the health and beauty lines—and they have thereby generated customer loyalty to the store as well as to the particular brands.

Where brand-name products have been successful, private brands or house brands of those products are now commonly introduced, as they achieve greater profit for the retailer. These private-label products are manufactured on contract to the retailer and labeled with a brand name unique to the pharmacy or chain of pharmacies. For example, vitamins and other products are manufactured for Shoppers Drug Mart and sold under the Life brand label.

Generic products are also currently popular. They do not bear a manufacturer's brand name, only the generic name of the drug. These products are sold on the basis of low cost and minimal advertising, other than stating that they are available.

TURNOVER

The merchandising philosophy of a pharmacy will influence its rate of inventory turnover. A pharmacy that achieves high sales volumes with low prices will have a high inventory turnover rate. On the other hand, smaller pharmacies and pharmacies with specialized inventories will have lower turnover rates in some of their departments. A high turnover rate is not usually characteristic of the high-price/high-quality merchandising philosophy—typical, for example, of cosmetics, which tend to have a lower turnover rate.

GROSS MARGIN

The gross margin on pharmaceuticals traditionally had been approximately 40 percent, but since the '70s this has eroded as a result of competition in the marketplace. The gross margin on non-prescription drugs is now 25 to 30 percent and on other product lines may be lower still. One of the challenges of pharmacy management is to maintain margins, attract customers, and remain a viable business. Product lines with less competition and higher margins are constantly sought, and the most promising among them are currently in the field of durable medical equipment (DME) and complementary health products.

ALLOCATION OF SPACE

The allocation of space to various product groups throughout the pharmacy is determined by calculating their relative sales and profitability per linear foot of shelf space. The principle behind the allocation of space is to maximize gross margin dollars per linear foot of selling area, hence to allocate more space to the most profitable product groups and less to the least profitable ones. Figure 9.8 (p. 222) shows a sample calculation of profit per linear foot in several different product areas. Sales in the various product groups should be monitored periodically to determine if adjustments are needed in existing allocations of space in the pharmacy.

Figure 9.8   *Calculating Sales and Profitability Per Square Foot*

1) Product Category	(2) Sales ($)	(3) Gross Margin (%)	(4) Gross Margin ($)	(5) Square Footage ($)	(2) ÷ (5) Sales per Sq. Ft.	(4) ÷ (5) Gross Margin Per Sq. Ft. ($)
Rx	150,000	40	60,000	400	375	150
Health and beauty aids	120,000	28	33,600	1,200	100	28
Tobacco	50,000	15	7,500	150	333	50
Cards	30,000	50	15,000	700	42.9	21.4
Cosmetics	30,000	40	12,000	200	150	60
Miscellaneous	120,000	31	36,900	1,350	88.9	27.6
Total	500,000	33	165,000	4,000	125	41.25

Source: Adapted from *Merchandising: Guide to Good Pharmacy Management* (Vaudreuil, Québec: Hoffman-La Roche, 1978), p. 13.

In some cases, space will be made available for merchandise or services that bear a low profit but are known to attract people into the store. This is usually the reason for introducing post office substations or lottery ticket sales in pharmacies and placing them at the rear of the store.

Promotional Displays

One important way of drawing customers into the pharmacy is special promotions, where featured items are sold at a special price over a specified period of time. In order for displays of the featured products ("promotional displays") to be effective in generating sales, they must have sufficient impact to attract the consumer's attention and interest. As customers look for the advertised items, they will be drawn into various parts of the store, where effective promotional displays will engage their interest in the full range of products offered there.

Promotional displays generally involve separating featured products from their regular product areas in the store through the use of floor displays, end displays, "side kicks," clip strips, dump bins, impulse units, and special areas promoting seasonal items. Experience has shown that sales per customer can be significantly increased in this way. In addition, promotional displays induce customers to travel through parts of the pharmacy that they might otherwise have no reason to explore.

The overall impact of a pharmacy's merchandise display will depend on the effective use and placement of the various types of promotional displays. Promotional displays can also feature "add-on" products—for example, a coffee maker with coffee beside it.

FLOOR DISPLAYS

Where space allows, one or two floor displays may be used—too many can detract from the pharmacy's orderly image. A floor display should contain quite a large amount of stock if it is to be visible and have impact, which means that the product used should have a high sales potential (otherwise, the amount of inventory needed to create a substantial display would be more than the store could sell). However, the display should not be so tall that it blocks the consumer's view of the rest of the store. Care should also be taken to allow adequate space for traffic to move around the display, as the aisles belong to the customer. The safety of the customer is equally important. Displays must be built and located in such a manner that they are secure and "shoppable"—that is, convenient to reach or access. Price signs are important for displays and should be prominently displayed. Floor displays must be continually replenished with stock, and taken down once their visual impact decreases because of depleted stock.

END DISPLAYS

Displays at the ends of shelving should have a theme, such as protection from the sun, and should feature no more than two or three different products, which must complement each other. A thematic approach tends to increase sales. It is generally held that competing products should not be placed together in an end display, as this will encourage comparisons and a process of looking for the best bargain. The purpose of the display is to convey clearly the single message that the product featured is an exceptional value and, in this way, to prompt customers to consider replenishing their home stock of the item. Accordingly, it needs to have prominent price signs to feature the value. End displays should be restocked regularly (ensuring that the number of facings remains sufficient to stimulate sales), and changed periodically to ensure that they do not lose their impact on consumers.

DUMP BINS

Dump bins are an inexpensive, versatile, and easy way of generating sales for promotional merchandise. Repositioning dump bins can give the store a new look and draw customers into its various departments.

If the bin is transparent, some of the product packages should be used to line the sides and the remaining stock can be dumped into the center. Another tip is to avoid putting a variety of products into a dump bin—no more than two different products (or, where applicable, two different colors or flavors) should be used, and preferably only one. Similarly, if two products are used, try to establish one price for both: confusion arises if there are several prices. When stock has been reduced and there is not enough to fill the bin, a false bottom can give the appearance of fullness. Dump bins should carry the same product for only a week or so. Bins are particularly useful for impulse, seasonal, or trendy items, but they should not be used to sell off damaged merchandise or products that could break or leak.

IMPULSE PURCHASE AREAS

Impulse items are normally located at or near the check-out counter where traffic flow is high and people have time to browse while waiting, cash in hand, to pay for their purchases. We have all seen the racks with candy bars and gum, batteries, or sunglasses. Other products, such as photo supplies, magazines, trial sizes of health and beauty aids, novelties, pens, and seasonal items, are also sometimes featured. Both counter units and free-standing units near the check-out counter are generally used for the display of impulse items.

SEASONAL ITEMS

Most pharmacies reserve a high-traffic aisle in the store for seasonal promotions, and rotate the product groups displayed there throughout the year. Seasonal promotional displays should be fully stocked and kept up to date. All seasonal merchandise should be introduced at the same time in one massive display that appears overnight and stays in place until the occasion for the display has passed. Treating a seasonal display as a new event in the store is much more effective than gradually building up partial displays as stock comes in. Additional displays of related merchandise (e.g., gift items and boxed chocolates during a Christmas promotion) should appear close to the main seasonal aisle where they will be noticed by the customer. It is wise to introduce seasonal items well in advance of the onset of the season, as many people shop early while selection is good, or want time to make price comparisons before purchasing. A pharmacy whose full seasonal display is not up early may lose some sales.

The progress of each seasonal promotion should be recorded in terms of changes in stock levels over time and total sales of each item (post-mortem), so that a plan for the next year can be prepared immediately upon the display's removal.

SIGNS

Signs are one of the most important sources of information about products in the store. People immediately look for information on prices, specials, and the location of particular products. The easier it is for the customer to find products, learn their prices, and determine how much of a bargain they are getting, the more likely they will be to make a purchase. Signs can be used in an effective way that will generate sales. They should be brief, simply worded, and clearly printed, with a consistent style used throughout the store. Prices should always appear in the largest characters to draw people to good values. The key element to remember is to use signs and to use them freely.

End units need signs, as they are separated from the regular product area and the consumer's attention must be drawn to them. The kinds of products in the display, the reason they are being displayed, and their price should be clearly identified. Floor displays also require signs. In this case, the signs must be easily read from all directions and, if possible, visible through the front windows to attract people into the store. Because the floor displays are quite large, correspondingly large signs should be used. Bin displays require signs that ensure clarity as to the products inside and their prices. When the bin contains more than one product, it is important that the sign be clear and specific about the contents.

WINDOW DISPLAYS

At one time window displays were important. They are rarely used now, but the windows of the pharmacy have potential for conveying information on image and promotions. Too often they are neglected and convey a negative impression by showing the backs of shelves, dust, and old posters.

LEGAL ASPECTS

In merchandising some legal aspects should be kept in mind. In each province there is a *Sales of Goods Act* that has been enacted as consumer protection legislation and sets out, to a large extent, the terms and conditions of a contract for the sale of goods and the rights and liabilities of the buyer and seller. This Act will apply to each and every sale a retail pharmacist makes in a community pharmacy, with a few exceptions. It sets out the following terms and conditions:

- The seller has title to the goods—that is, the legal right to them in order to have the legal right to sell them.

- Description—where the seller has described the goods to the purchaser, there is an implied condition that the goods will correspond to the description.

- The goods must be fit for their purpose. If the seller knows the purpose for which the buyer is buying an item and the circumstances are such that one knows the customer is relying upon one's judgment that the item is suitable, then there is an implied condition that the goods are reasonably fit for that purpose. This is the case whether or not the seller is the manufacturer. Where the buyer asks for a specific item under its trade name, and it is clear that the buyer is not relying on any advice from the seller, this condition will not apply.

- The goods must be of merchantable quality. The goods should be useable for their ordinary purpose and, if there is a defect, it should be so minor that a reasonable person would still pay the full price for them. Where the buyer has had an opportunity to examine the goods before the purchase and the defect would have (or should have) been discovered during that examination, it will be assumed that the buyer agreed to buy the goods with the defect.

It is possible to contract out of the *Sale of Goods Act* by setting out a written contract with specific terms.

SUMMARY

The marketing of the consumer products found in a pharmacy calls for anticipating and meeting the needs of the public. This entails keeping abreast of new products and the changing demands of consumers. Hence, pharmacy managers should know and apply the principles of environmental scanning and market research. Analyzing and meeting the special needs of selected consumer groups is also a critical tool, known as market segmentation.

Marketing information is essential to pharmacists in managing their stores. It is becoming increasingly important for pharmacists to establish market research programs that will keep them in touch with the attitudes, needs, or complaints of their customers. These can be informal systems or more formal methods of data collection. Questionnaires are now being used more frequently by pharmacies to collect market information.

A pharmacy's marketing plan should take into account the competition, ways of attracting customers, product lines to be carried, and the image of the store that is to be projected. It should set out the responsibilities and duties of staff members in reaching the stated objectives. Control procedures that trigger corrective action when objectives are not being met should also be established.

A key component of marketing is merchandising, which refers to the assembly, promotion, and presentation of products in a visually appealing way. Merchandising guidelines should include variety, price and quality, brands, turnover, gross margin, and inventory balance. Decisions relating to these factors will combine to create a particular image for the pharmacy.

Merchandising is sometimes defined as visual selling, in recognition of the power of visual impact in promoting sales. Product display is consequently a central concern in merchandising. Pharmacists can increase sales and profitability in their stores by observing certain proven principles for effective stock presentation. Some of the factors influencing product display are visual balance, facings, and space allocation according to a product's sales potential and profitability. These factors inform the design of planograms, which are an invaluable aid to pharmacy owners in achieving effective stock presentation. Equally important in stimulating sales is the creative use of promotional displays and signage throughout the pharmacy.

References

1. Anon. "The 1996 Pharmacy Business Trends Report." *Pharmacy Post*. Toronto: Eli Lilly Canada, 1997.

2. Anon. *The AltiMed CFP Report on Pharmacy Services 1997*. Toronto: AltiMed, 1997.

3. Reardon, J., Hasty, R., and Coe, B. "The Effect of Information Technology on Productivity in Retailing." *Journal of Retailing* 92 (1996): 445–461.

4. Ramsay, L. "A Balanced Shelf: Data Warehousing Software Helps Retailers Ensure There Are Always Products in the Store but Not Too Many in the Storeroom." *Financial Post*, 8 July 1997.

5. *Merchandising: Guide to Good Pharmacy Management*. Vaudreuil, Québec: Hoffman LaRoche, 1978.

6. "Impulse Behind Many Purchases: POPAI/DuPont Study." *Drug Merchandising* 66 (1985): 40–43.

7. Archambault, A., and Segal, H. *Merchandising: Pharmacy Management Program Module 3*. Kirkland, Québec: Nordic Laboratories.

8. Murphy, J.M., ed. *Branding: A Key Marketing Tool*. London: Macmillan, 1987.

10

FIXTURE DESIGN AND LAYOUT

INTRODUCTION

Among the responsibilities of the pharmacy owner or manager is the direction of the design and layout of physical facilities for the pharmacy, including its fixtures and equipment. Other considerations are pharmacy security against theft and/or drug diversion, and proper storage conditions for perishable pharmacy items. We shall focus on the essential requirements for the physical facilities of a well-operated community pharmacy.

The owner or manager, in developing an operational plan for the pharmacy, will decide on an underlying approach and a set of objectives for the practice. This will entail projecting a desired image for the pharmacy, which will in turn determine the guidelines for its design and layout.

Once such general guidelines have been developed, the manager would be well advised to seek expert assistance in both the design of the pharmacy and the selection of fixtures and equipment. Many firms in Canada specialize in pharmacy design and it is recommended such a specialist be used. Some community pharmacies seek the services of interior decorators as well, to co-ordinate the decor of the premises. Companies that supply fixtures also generally provide assistance in design and layout.

The essence of a good store design is different for the dispensary and the front store. In the dispensary, both design and fixture selection should focus on efficiency in dispensing operations. In the front store, a good design pays attention to all aspects of the customers' experience. How does one want the customers to feel in this new environment? Does one want them to stay longer and linger? Or is one more interested in having them feel comfortable running in quickly for something—always knowing they will be able to find it easily? A properly designed store will find the proper balance.

BASIC PHARMACY DESIGN PARAMETERS

Results of an industry survey conducted in 1987 indicated that the size of the average Canadian pharmacy was just under 4,000 square feet.[1] A 1996 survey of pharmacies by the *Pharmacy Post* showed an average Canadian pharmacy at 2,948 square feet, with a 511-square-foot dispensary.[2] The franchise stores were larger, at an average 5,354 square feet, and independents were 2,339 square feet.

Experts suggest that the ideal shape for any retail outlet, irrespective of size, is rectangular. A pharmacy should have a sign or signs clearly identifying it. The entrance to the store should be designed for easy access, presenting no barriers to customers. Doors that are difficult to open and entrances that are difficult for elderly or disabled people to manoeuvre should be avoided. For example, the use of turnstiles can make entry impossible for the elderly and disabled. During the past several years, many of the larger pharmacies have installed double-door entrances. Originally, these presented a significant obstacle to entry for disabled persons. The use of push-plate automatic door openers for the disabled has alleviated this problem. Exits should also observe the easy-access principle, but they should be well controlled and positioned in such a way that customers must pass through a check-out area to leave the pharmacy. Some pharmacies have more than one customer entrance, but most have only one exit.

The overall decor of the pharmacy should be inviting and tasteful. Perhaps most important, however, is that the store have excellent lighting. The importance of lighting in the front store is to get the best possible illumination of the product. Good lighting is also valuable to the overall security of the store.

With regard to floor coverings, it should be noted that because carpeting tends to absorb rather than reflect light, it can reduce the lighting level in the store. It is therefore preferable to avoid it, and to maintain clean, polished floors at all times, which will best set off the pharmacy's image. If floor coverings are required, they should blend in with the overall decor of the pharmacy, and should be easy to maintain. A commercial grade of carpet is now commonly used. In the dispensary, commercial anti-bacterial carpeting with a good cushion should be used to maintain cleanliness while reducing noise and fatigue.

Front-store aisles should be uncluttered and wide enough both to facilitate traffic flow, especially where shopping baskets and carts are involved, and to enhance the consumer's view of the merchandise. The recommended aisle width is six feet. Depending on the size of the overall store and the height of the shelving, this may be reduced.

Signage is extremely important in a pharmacy. All departments should be identified clearly, and particular attention should be given to the prescription department. Whenever possible, the sign identifying the professional department should be visible from any point in the pharmacy. All department signs should be easy to read, durable, and at a height calculated for best visibility by the consumer. One of the most important things to remember about in-store signage is that it should reinforce, not force, customers' shopping patterns.

If at all possible, the pharmacy's receiving area should be separate from the customer entrances and exits, and, for convenience and efficiency, the stockroom should be located near the receiving entrance. The stockroom must be made as secure as possible: any exterior doors and windows should be kept locked at all times, keys should be assigned to only a few selected staff members, and an alarm system should be installed. Stockrooms in contemporary pharmacies are normally small, partly because the current trend is to display as much inventory as possible in the front store and partly because, as rental costs rise, less space is being devoted to non-selling areas. Inventory management is facilitated when stock is concentrated in one area. Other non-selling areas include employee areas, such as staff rooms and washrooms. While these are likely to be quite small, they should be made as comfortable as possible. It is also important to check building codes to ensure that washroom facilities meet the required standards.

PRESCRIPTION DEPARTMENT

The *Pharmacy Post* 1997 survey found that prescription sales account for 63 percent of total sales in the average Canadian pharmacy. This may be distorted upwards, as many supermarket pharmacies report only dispensary sales. In a store of approximately 3,000 square feet, the prescription department would normally occupy approximately 500 square feet, or 15 percent of the total area of the store. The prescription department is most often located at the rear of the pharmacy. It is critical that it is clearly identified, visible from all points of the store, and that the reception be in a direct line of sight from the store's entrance.

For many years now, prescription departments in pharmacies have been constructed on platforms raised six to eight inches above the floor. This has afforded pharmacists a good view of both the professional area and the front store, thereby contributing to store security. Recently, however, with growing emphasis on patient counseling, this design has come to be considered a barrier to effective communication with patients. As a result, most new pharmacies have had their prescription departments constructed at floor level, while others have introduced a step-down area where patients can communicate more easily with the pharmacist. Pharmacy owners who have elected to keep the dispensary at floor level believe that the benefits of direct contact with their patients, at eye level, outweigh the greater security afforded by the raised platform. Some also argue that claims of increased security are exaggerated, since dispensary staff seldom have (or take) the time to observe activity in the front store from the higher vantage point. The step-down area would thus seem to be a reasonable compromise.

Pharmacy licensing bodies in each province may have specific requirements pertaining to the size of the prescription department. It is essential to check the provincial regulatory agency's requirements, and to conform to them.

Certain design guidelines contribute to the efficient operation of a dispensary. For example, since pharmacists and other dispensary staff are often required to stand on their feet for six to eight hours per shift, their comfort should be considered a design priority. The dispensing counter should be of a height that is comfortable for the dispensary staff who use it—usually the recommended height is 34 to 39 inches.[3] Standard height found in most Canadian pharmacies is 36 inches. "Fatigue" mats are often used to provide cushioning from hard floors.

Each pharmacist should have sufficient space to work: most dispensing counters allow for two pharmacists, with about six to eight feet of counter space for each. Prescription counters should be 24 to 30 inches deep, to accommodate computer terminals, keyboards, and printers. Today, it is common for each pharmacist to have his or her own computer terminal, and there is often one at the prescription check-in area, to facilitate customer service for refill inquiries or cost questions. On the whole, the dispensary should be designed for economy of movement, reducing the need for excess steps, hence saving time for both the pharmacist and the technician.

Storage facilities for products in the prescription department vary among pharmacies. Three styles discussed here are: drug-a-door, bay, and adjustable. The familiar white, closed cabinets are drug-a-doors. They are secure, and thus suitable for pharmaceuticals, and designed for easy cleaning and maintenance. They are also tidy and professional looking. The main drawback of this style of shelving is the need to open and close the doors each time product is required, which can contribute to injury if one forgets to close the doors.

Bay shelving is another storage facility chosen by many pharmacists. Six to eight inches deep, this thin metal shelving gets its name from the standard "bay" layout in which it is normally arranged. The ends of the bays facing consumers are often attractively finished in woodgrain or decorative colors. Those who prefer bay shelving claim it facilitates inventory monitoring and saves time by eliminating the need to open and close cabinet doors. Since it is exposed to customers, bay shelving requires more effort to keep the shelves and the stock itself clean at all times.

The newest shelving to emerge on the market is "adjustable tray shelving" (see Figure 10.1, p. 234). Shallow trays, each 16 inches wide and six inches deep, fit onto a slatwall-style backing. Normally arranged in bay fashion, this kind of shelving increases capacity by up to 30 percent. It is easy to adjust, restock, and keep clean.

Particular attention must be paid to the security of storage areas designated for narcotic and controlled drugs, especially as governed by the applicable legislation. The dispensary must also be equipped with a refrigerator for storing insulin, vaccines, injectables, and similar products. Finally, cabinets are needed for containers and labels, and a number of functional designs are currently available.

In addition to fixed shelving, automated dispensing systems should be considered. If current or future plans include automation, space must be allocated in your design, as an automated dispensary often requires a different workflow from a conventional dispensary.

Housekeeping and lighting are both extremely important in the dispensary. Cluttered, disorganized, and unkempt professional departments not only project a poor image, but can also contribute to confusion, error, and even accidents. Optimizing dispensary function requires an analysis of activities and innovative processes.[4] Cleanliness and good maintenance will contribute to greater efficiency. Good lighting will improve the department's image, facilitate the pharmacist's work, and decrease errors.[5]

Figure 10.1   Adjustable Tray Shelving

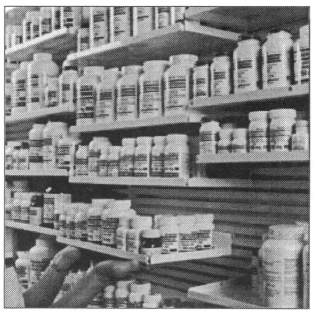

Source: Wilson Display, Mississauga, Ontario.

Check-out areas are often installed in prescription departments, to improve both customer service and store security. These check-outs serve the professional-product areas located near the dispensary as well. With patient education becoming increasingly popular, sophisticated consumers have come to expect information sources such as self-help computer kiosks with touch-screen technology, as well as hard copy to take home. Finally, for the convenience of customers, a waiting area should be located near the dispensary, within view of the counseling and cash-out areas. It need not be elaborate nor occupy a great deal of space, but it should be furnished with at least a few chairs. Some pharmacies display patient-education material and show health-related videos in the waiting area. Some even provide self-administered blood pressure monitoring units, free of charge, and a play area for children.

Each of the provincial licensing authorities has certain requirements regarding the involvement of a pharmacist in the sale of certain non-prescription drugs (e.g., Schedule C products in Ontario). Regulations often require that such products be displayed in an area of the pharmacy where a pharmacist's services are immediately available. One must be sure to consult the provincial pharmacy legislation with regard to such matters.

Other Professional Departments

Since patient counseling has gained in prominence and consumer demand, some provinces have recommended, and mandated, the introduction of private, or semi-private, patient-counseling areas. These should be adjacent to the prescription department, but separate from the general waiting area to ensure privacy. In cases where it is impossible to create a separate area, patient counseling may be conducted in the pharmacy owner or manager's office or, where applicable, in the home-health-care department's fitting room. Patient response to a fully private counseling area is not all positive, as patients often feel uncomfortable entering an office and having the door closed behind them. An alternative design is an "open-private" counseling area that offers acoustic insulation even though walls are mostly glass and doorways are only partially closed. In addition to fully private counseling areas, one may provide a semi-private area, separated from the cash by smoked-glass panels. Whatever the style(s), the area designated for counseling should be comfortable, well lit and well ventilated. It is also a good idea to display health-education literature in this area.

Pharmacies planning a home-health-care department should also locate it near or adjacent to the prescription department. If the department will be fitting surgical garments, prostheses, or ostomy supplies, a fitting room must be provided. This room must be large enough to accommodate a fitting table, have proper heating and ventilation, and be completely private. A washroom for the exclusive use of patients should also be available. Like the patient-counseling area, the home-health-care department must offer privacy. Like all departments, it should have a clearly visible identifying sign.

THE FRONT STORE

The main objective in the design of the front store is to promote the merchandising goals of the pharmacy owner or manager, which involves planning a layout that promotes desirable traffic flow, designing fixtures for the optimal display of merchandise, and, of course, providing adequate security.

Layout and Traffic Flow

The physical layout of the pharmacy plays an important role in the image that is created, and in the store's efficiency and sales activity. Traffic flow should be the critical consideration in designing the layout of the front store and dispensary. The main concern of layout design is to activate all areas of the store. Customers who enter the pharmacy should be exposed to as many products as possible while they are there, to encourage impulse purchasing. It has been estimated that approximately 60 percent of customers' purchasing decisions are made while they are in the store.[6]

The location of the different departments will determine traffic flow and hence is critical to stimulating sales activity. For example, as we mentioned earlier, the prescription department is normally located at the rear of the pharmacy, so that customers will have to pass through a number of other departments and see the range of products offered there before they reach the dispensary. Impulse items (those that the customer had not planned on purchasing) and seasonal items are usually displayed at the front of the pharmacy, in the high-traffic area of the check-out counter, or near other active service areas. On the other hand, demand items should be located toward the rear or along the center aisles, drawing consumers further into the pharmacy. Health and beauty aids are frequently found along the wall to the right of the entrance, where consumers tend to be drawn upon entering the store.

The layout of the pharmacy should take advantage of the sales potential inherent in displaying associated items in proximity to one another—baby gift items near infant products, gift items near greeting cards, oral hygiene products near dental products, and so on. It is sometimes helpful to visit a number of pharmacies, observe the layout of departments and promotional displays, and draw on what one has seen as an aid to planning one's own store (a basic layout is shown in Figure 10.2). Discuss the plan with the company engaged to design the pharmacy and supply fixtures. Wholesale drug companies, pharmacy design firms, and suppliers of store fixtures will often provide pharmacists with customized traffic-flow analyses of their stores. The results of such studies will supply the information necessary to decide on a design or determine whether an existing layout requires improvement. Whatever layout is finally agreed upon, it will be necessary to assess its effectiveness over time. One of the tasks of management is to evaluate and re-evaluate decisions taken, and be prepared to make changes when they are required.

Figure 10.2   Pharmacy Layout (Sample)

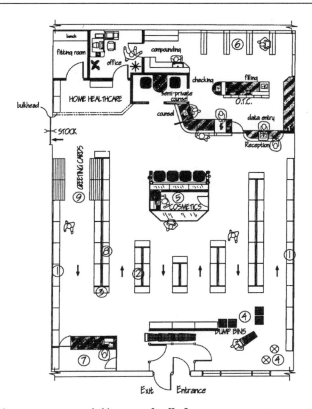

Note: Solid arrows represent probable routes of traffic flow.

1.   Wall cases: Fitted with shelving and/or pegboard or slat wall.

2.   Gondolas: As above.

3.   End displays: May be fitted with pegged or clip strips or slat-wall backing. Merchandise may also simply be stacked.

4.   Floor displays or dump bins: Normally used to display promotional items. Floor stands may also be supplied by manufacturers.

5.   Showcases: Usually contain cosmetic items or high-ticket items.

6.   Bay shelving: Used in the dispensary for pharmaceuticals.

7.   Check-out counters: One is shown here, but there may be more as necessary.

8.   Magazine rack: May replace gondolas in location near check-out counters.

9.   Greeting card cabinets: Usually located to the rear of the store and may replace gondolas.

Each department would have proper signage and lighted canopies may be placed over wall cases.

Merchandise Display and Fixtures

Merchandise in the pharmacy should always be attractively displayed within clearly identified departments. As shown in Figure 10.2 (p. 237), wall cases may line the perimeter of the store. Such fixtures are normally seven feet high and often have a lighted canopy to heighten the effect of displayed products and enhance the overall decor of the store. In the remainder of the floor area, merchandise is displayed on gondolas (free-standing fixtures that hold shelving), which should be positioned to create six-foot aisles. Both wall cases and gondolas are normally constructed of metal, with adjustable shelving. Gondolas typically run parallel to the wall cases and perpendicular to the dispensary. In recent years, gondolas have more frequently been set up to extend without interruption from the check-out area at the front of the store to the prescription department at the rear. This arrangement exposes customers to a wide range of merchandise as they travel from the entrance to the rear of the store. The resulting alignment also improves control over the store by giving personnel a better view of customer movement. While opinions on this point differ, some experts recommend that gondolas not exceed a height of four feet, since anything taller impedes visibility. A clear view across aisles not only helps customers to locate the items they are looking for, but also exposes them to a wider range of products; for staff, it facilitates monitoring customer movement and thereby improves store security. Promotional displays are often situated at the ends of the gondolas.

The display of paper products, in particular disposable diapers, had posed a problem until manufacturers increased the width of shelving in gondolas to 24 inches or more. This has proved useful for the display of infant formula as well, and indeed many products can now be stocked in greater depth on the shelves, alleviating the problem of reduced storage space in contemporary stores.

In addition to wall cases and gondolas, display cases are used, particularly for high-ticket items such as cosmetics, clocks, or cameras. Cosmetics departments usually consist of a square arrangement of display cases, frequently in the center of the front store, or a line of display cases on the incoming wall. These are referred to as service areas in that a cosmetician is normally present to serve customers. Cosmetics departments tend to be distinctively identified by color, floor coverings, lighting, and fixtures, and are usually equipped with their own cash register.

Suppliers will often provide display stands for their products, some designed for temporary use and others for more permanent use. It is up to the pharmacy owner's discretion whether to use them in the store. While some of the temporary stands are ideal for special promotions of particular products, care should be taken to integrate them properly with the pharmacy's other promotional displays and to avoid cluttering the aisles. With the more permanent type of suppliers' displays, consideration should be given to their suitability for use in the store: they should blend in well with the other fixtures and the general decor.

The use of pegboard, a hard backing with movable hooks, has been popular in pharmacies for several years now. It is inserted into sections of wall cases or gondolas, to display items such as carded cosmetics, blister-packed hair-care items, first-aid supplies, or school supplies. More recently, however, slat wall has been gaining in popularity among pharmacies. A slat wall, as the name suggests, is a slatted or grooved backing that can be fitted with either shelves or rows of hooks. Slat walls, which can be painted, can be very attractive and are perhaps even better suited than pegboard to the display of blister-packaged products.

Other display techniques and fixtures that deserve attention include "profit panels," which hook into the ends of gondolas and can periodically be moved to different positions in the store. They are made of pegboard and can be used for products such as notions and baby toys. Profit panels should not be installed in areas where they could obstruct traffic flow. A display device called a clip strip is currently on the market. As the name suggests, it facilitates the display of packages that can be held by a clip. This device resembles a potato chip stand except that it is a free-standing, single strip.

The sale of pantyhose in pharmacies can be reasonably high, and consists mostly of impulse purchases. Normally pantyhose are displayed on revolving wire racks or on lucite-faced pull-out trays that will fit into gondola or wall-case sections.

Other innovations include a convenient gravity-feed display case for trial sizes of products. It is made of transparent acrylic and allows the customer to select the product(s) desired. Attractive new designs of upright refrigerated cabinets are now available for soft drinks, ice cream, or other food products. Some pharmacies used sloped shelves in wall cases and gondolas to give the appearance of greater depth with a minimum of inventory. Products displayed on sloped shelving are easier to see, particularly if they are contained in a flat type of packaging.

GREETING CARDS AND STATIONERY

Another department for which special fixtures are required is the greeting card section. Greeting card cabinets are normally provided by the card suppliers, with whom payment arrangements may be negotiated. The location of this department is important and will depend on whether cards are a demand item or an impulse item in the particular store. If there are no specialty stores in the area that carry them, greeting cards are more likely to be a demand item in the pharmacy and can be located toward the rear of the store (near the post office substation, where applicable). Greeting cards and gift wrap generally have a relatively high gross margin but a low turnover rate, so their profitability should be carefully assessed to determine the appropriate amount of space that should be allocated to them. (Remember, allocation is determined by a product group's profitability per linear foot.) Display fixtures for stationery products include separators for paper products and specially designed stands for bristol board and wrapping paper.

MAGAZINES

Fixtures for magazines may be either obtained from the magazine dealer or custom built. Pharmacies that sell paperback books often display them on revolving wire racks. Again, attention to space allocation is important, since magazines bear a low gross margin but tend to have a relatively high turnover. Magazines are often a source of security problems and should therefore be located near a check-out counter or service area.

Check-out Counters

Check-out counters are located near the store exit. Large independent pharmacies typically have at least two cash registers in the check-out area. Impulse items are best located at or near the check-out counters.

Post Office Substations

Some pharmacists provide post office substation services, which can generate considerable traffic. They are generally located in the rear of the pharmacy. Care should be taken to prevent post office line-ups from impeding traffic flow in adjacent areas. Post offices must be equipped with a safe to protect the substantial amounts of cash and inventory that they often handle.

FIXTURE SUPPLIERS

A number of suppliers offer fixtures for sale or lease to community pharmacies. They are usually listed in professional publications or they can be reached through wholesale drug companies. When deciding on a supplier, pharmacy owners and managers should observe the following guidelines:

- Choose one who can supply all or most of your fixtures.

- Be familiar with the services they offer. Do they provide traffic-flow analysis?

- Seek proposals from more than one supplier.

- Discuss the subject with local wholesalers.

- Seek references and advice from other pharmacy owners.

In planning the fixture design and layout of their pharmacy, pharmacy owners and managers should not only follow the above guidelines, but also keep the checklist of fixtures and equipment (see Table 10.1) close at hand to ensure that all necessary items are included.

Table 10.1   Fixtures and Equipment Checklist

Fixtures (Front Store)
Gondolas
Wall cases
Display cases
Display bins
Greeting card fixtures
Magazine racks

Signage
Department identification signs
Promotional signs
Prescription-department identification

Furniture and Office Equipment
Furniture as needed for patient-counseling area, waiting area, fitting room, and office

Calculator

Filing cabinet

Bookcase

Typewriter/computer

Dispensary

Dispensing-container fixture

Dispensing counter

Pharmaceutical equipment (check provincial regulations)

Refrigerator

Dispensary cabinets or shelving

Dispensary computer and printers

Patient-record system

Electronic tablet/capsule counter(s)

Typewriter/computer

Narcotic cabinet or safe

Sink unit

Check-out Areas

Check-out counters

Cash registers (terminals)

Scanners

Pricing equipment

Stockroom

Stockroom shelving

Safe

References

1.   Meere, V. "Average Rx Price Up 10% to $15.45." *Drug Merchandising* (1987): 40–44.

2.   "1977 Pharmacy Business Trends Report." Pharmascience, *Pharmacy Post*. Toronto: Lilly Canada, 1998.

3.   Panero, J., and Zelnik, M. *Human Dimension and Interior Space*. New York: Whitney Library of Design, 1979.

4.   Panke, K.K., and MacLeod-Richards, C. "Initiating Practice Change: Analysing Pharmacy Systems and Optimizing Dispensary Functioning." *Canadian Pharmaceutical Journal* 130 (1997): 37–40.

5.   Buchanan, T.L., Barker, K.N., Gibson, J.T., Jiang, B.C., and Pearson, R.E. "Illumination and Errors in Dispensing." *American Journal of Hospital Pharmacy* 48 (1991): 2137–2145.

6.   Archambault, A., and Segal, H. *Merchandising: Pharmacy Management Program, Module 3*. Kirkland, Québec: Nordic Laboratories.

Recommended Reading

Caverly, W. "Patient Counseling Areas." *The Efficient Pharmacy* 2 (1). Burlington, Vermont: Saxe Communications, August 1998.

Smith, H.A. *Principles and Methods of Pharmacy Management*. 3rd ed. Philadelphia: Lea and Febiger, 1986.

Panero, J., and Zelnick, M. *Human Dimension and Interior Space*. New York: Whitney Library of Design, 1979.

11

INNOVATION AND TECHNOLOGY IN PRACTICE

INTRODUCTION

Our society is undergoing profound changes in this post-industrial era of information and services. Pharmacy cannot avoid being affected by these changes and pharmacists must acquire the modern tools and adopt the required philosophy that will not only enable them to fully and efficiently perform their professional duties, but to survive as a valued profession.

Pharmacy has always been characterized by its dual aspect of offering both products and professional services—that is, medications and advice. However, in the information age, pharmacists must enhance this dual role entrusted to them by society in the most complete and efficient manner possible, while at the same time complying with the socio-economic requirements imposed on them by governments, provincial licensing boards, third-party insurers, and the patients themselves. Consequently, pharmacists must understand the future requirements of their industry, define their services more precisely, evaluate their costs more accurately, and make the necessary increases to the range of services they provide. They will be called upon to free themselves from routine and mechanical tasks in order to devote more time to informing and advising the public and other health professionals about pharmaceuticals and related issues. These information and counseling functions will assume a greater importance as pharmacotherapy becomes more complex and as disease management and outcomes monitoring become functions of the pharmacist.

In its 1986 report on pharmacy, a committee of inquiry created by the Nuffield Foundation in Britain concluded that the dispensing of medication would continue to be an important activity of pharmacists, but that their professional role should be construed in terms of increased collaboration with other health professionals and increased interaction with the public. This would be accomplished chiefly through participation in public health-education programs and the provision of pertinent information to consumers about the proper use of prescription and non-prescription drugs.[1] Several Canadian studies in recent years have also emphasized the need for pharmacists to inform, advise, and teach the public about drug-related matters.[2]

This chapter will show how recent innovations and technology can help pharmacists play their part to the fullest, as both dispensers of medication and providers of information. We shall not attempt to describe and analyze each of the existing (or potential) new technologies in detail, but will focus on their application and usefulness for the pharmacist.

AUTOMATION OF TECHNICAL FUNCTIONS

One of the pharmacist's fundamental tasks is to prepare and dispense both prescription and non-prescription drugs to members of the community. In its practice guide published in 1981, Québec's Order of Pharmacists described each of the functions and tasks involved in preparing and dispensing a prescription.[3] A study performed at Auburn University established that 39 successive actions were involved in filling a prescription, from the moment the prescription was received to the moment the medication was dispensed to the patient.[4] Many of these actions can be performed by technical personnel, but most can now be automated.

Automated Tablet- and Capsule-Counting Systems

Automation in the retail pharmacy is fast becoming a large part of the answer to the profession's need to dispense faster, be more accurate, and counsel more.

BakerAPS introduced one of the first tablet- and capsule-counting systems in 1971.[5] "Baker Cells" were designed and employed primarily for storage and automated counting of the most high-volume oral-solid medications dispensed in the community pharmacy. In the last several years, the industry has seen an explosion of new technologies (in both hardware and software) designed to further automate the community pharmacy.

Although several reasons are given for installation of an automated counting system, the most frequent one is that the system can provide the pharmacist with the tools necessary to dispense an accurately filled prescription with the least amount of pharmacist involvement. The hope is that the additional time gained by using the system will be used to provide the patient with pharmacist-patient interaction. Other reasons stated are to:

- improve customer service by decreasing wait times;

- reduce labor costs by filling more prescriptions by the same number of people;

- improve accuracy, thereby reducing liability costs;

- provide a better work environment to reduce the costs of employee turnover;

- comply with federal, provincial, and local regulations including but not limited to patient counseling.

Also, as competition becomes more intense, the investment in automation today will mean the difference between staying in business or closing the doors tomorrow.

The entry level to automated tablet- and capsule-counting machines are the "counter-top" or "universal" machines. The Baker Universal 2000 (see Figure 11.1) uses a class 1 electronic pharmacy scale to weigh the tablets or capsules. Using a built-in database, the unit instantaneously computes the number of tablets or capsules counted. The Kirby Lester uses photoelectric eyes to "see" product as it is poured through the machine into a collecting tray. Care must be taken to ensure the units are kept clean, and, in the photoelectric eye versions, some skill is involved in maintaining accurate counts.

The "semi-automated" counting machine is a low-cost method for automating the counting of a large number of tablets and capsules. With this category, we begin to see the benefits of stock bottle elimination. Semi-automated systems replace stock bottles with multiple tablet/capsule storage units or product "cassettes" which are placed, one at a time, on a counting device.

Drug-O-Matic (see Figure 11.2) and Baker Cassettes provide fast counting on a wide range of products. These systems are faster than the universal machines mentioned above; however, they count only a limited number of products (the number of product cassettes).

Figure 11.1   *"Counter-Top" or "Universal" Automated Tablet-*
and Capsule-Counting Machine: the Baker
Universal 2000

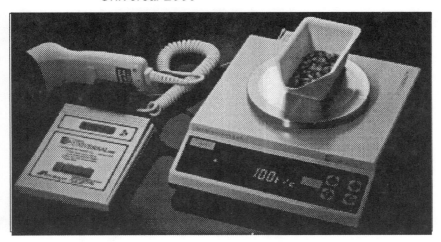

Figure 11.2   *Automated Tablet- and*
Capsule-Counting Machine:
the Drug-O-Matic

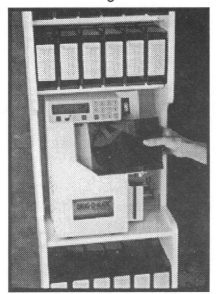

The Baker Cells[6] (see Figure 11.3)are a fully automated system of storage and counting devices that do not require staff intervention until the count is completed. Activation of the system is via the pharmacy's "fill and bill" computer. As the tablets or capsules are counted, they are stored temporarily in a product-specific "drop-out" chute until a technician or pharmacist releases them into a vial. By using a separate product cell to store, count, and hold each product, this system is free of cross-contamination and requires minimal maintenance. At a count rate of 7.5 pills per second on average, most counts will be completed before the technician arrives at the machine.

Figure 11.3   Automated System of Storage and Counting Devices: Baker Cells

As with semi-automated systems, the major benefit of a fully automated system is the elimination of the stock bottle from the active prescription-filling tasks, thus eliminating the technician's time traveling to the shelf, retrieving, and replacing the stock bottle.

These automated counting systems have several features in common. Most require a pharmacy host-system interface to a separate computer or computer network that controls the pharmacy workflow and automation equipment, either directly or through a series of barcode scans. All require technicians to retrieve medications kept in the automation equipment, and all require the pharmacist to verify the end product.

Dispensary automation also includes liquid dispensing. Pioneered by Innovative Medical Services, this equipment is used to automatically and accurately dispense pharmacy grade water. The Fillmaster 1000E (see Figure 11.4) includes a bar-code scanner to automatically dispense the right quantity—in the required stages. Fillmasters connect directly to the incoming water supply and include the necessary filters and water purification equipment. A new Canadian entry into this market performs the same functions, but uses familiar bottles of pre-distilled water.

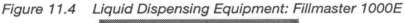

Figure 11.4   Liquid Dispensing Equipment: Fillmaster 1000E

Automated Dispensing Systems

One of the complete systems is the Baker Pharmacy 2000 (see Figure 11.5). This combination of hardware and software requires the pharmacy to be arranged into workstations, an idea used by successful manufacturing companies for years. Each workstation requires personnel to be dedicated to a set of specific tasks allowing simultaneous processes to occur, and effectively reducing the total time required to fill a prescription. The data-entry station receives the prescription from the patient and enters the information into the host system, a barcoded label is printed in the filling station and may be filled concurrent with the data-entry technician scanning the original prescription into the Pharmacy 2000 system. The fill technician prepares the medication by filling and labeling each order, and is directed by the system to place the prescription into a specific packing bin. When all the prescriptions for the order are filled, the system directs the pharmacist to check the order. The scanned image of the hard-copy prescription will be displayed at

*Figure 11.5   Automated Dispensing System:
Baker Pharmacy 2000*

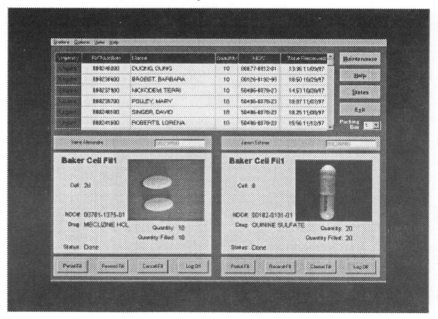

the pharmacist check station, along with a full-color photograph of the medication and other pertinent information. The pharmacist then verifies the accuracy of the prescription and dispenses it.[7]

The most automated level of dispensing systems includes ScriptPro, PharmAssist, Optifil, and AutoScript III. These machines use barcodes and computer-controlled robotics to choose and label vials, count the required medications (high-volume oral solids), place the counted medication in the vial, and present the completed prescription to the checking pharmacist. The first such system was Baker's AutoScript II (1990), which was replaced by their BK series (1993), and now AutoScript III (1997) (see Figure 11.6). AutoScript III utilizes a fully articulated robotic arm with between 150 and 300 Baker Cassettes and Cells. The arm retrieves the appropriate cassette and places it on the counting head. While the medication is being counted

Figure 11.6   Automated Dispensing System: AutoScript III

into the chute, the arm picks up the appropriate vial, deposits it into a labeling machine, and then places the labeled vial underneath the chute. After the medications are released into the vial, the arm places the vial on a conveyor that delivers it to the pharmacist check station. The pharmacist verifies the prescription information and caps the vial. Output of these systems range from ScriptPro, at 60 prescriptions per hour, to AutoScript III's C series, at 240 prescriptions per hour.

Mail-Order Dispensing Services

In the last few years, mail-order drug-dispensing services have been offered to employer-benefit groups in Canada. In the US, approximately three percent of all prescriptions filled are now dispensed through such systems. In Canada, mail order had grown to 0.4 percent of the market by 1997.[8]

In the US, these mail-order services enable members of organizations such as the American Association of Retired Persons (AARP), trade unions, and war veterans' groups to obtain medication at lower cost. The use of highly automated procedures, computerization, technical personnel, volume-purchase discounts, and the provision of long-term drug supplies to their members have enabled these companies to dispense drugs at lower cost, which has resulted in substantial savings for the patients.[9] User organizations and companies also benefit from decreased administrative costs for group programs. The companies operating such services claim that they are the consumer's answer to the current high cost of prescription drugs.

Over and above monetary savings, organizations that purchase from mail-order dispensing services also gain access to data banks with information on the use and cost of the drugs prescribed to their members or employees. The mail-order companies also offer employers and other user organizations a management system for their drug insurance plans. In addition, they provide detailed and complete information on product selection, physicians' prescribing patterns, savings for contributing organizations and their beneficiaries, a drug-utilization review (by drug and by therapeutic class) for each plan, and a list of potential drug abusers. Finally, such services take extensive precautions to prevent fraud and abuse.

Mail-order services have some obvious limitations: they cannot offer the convenience of same-day prescription service, and are appropriate only for chronic-care drug therapies; they cannot provide personal services nor the continuity afforded by community-pharmacy practice. Even the term "mail-order" highlights one of their limitations: in Canada, it is illegal to send prescriptions through the mail. Canadian "mail-order" services actually use more expensive courier service and have employees pick up their medication at their place of employment. Mail-order services do give evidence that it is possible to fill prescriptions in a safe and efficient manner at reasonable costs. Automation, computerization, and skilled technical personnel are highly instrumental in achieving that goal.

Community pharmacists would be well advised to analyze such operations and to automate and computerize as many technical tasks in their own pharmacies as possible. They would then have more time to devote to other professional tasks, such as personalized services and counseling for their patients. As the president of one mail-order company said, "The best way to fight mail-order is for the pharmacist to sell his personality to the customer; if the pharmacist is liked, he or she has the edge."[9] It seems evident that, in the near future, in face of the considerable increase in demand for medication in our society—especially among the growing proportion of senior citizens—governments and other third-party insurers will put considerable pressure on pharmacists to contain the costs generated by prescription-drug use.

COMPUTERIZATION

Computerization is probably the technology that has in recent years had the greatest impact on the community pharmacist's daily practice, and will continue to do so in the near future. The computer systems and software currently available allow pharmacists to free themselves from technical and routine tasks and to focus their attention on professional duties. Numerous data banks now contain extensive information on the effectiveness of drug products, adverse effects, directions for use, precautions to be taken, contraindications, clinical indications, possible interactions with other medication or with food, and advice that should be given to patients. In the very near future, with the help of computers and peripheral systems, pharmacists will be able to control the use of medication much more closely than has ever been possible before.

Patient-File Analysis

In addition to preparing and dispensing drugs, pharmacists are responsible for monitoring drug use and helping patients to understand their drug treatments. The computerized patient file has given pharmacists a valuable tool to assist in performing this function. The pharmacist's professional activity is based on the patient file, the study of which enables him or her to provide patients with optimal pharmacotherapy. We shall now explore further some of the factors of which pharmacists should be aware in their use of computer systems for such analysis.

DETECTION OF DRUG INTERACTIONS

Computerized drug-interaction data banks, compiled from the existing literature on the subject, have been on the market for some time now. Although they are an invaluable aid, these data banks have often been found to be incomplete or dated, due to the rapid development of scientific knowledge and the considerable delay between the publication of new research and its incorporation into the data banks. A number of software companies have attempted to address this problem by regularly updating their data banks to reflect recently published clinical information. An example is *Hansten's Drug Interaction*, which is available on diskette and CD-ROM and can be integrated with most pharmacy systems, and whose purchasers are provided with updating services.

Care must be taken in the choice and maintenance of a drug-interaction detection system.[10] Good systems are characterized by exact and complete data and an adequate means of identifying drugs, the products that contain them, and their therapeutic class. The system must also require pharmacists to keep complete and up-to-date files on each patient's drug history. Above all, a good drug-interaction detection system should generate precise, relevant information without a lot of unnecessary or unimportant detail, which could cause the pharmacist to mistrust the system and hence ignore its messages.

Such detection systems are not intended to replace the pharmacist. With their great operating speed, however, they are an excellent tool to help the pharmacist make professional decisions and assume more fully his or her responsibilities in the area of patient care.

DETECTION OF ADVERSE EFFECTS

The detection and prevention of adverse effects associated with drug products is another field to which modern pharmacotherapy pays particular attention. Systems that monitor such effects have been in existence in Canada and elsewhere for some years now. Such systems are, as a rule, based on two main sources of information. The first consists of the results of compulsory clinical trials designed to determine any adverse reactions caused by new drugs, which are conducted by pharmaceutical companies seeking authorization to release those drugs commercially. The incidence of reactions documented this way is bound to represent only a partial measurement, since only a limited number of individuals are exposed to the new drug during clinical trials. The second source of information comprises, in large part, statements volunteered by health professionals to government bodies such as the Health Protection Branch of Health Canada, which is responsible for public health protection and drug-release authorization. The two main sources are supplemented by data from certain other countries, such as Great Britain, where such information is collected in a more systematic manner.

It stands to reason that computerization of the results of clinical research, together with a systematic monitoring of patients, will yield much more dependable data about the actual incidence and seriousness of adverse reactions to drugs, and will assist in developing more complete and more reliable data banks. Until that time, Canadian pharmacists can, nevertheless, benefit greatly from currently available data in their efforts to detect and prevent the occurrence of adverse drug reactions among their patients.

Pharmacists in Canada benefit from the CPhA's computerized *Compendium of Pharmaceuticals and Specialties (CPS)*. Pharmacists are now able to integrate the CPS into their computer systems and draw on it to detect any adverse reactions that their patients might experience. The computerized *Compendium* also represents an invaluable data bank from which pharmacists derive assistance in their other professional tasks, such as informing and counselling patients. The *United States Pharmacopoeia—Drug Information (USPDI)*, also available in electronic form, is another invaluable source of information for pharmacists.[11]

It will probably take a few more years, however, before computerized programs capable of systematically detecting adverse drug reactions are available on the market. Present-day technology would permit it, but adequate information-gathering systems are still lacking. As drug specialists, pharmacists must avail themselves of all the currently existing tools, which are essential to acquiring the requisite knowledge of drug products.

PATIENT COMPLIANCE

Failure among patients to comply with prescribed drug treatments constitutes a major problem in pharmacotherapy—one that community pharmacists can help resolve. Being the last health professional in contact with patients before they take their medication, the pharmacist can intervene to make them aware of the importance of adhering faithfully to the treatment prescribed. In this regard, the computerized patient file gives pharmacists a powerful tool to identify patients who are not compliant, and enables them to remind those patients regularly about their drug treatment.[12]

Smart Cards

The "smart card" is the size of a credit card and contains a computer chip. It can carry large amounts of information regarding its bearer—for example, the person's complete medical and drug history. Early testing of smart cards in Canada has had physicians encoding prescriptions onto a patient's card, and pharmacists decoding them, with the help of special equipment that "reads" the cards. The implications are clearly immense—an entirely paperless process from the physician's order to the dispensing of medication and, combined with existing computer-system capabilities and the health-services cards, the billing of third parties. Furthermore, theoretically at least, smart cards could make in-house patient-profiling systems obsolete. They would also allow patients even greater flexibility in their choice of both physicians and pharmacists, while simultaneously permitting immediate detection of any attempt on the patient's part to engage in double-doctoring. They would, in general, reduce the possibility of fraud, duplication, and error.

Smart cards at present have significant limitations. One that will probably be overcome in time is the current inability of the card to hold a sufficient number of prescriptions. Serious ethical issues—protection of privacy being the most obvious—will have to be debated and resolved before smart cards gain authorization and widespread acceptance. Pharmacists should, however, be watchful of developments in the near future.

Computer-Assisted Self-Care

Self-diagnosis and self-medication have been known to exist from time immemorial, and there is little doubt that self-medication will increase considerably in the years to come. Confronted by the growing costs of health programs, governments are likely to encourage this trend by moving medication from prescription to non-prescription status (a process colloquially referred to as "switch"). In this regard, the Canadian government is following the lead of the US, which has already authorized the change in status of several drugs, thus aiming at limiting government spending, since most non-prescription drugs are not reimbursed by drug benefit plans.

Consumers at large, as well as general practitioners, trust and seek out pharmacists' advice on drugs, especially those sold without prescription. As a result, there is a general expectation that community pharmacists will assume this increased responsibility as the trend toward self-medication grows, and will take an even more active role in patient counseling.

Further technological developments, such as artificial intelligence and human-interface capacity, will certainly stimulate self-care services in the future.

Automated Telephone Refill Systems

The next area to look at is the pharmacy telephone system. Too often, pharmacy staff are interrupted from professional tasks to answer routine questions. These interruptions take time away from true dispensary duties and their distractions are a leading cause of dispensary errors.

Simple IVR (Interactive Voice Response) systems are one answer to reducing phone calls. However, a new level of IVR is emerging in North American pharmacies: automated prescription refill systems.[13]

Automated prescription refill systems offer one of the most cost-effective ways in the marketplace today to improve pharmacy productivity and customer service. These hardware/software systems answer pharmacy phones and allow patients to refill their prescriptions using the telephone keypad. Refill systems are relatively inexpensive and, by using potential productivity gains, reach break-even quickly.

One of the main benefits to pharmacies is that telephone calls coming into the pharmacy are reduced by, on average, 30 percent or more, which in turn reduces staff interruptions. Because of the reduced number of telephone calls, pharmacists and their staff can remain more task-focused, reducing errors and increasing productivity. Improved productivity means that labor costs can be reduced, which of course improves profitability. In addition, pharmacy staff can spend more time counseling their clients, thereby improving customer service and loyalty.

Consumers benefit because they can call in their refill requests 24 hours a day, seven days a week. With automated prescription refill systems, some 15 percent of all refill calls are placed after hours or before the pharmacy opens in the morning. Perhaps the greatest benefit to customers is avoiding long ringing and hold times. Customers find that time on the telephone is reduced dramatically, and they can call at all hours. Callers can elect to transfer to the pharmacy at any time, and anyone using a rotary telephone, or who gets confused, will automatically be transferred to the pharmacy.

Doctors benefit from the system by being able to quickly leave refill or new prescription messages (where allowed by law) and by having the ability to transfer to a pharmacist-only line.

Once patients have entered their refills into the system, the information can be presented to the dispensary staff in two ways. Refill script information can be presented on dedicated or network printers for manual re-entry to the fill and bill system. The IVR system can be interfaced with the fill and bill host, with refills entered immediately upon verification. This second is the preferred method, as it optimizes the system and allows refill verification while the patient is on the line.

Important features to look for include call-routing applications, host integration, and quick-disconnect (50ms). Caller ID of both customers and doctors aids in identifying calls and can be used to route them to special destinations or to allow customers to by-pass the system entirely.

SUMMARY

We have outlined briefly the opportunities that technology, especially computer systems, offers community pharmacists in helping them pursue their professional responsibilities. Assisted by modern technology, pharmacists can noticeably diminish their technical tasks and devote the time saved to the performance of their professional duties. Computerization can also help them in their professional tasks by providing easy access to impressive quantities of stored information. It is important that community pharmacists make the most of these modern tools, both in their own interests and in the interests of the patients they serve.

References

1. *Pharmacy: Report of the Committee of Inquiry Appointed by the Nuffield Foundation.* London: Nuffield Foundation, 1986.

2. Poston, J., Kennedy, R., and Waruszynski, B. "Initial Results from the Community Pharmacist Intervention Study." *Canadian Pharmaceutical Journal* 127 (1995): 18–25.

3. *Guide de pratique.* Ordre des Pharmaciens du Québec. Montréal: September 1981.

4. *Autocount: The Baker Cell System.* Dorval, Québec: BakerAPS Canada, 1985.

5. "Looking Back." *The Efficient Pharmacy* 1(3), 1998. [editorial]

6. Anon. "Robot in the Pharmacy: Automated Prescription System for 48 Most-Prescribed Rxs, Counts 100 Capsules in 10 Seconds." *Drug Merchandising* (1984): 16–18.

7. Welin, D. "Pharmacy Software." *The Efficient Pharmacy* 1(2), 1997.

8. *IMS Academic Reference Manual.* 1997 edition. Montréal: IMS Canada, 1998.

9. Glaser, M. "Mail-order Rxs: Separating Facts from Fiction." *Drug Topics*, February 1984.

10. Koup, J.R. "Therapeutic Drug Monitoring and Other Clinical Applications." In W.E. Fassett and D.B. Christensen, eds. *Computer Applications in Pharmacy.* Philadelphia: Lea and Febiger, 1986.

11. Poston, J. "Pharmacy Software in the Future." *The Efficient Pharmacy* 1(1), 1997.

12. McLaren, S. "Automated Dispensing: Will New Technology End Drudgery or Automate Chaos?" *Canadian Journal of Pharmacy* 128 (1995): 16–23, 44.

13. Smith, T. "Automated Telephone Refill System." *The Efficient Pharmacy* 1(3), 1997.

Recommended Reading

1. Bezold, C. Halperin, J.A., Blinkley, H.L., and Ashbaugh, R.R., eds. *Pharmacy in the 21st Century: Planning for an Uncertain Future.* Washington: Institute for Alternative Futures and Project Hope, American Association of Colleges of Pharmacy, 1985.

2. Fassett, W.E and Christensen, D.B., eds. *Computer Applications in Pharmacy.* Philadelphia: Lea & Febiger, 1986.

12

MERCHANDISE MANAGEMENT—INVENTORY

INTRODUCTION

The key to effective control of inventory lies in the appropriate balance between the sales of specific items and the amount of funds invested in those items. Inability to achieve this "ideal" balance often results in a situation where a retailer is overstocked in slow-selling items and understocked in faster-selling items. This further exacerbates management because it creates a decrease in inventory and asset turnover—as well as lost sales and dissatisfied customers. The solution is to allocate investment dollars in inventory to obtain an appropriate balance between sales and inventory levels in order to achieve a planned level of profitability. Thus, it is necessary to link the two activities of inventory control and purchasing. These two activities comprise what is called merchandise management and it, in turn, affects profitability.

The breadth (number of brands or variety), and depth (number of units of each size) of inventory in a pharmacy should reflect the needs and wants of its clientele. Individual items of inventory are referred to as stock keeping units (SKUs). These SKUs reflect the variety and sizes of the spectrum of available inventory that the individual responsible for merchandise management must purchase on behalf of the pharmacy's clientele. The merchandise manager's personal likes and dislikes are of secondary concern.

A merchandise manager must consider the following to plan and control merchandise offered for sale.

Type of Pharmacy

- Is the pharmacy organized to provide self-service of products or will it stock items requiring personal selling/service such as cosmetics?

- Is the pharmacy independently owned and operated or part of a chain or franchise? This may influence whether the pharmacy stocks national brands in addition to private label products.

Location of Pharmacy

- Is it located in a strip mall, neighborhood, or major mall? This will influence the merchandise mix because of the demographics of the clientele attracted to the practice.

- Availability of parking will determine accessibility to the pharmacy.

Practice Objectives

- The degree of specialization that the pharmacist(s) provides will determine the type of products available. For example, an interest in sports medicine, homeopathy, or parenteral nutrition requires specialized knowledge of products.

Size and Amount of Shelf-Space and Investment Dollars Available

- Larger pharmacies may simply carry larger amounts of inventory and consequently assume larger investments.

Other considerations include whether to make less frequent, but larger, purchases or smaller ones more frequently. The terms and process of purchase require decisions about price discounts, supplier choices, and delivery dates. Automatic shipments of new products from established suppliers are a mechanism to assure having the latest size, shape, or innovation, but have implications for space and financial resources. Lastly, returning dated, soiled, or unsaleable merchandise to a supplier is not always straightforward and often must be negotiated. This has implications of staff time, storage space, and an investment that is not generating a return.

While qualitative issues are considered in the planning and control of merchandise,quantitative factors must also be considered. In an average community pharmacy, the value of inventory represented 46.9 percent of total assets in 199y, up from 42.9 percent in 199x. Similarly, purchases represented an expenditure of $1,788,674 in 199y compared to $1,535,629 in 199x.

In order to achieve a situation in which sales are maximized with a minimum inventory, the pharmacist owner/manager must meet the clientele's demand for products by not overstocking or understocking. This can be accomplished by a mix of unit controls and dollar controls, illustrated in Figure 12.1.

Figure 12.1   Relationship between Unit and Dollar Control of Inventory Merchandise Management

Unit Control		Dollar Control	
Planning	*Control*	*Planning*	*Control*
planograms	visual systems	purchase planning	book value of inventory
stock cards	periodic count	planned sales	physical value of inventory
point-of-sale data	perpetual unit	planned reductions	
		planned initial markup	point-of-sale data
		planned inventory levels	EOQ* OTB†

* EOQ = economic order quanity
† OTB = open-to-buy

UNIT CONTROL SYSTEMS
Visual System

This method of inventory control consists simply of examining the merchandise on the shelves by walking around the pharmacy and reordering if it is below a desired level or out of stock. Order quantities are determined largely by intuition: the pharmacy manager estimates an amount, based on experience, that will satisfy consumer demand. The visual method is inexpensive to operate and simple to conduct, but, to be effective, must be performed frequently and should be used only in low-volume situations. This method clearly involves a high risk of error, and it can be difficult to control. A "wantbook" is often used to keep a simple record of items to be reordered and can also be used to fill in merchandise between ordering cycles.

Systematic Wantbook

This method is essentially a more systematic version of the visual method, employing wantbooks by product classification or by each supplier that sells directly to the pharmacy. Generally, minimum and maximum order quantities are noted for each product: the minimum serves as a reorder point; the maximum prevents overstocking. Similar notation may also appear on shelf labels to assist in checking inventory. Frequent review of wantbooks by management can help to make this system more reliable and more sensitive to fluctuations in product movement. This method also finds use for "fill-ins" to supplement existing stock levels or for special orders.

Periodic Inventory System

The periodic method involves monitoring sales of products over specific time periods, as well as conducting periodic physical counts of products on the shelves. This approach to inventory management is also known as the stock-record card system, as a stock-record card for each product is commonly used to record the number of units on hand, sold, and on order within a given period. The card also bears supplier information (name, address, salesperson's name, terms of payment, supplier's special offers) and product information (format, size, cost, retail price, minimum/maximum order quantities). Figure 12.2 (p. 264) shows two typical stock-record cards. The clear advantage of the periodic system, when properly maintained, is to show, for example, monthly opening and closing inventories and rates of

Figure 12.2 Two Sample Stock-Record Cards

Manufacturer's Name				Address									
Salesman's Name				Address						Phone			
Discount Terms 2%, 30 days, 10th of Mo. (Books close on 12th)*													
Item	Size	Cost	Retail Price	Min/Max	Deal Periods		1/11	2/11	3/11	4/11	5/11	6/11	
Antacid Brand Q Liquid-Plain	15 oz.	8.52	11.95	¹/₂ doz./ 2 doz.		S.O.H.	5	4	1				
						ORDER	12	12	18				
						SOLD	13	15					
Antacid Brand Q Liquid-Plain	12 oz.	5.32	7.45	¹/₂ doz./ 2 doz.	Nov. 1 doz. + 2 free	S.O.H. ORDER SOLD							
Antacid Brand Q Liquid-Plain	5 oz.	3.16	4.45	1 doz./ 3 doz.		S.O.H. ORDER SOLD							

Manufacturer's Name				Address									
Salesman's Name				Address						Phone			
Discount Terms 2%, 30 days, 10th of Mo. (Books close on 12th)*													
Item	Size	Cost	Retail Price	Min/Max	Deal Periods	Quantity Savings	1/11	2/11	3/11	4/11	5/11	6/11	
Antacid Brand Q Liquid-Plain	15 oz.	8.52	11.95	¹/₂ doz./ 2 doz.		beginning inventory	5	4	1				
							12	12	18				
Antacid Brand Q Liquid-Plain	12 oz.	5.32	7.45	¹/₂ doz./ 2 doz.	Nov. 1 doz. + 2 free	quantity ordered							
Antacid Brand Q Liquid-Plain	5 oz.	3.16	4.45	1 doz./ 3 doz.									

*"2%, 30 days, 10th of Mo." means that a two percent discount will be given if the invoice is paid no later than the 10th of the month that falls after 30 days from the invoice date; in other words, within (30 + 10) 40 days of the invoice date.

Source: Adapted from *"Inventory Control Guide to Good Pharmacy Management"* (Vaudreuil, Que.: Hoffmann-LaRoche, Inc., 1978).

sale for particular products, thereby allowing the pharmacist-manager to identify shrinkage (and possibly some of its causes, depending on the extent of detail recorded), as well as to analyze sales in different time periods to determine patterns and adjust ordering habits accordingly. This is the most accurate of the manual unit-control systems, especially if order periods are shortened so that purchasing decisions are made more frequently. It is considered good policy to verify inventory levels that are counted by non-store employees (i.e., sales representatives) as a further method of control.

Perpetual System

This type of system records sales as they occur, continually calculating increases in inventory as products are received into stock, and reductions as products are sold. It is the most accurate and effective of all inventory-control systems, but only when it is computerized. Performed manually, perpetual systems are the most time consuming and costly to operate, requiring constant maintenance to be kept current and, given the number of products in a pharmacy, are virtually impossible to implement. (Figure 12.3 shows a manual perpetual inventory-control record). Rendered much

Figure 12.3   Sample Perpetual Stock Card

Manufacturer: A & B Manufacturing Co.   Salesman: W. Jones

Address: 23 First Street

Product: Hair Dryer   Unit Cost: $11.50   Retail Price: $22.99

In Stock		Re-Order Time	Terms
Minimum	Maximum		2/10 net 30 (books
3	12	7-10 days	close on 10th)

Date	Received	Sold	Balance
3 Jan.	5	2	8
5 Jan.		2	6
7 Jan.		1	5
7 Jan.	One returned damaged		
10 Jan.		2	3
10 Jan.	P.O. #1234 issued		
17 Jan.	6		9
18 Jan.	Cheque # 0456 issued against invoice # 2678		
19 Jan.	Damaged hair dryer returned via salesman. Credit note to follow.		
20 Jan.		2	7

Source: Courtesy of H.J. Segal.

simpler, more accurate, and more effective through automation, perpetual systems are gaining wide acceptance. A computer running a perpetual inventory-control program is able to generate data at any time on the units-on-hand and sales activity of any product that has been entered into the system.

In recent years, computers have played a significant role in inventory control and have improved the profitability of pharmacies both in the dispensary and in the front store. Initially, the emphasis in automated systems for pharmacies was on the dispensary, where computers programmed for perpetual inventory control were able to generate information in several extremely useful ways, and to perform additional functions as well as:

- provide information on the categories and quantities of drugs dispensed during specified periods;

- provide data on the categories of drugs not dispensed during specified periods;

- provide current data on dollars invested in dispensary inventory by selected periods or "year-to-date";

- notify pharmacists of quantities of products on hand to enable them to reorder; also, if invoices are entered when a new stock of drugs comes into the dispensary, track increases in stock-on-hand;

- in the most sophisticated systems, automatically generate orders when stock levels fall to previously established reorder points, and adjust those reorder points automatically in response to fluctuations in sales patterns.

Figure 12.4 illustrates a computer print-out of selected confectionary sales for a specific day and Figure 12.5 (p. 268) is an item movement report. Figure 12.6 (p. 269) illustrates a stock control method when transferring stock to another unit within the same corporate entity. The operative word here is "control."

Point-of-Sale System

More recently, pharmacies have started to use what are known as point-of-sale (POS) systems to provide efficient inventory control of merchandise in the front store. These systems have the ability to track inventory from the time it is received to the time it is sold. Once item files are built and order

Figure 12.4   Daily Sales Report—Detail

JUNE 9/97
All Departments   Regular/Promotional/Non-Profit Sales

Item (Bar Code)	Item Description	Size	NPR FI	Qty	Actual Retail	Unit Cost	Extended Sales	Extended Cost	GM%
05954222014	CANDY BAG CHERRY LOOPS	1	R	2	0.50	0.2800	1.00	0.5600	44.0
05954222011	CANDY BAG COLA	1	N	2	0.28	0.2800	0.56	0.5600	
			R	1	0.50	0.2800	0.50	0.2800	44.0
05954222013	CANDY BAG FROGS	1	R	1	0.49	0.2800	0.49	0.2800	42.8
			R	2	0.50	0.2800	1.00	0.5600	44.0
0594222015	CANDY BAG JUICE BERRIES	1	N	1	0.28	0.2800	0.28	0.2800	
			R	3	0.50	0.2800	1.50	0.8400	44.0
07276017493	CRAYON POP	1	R	3	0.99	0.5800	2.97	1.7400	41.4
07484800001	LOLLIPOP INDIVIDUAL	1	N	5	0.41	0.3900	2.05	1.9500	4.8
			R	38	0.69	0.3900	26.22	14.8200	4.34
77484800005	LOLLIPOP REG REFILL MINI CASE	1	N	5	0.41	0.3900	2.05	1.9500	4.8
07531201725	THOMAS GUMMY CANDY	113.4	I	1	0.70	0.3500	0.70	0.3500	50.0
			I	1	0.79	0.3500	0.79	0.3500	55.6
07279900905	WERTHER'S ORIGINAL	198	I	1	2.49	1.6100	2.49	1.6100	35.3
TOTAL FINELINE: 004	CANDY LARGE BAG	1		77			58.69	35.4900	39.5

N = non profit   R = regular   I = interim special value   F = flyer

Figure 12.5   Item Movement Report

Date Printed: JUNE 12, 1997
Range ——— ; SELECTED VENDORS (MANUFACTURER)
Vendor ———: 3M1   3M

Sales Department: 13
Department ——— : HH
Category ——— : 083
Findine ——— : 423

Household
Household Products
Cleaners & Equipment
Household Sponges, Brush & Towel

Item (Bar Code)	Item Description	Quantity on Hand	Ordered not yet Arrived	Period Total Sold	05 May 18 97	04 Apr 20 97	03 Mar 23 97	02 Feb 23 97	01 Jan 26 97	13 Dec 29 96	12 Dec 01 96
05113163369 1) C 9	3M BBQ Sted Scrub Display PPK R S.V.	1 UNIT Q N									
05113163489 2) C 5	3M Cellos/Utlty Spng Dsply PPK R S.V.	1 UNIT Q P									
05113163553 3) C 0	3M Non-Scratch Scouring Pads R 1.79 S.V.	2 PK C N									
05113163604 4) C 7	3M Scour Pads/Spngs Dsply PPK R S.V.	1 UNIT Q N									
05113163538 5) C 9	3M Scouring Pads R 2.99 S.V.	4 PK C N									
05113163610 6) C 2	3M Stay Fresh #HP4 Clip/S PPK R S.V.	1 UNIT Q P									
06032700009 7) C 5	3M Stay Fresh Ktchn Scrub Spng R 2.49 S.V.	2 PK C N	Regular	60	4	8	9	8	7	13	11
05113163552 8) C 9	3M Stay Fresh Scour Scrub Spng R S.V.	1 UNIT C N									

QUANTITY SOLD EACH 4-WEEK PERIOD

Figure 12.6   *Sample Claims Report: Example of a Computer Generated Report—Transferring Stock to Another Store*

TO: FROM: 0824

Claim #:   484 Reason Code: TO TRANSFER OUT   June 11, 1997
P.O. #:   0   Ref #:   Conf #:   Auth #: 2594352

FNL	Upc / Plu	Description	Size	Qty	Store /Rec Cost	Inventory Cost	General Ledger
426	77230524569 0	Tide Powder Trial Size	60 G	156	0.3500 B	0.3500	13

TOTAL CLAIM $54.6000

Summary:

13   HOUSEHOLD   54.6000

G.S.T.   3.82
TOTAL CLAIM   58.4200

**** END OF REPORT ****

levels established, the system can generate purchase orders at the appropriate times, its accounting functions can create all the necessary records, and, when the ordered merchandise is received, can add it to the inventory and even generate price stickers and shelf labels. A POS system can produce daily transaction reports, regular gross margin reports, product movement by department, purchasing reports, and gross margin return on inventory investment (GMROI) by product or department. In fact, reports can be customized as required; for example, turnover rates can be plotted and new product lines evaluated. It is said that such systems, if properly designed, can reduce inventories by ten percent or more. This is perhaps not surprising when one considers the vast increase in control that is afforded by such a system. Not only can POS systems reduce inventory, but they can increase sales dramatically by focusing clearly on what sells. A process called SKU rationalization can be implemented, whereby the correct number of facings of product is adjusted according to sales and not to what is bought.

Practically all the merchandise carried in pharmacies today bears a Universal Product Code (UPC) identification, as shown in Figure 12.7 (p. 271), which makes it possible to scan products on scanning counters or with hand-held scanners, and thereby register in the system all necessary product information and appropriate prices. (Cash registers—in fact, terminals—are specially equipped.) In addition, companies offering POS systems have developed assigned product codes for items that do not yet bear UPCs; they also supply labels bearing assigned UPCs for shelves and for products. For those products that do not have assigned bar codes, systems are available to create the necessary bar codes. Some suppliers provide the purchaser with an item file of up to 30,000 items of merchandise, all priced. The purchaser may have to customize this file to ensure that the prices are appropriate for his or her store. POS data should be compared constantly to physical inventory data to monitor shrinkage. Further, POS data should be reviewed often for price reliability in the system. Also, data on existing inventory and minimum stock levels must be entered. If desired markup information is entered, the system will provide the appropriate retail prices. POS systems thus feature the capability to search prices and can be programmed to bring discounted prices into effect on specified dates for purposes of sales or special offers, resume regular pricing on a preprogrammed selected date, and generate new price stickers and shelf labels. The resultant savings in labor cost and increased productivity will repay the cost of the equipment over time.

The principal advantage of POS systems is that they provide more accurate information more promptly. Overstocks and out-of-stock situations can be reduced through early detection: fewer sales are lost, turnover increases, and profitability increases. All this contributes to improving the pharmacy's cash position as well. It has been suggested that, with the aid of a POS system, the 65 percent of products that yield only five percent of sales can virtually be eliminated, or at least dramatically reduced. POS systems also help to control procurement costs in that they reduce the labor costs associated with order generation, as well as with price marking and price changing. Finally, the carrying costs of inventory will be reduced proportionally to the reduced stock. The system allows discrepancies between inventory levels in the computer and physical inventory levels to be detected more promptly, and hence affords greater control over shrinkage, waste, and damaged goods.

Figure 12.7   Sample Universal Product Code

DOLLAR-CONTROL SYSTEMS
Open-to-Buy (OTB) Budget Method

As mentioned earlier, dollar-control systems are concerned with controlling the money invested in inventory rather than the actual items in stock, their balance, and assortment. The OTB budget method is based on establishing overall monthly purchase budgets in advance, monitoring actual sales and purchases during each month, and adjusting the purchase budget for the following month to compensate for documented overspending or underspending, and sales declines or increases in the previous month. This method protects the pharmacy, on a monthly basis, from either exceeding or falling too far below its intended inventory investment for the year. However, it does not address understocking or overstocking of particular products, and, where this does occur, permits the problem to continue. Used in conjunction with an item-specific, unit-control system such as the periodic method, it ensures a more balanced and accurate overview of the inventory situation. The OTB method may be applied by section, by department, or to the entire store.

The estimated or "unadjusted" purchase budget for each month is in fact an estimate of cost of goods sold for that month. To arrive at this estimate, sales are projected for the month and the anticipated gross margin deducted. In some systems, the sales figure is simply taken from the same month last year, and an average gross margin percentage—for the sake of this discussion, let us say 40 percent—is deducted. At the end of the month, actual sales are recorded, together with actual purchases. Variances between the estimated and actual sales figures, and between the purchase budget and actual purchases, are the factors that will determine the adjustment to each following month's purchase budget.

Figure 12.8 (p. 274) shows a completed annual OTB budget chart. Refer to the chart as you read the following steps involved in the method:[1]

While this option is effective, fewer pharmacies are using it for the entire pharmacy. It does find use in the dispensary.

1. At the beginning of the year, a chart is set up with column headings similar to those in our sample and with a row for each month. Estimated sales for each month are entered in column 1 and the corresponding cost-of-goods-sold (COGS) figures in column 2, to represent the unadjusted purchase budget.

2. At the end of January, that month's actual sales and purchases are entered in columns 6 and 7, respectively. (Note that no adjustments can be made to the purchase budget in the first month of implementing this system.)

3. The February purchase budget must be adjusted to reflect activity in January. In this case, $1,400 more merchandise was purchased than had been allowed for in the purchase budget. Also, January's purchase budget was based on estimated sales of $21,000; actual sales that month were $1,000 less. At cost (60 percent of $1,000), this means that $600 less merchandise was sold than anticipated. The net result is that inventory went up by $2,000 ($600 + $1,400) in January (see column 8). February's purchase budget must therefore be reduced by $2,000 (as entered under February, columns 4 and 5 in the chart) to bring inventory back to its original level.

4. At the end of February, actual sales and purchases are entered and adjustments calculated for March. The process continues in the same way each month throughout the year, with purchase budgets being changed each month to compensate for actual events of the previous month that affected inventory.

Figure 12.7   *Sample Open-to-Buy (OTB) Budget Chart*

(This example is based on an estimated gross margin of 40%)

Month	Estimated Sales	Unadj. Purch. Budget (Est. COGS)	Adjusted Purchase Budget	Adjustments	Actual Sales	Actual Purchases	Cumulative Change in Inventory
Jan.	$21,000	$12,600	$12,600	not available	$20,000	$14,000	+ $2,000
Feb.	18,000	10,800	8,800	– $2,000†	17,500	9,300	+ 800
March	19,000	11,400	10,600	– 800‡			
—	—	—	—				
—	—	—	—				
—	—	—	—				
—	—	—	—				
—	—	—	—				
—	—	—	—				
—	—	—	—				
Dec.	20,000	12,000					

$$† – \$\ 1,000 \times 0.6 = \quad – \$\ 600$$
$$\$12,600 – \$14,000 = \quad – \quad 1,400$$
$$– \$\ 2,000$$

$$‡ – \$\ 500 \times 0.6 = \quad – \$300$$
$$\$8,800 – \$9,300 = \quad – \quad 500$$
$$– \$800$$

Source: B. McCormick and H.J. Segal, *Systems Management Program: Inventory Control,* Toronto: Ontario College of Pharmacists, 1980, p. 9.

In addition to revising monthly purchase budgets, the OTB budget method involves tracking actual orders placed to keep an eye on the balances left to spend during the month on merchandise purchases. See Figure 12.8, which depicts this sort of OTB worksheet, using the figures from Figure 12.7 (p. 273).

Our sample describes a situation wherein the inventory is maintained at the same level as it was at the end of the previous year. If the pharmacist-owner planned to reduce the pharmacy's investment in inventory during the year, the monthly adjustments could be reduced by a desired average percentage.

Economic Order Quantity

The economic order quantity (EOQ) method, as its name suggests, seeks to minimize inventory investment by determining the most economical quantities to be ordered, and the frequency with which these orders should be placed. Unlike the methods discussed thus far, the calculation of the EOQ takes into consideration the effects of the value of an order (and frequency

Figure 12.8   Open-to-Buy (OTB) Worksheet

Order No	Supplier	Jan. Amount	Jan. Bal	Feb. Amount	Feb. Bal	March Amount	March Bal	April Amount	April Bal	May Amount	May Bal	June Amount	June Bal
	Planned purchases	25,000		12,500		25,000		22,500		12,500		6,250	
	Dec. adj.	3,100	22,000										
1491	Blain Co.	3,000	19,000	4,000	8,500	3,000	22,000						
1492	Acme Macrame	5,000	14,000	3,000	6,500								
1493	Hobby Crafts	2,000	12,000	2,000	4,600								
1494	Models Ltd	1,000	11,000										
1495	Blain Co.	4,000	7,000										
1496	Acme Macrame	2,000	5,000	2,000	2,500	1,000	2,000						
1497	Jan. adj.	500	–	(500)	7500								
1497	Hobby Crafts			2,000	5,500	3,000	18,000						
1498	Blain Co.			6,000	(500)	5,000	13,000						
	Feb. adj.			500	–	500	12,500						
1499	Acme Macrame					3,000	19,500	5,000	23,500	5,000	7,500		
1500	Models Ltd					3,000	7,500	3,000	14,500	3,000	1,500		
(1499)	May order cancelled									(5,000)	7500		
1501	Blain Co.					4,000	3,500	500	14,500				
1502	Hobby Crafts					3,500	–	3,000	11,500				
	April adj.							1,500	–	11,500	14,000		
1503	Acme Macrame									3,000	16,000	3,000	3,250

Source: Adapted from *Minding Your Own Business*, Vol. 2, Montréal: Federal Business Development Bank, 1980, p. 94.

of ordering) on the two sets of costs associated with purchasing—procurement costs and carrying costs. The EOQ is the dollar volume of purchases or level of inventory at which combined procurement and carrying costs are lowest. Although this method is not commonly used by community pharmacies, the principles on which it is based are important and worthy of consideration by the pharmacist-owner or manager.

A procurement cost is incurred with each order placed; hence, to keep procurement costs down, orders should ideally be made larger (i.e., of a higher dollar volume) and placed infrequently. Carrying costs, on the other hand, increase with the value of the inventory, and can hence be minimized by placing smaller orders more frequently. This inverse relationship, finds a balance at a particular size of order at which procurement costs are (theoretically) equal to carrying costs (practically, it is the point at which the two sets of costs are closest to one another). This is the EOQ, in that it results in the lowest combined cost for each item identified.

Table 12.1 (p. 276) illustrates this relationship between the value of orders and total cost. The example assumes a procurement cost of $3 per order and a carrying cost of 20 percent of the average inventory value (beginning inventory plus ending inventory divided by two). The cost of the product in the example is $720 for a full year's supply and, assuming depletion of the order at the end of the period, average inventory is calculated as ($720 − 0) ÷ 2 = $360 on a one-time order. Total costs are minimized at five orders per year.

The EOQ method is best suited to high-volume products that incur high procurement and carrying costs; it is not useful with seasonal merchandise, nor with items that demand particular reorder cycles by virtue of limited shelf life or for other reasons. Similarly, the results of EOQ calculations must be weighted against outside factors such as suppliers' terms of payment, order cycles, and available volume discounts, and order quantities must be modified as necessary to obtain optimal returns on investment in inventory.

ASSESSING THE EFFECTIVENESS OF INVENTORY CONTROL

An examination of the various inventory-control systems available is necessary to decide which ones are best for a particular practice. But it is important to recognize that not every product in a pharmacy needs to be formally

Table 12.1   Value of Orders and Total Cost

No. of orders per year	1	2	3	4	5	6	7	8
Value of order	$720	$360	$240	$180	$144	$120	$102.85	$90
Procurement costs	3	6	9	12	15	18	21	24
Ave. active inventory	360	180	120	90	72	60	51.43	45
Carrying costs (20%)	72	36	24	18	14.40	12	10.29	9
Total cost	75	42	33	30	29.40	30	31.29	33

Source: Adapted from B. McCormick and H.J. Segal, *Systems Management: Inventory Control,* Toronto: Ontario College of Pharmacists, 1980, p. 10.

controlled. There is a guideline known as Pareto's Law, which holds that 20 percent of all products stocked generates 80 percent of total dollar sales, 15 percent of inventory generates another 15 percent of sales, and the remaining 65 percent of the stock generates only five percent of sales. Identifying the products that produce the greatest percentage of revenues and managing them properly is therefore extremely important; conversely, undue attention to the 65 percent of inventory that generates minimal revenues could be potentially disastrous.

One important measure of how well or how poorly inventory is being managed is the turnover rate. This is a ratio calculated by dividing the cost of goods sold by the average inventory at cost. For example, if the annual cost of goods sold is $800,000 and the average inventory at cost is $200,000, then the turnover rate is four; that is, merchandise has been ordered and sold four times in the course of a year. When the turnover rate is too high, the level of inventory is likely to be too low and out-of-stock situations frequent; when it is too low, inventory levels are probably excessive, tying up funds that could be used more profitably otherwise and leading to lower profits. The appropriateness of a pharmacy's turnover rate may be judged against past performance or against industry standards. It is reported that the average turnover rate among pharmacies is currently about four to five.

Another measure of the efficiency of inventory control is the GMROI, which is calculated by dividing the annual gross margin by the average inventory at cost, and multiplying by 100. According to the most recent Survey of Community Pharmacy Operations, the average pharmacy in 1994 had a gross margin of approximately $639,656 and an average inventory of $263,777, giving a GMROI of 242 percent, that is, a gross margin of $2.42 for every dollar invested in inventory. Some authorities claim that pharmacies should be able to achieve of GMROI of 150 to 300 percent.[2]

Good pharmacy management can contribute to both increasing the gross margin and reducing inventory, thereby improving the GMROI. Since the goal of 150 to 300 percent represents an overall GMROI, it is important to consider the performance of each of the pharmacy's departments to ensure that the overall objective is reached. Both greeting cards and cosmetics may have relatively high gross margins (approximately 50 and 40 percent, respectively), but also relatively high average inventories, producing poor GMROIs. The dispensary typically has a good gross margin (approximately 30 to 35 percent on average) and a low average inventory, producing a very good GMROI. It follows that, if the percentage of prescription sales (and sales of other product groups yielding high GMROIs) is high relative to total sales, it will be easier to achieve the desired GMROI for the pharmacy as a whole. In other words, pharmacy managers should regularly monitor the effect on overall GMROI of the varying contributions by the different departments, striving to increase the sales of those departments that yield a high individual GMROI so that they will represent a greater percentage of the pharmacy's total sales.

References

1.   Archambault, A., and Segal, H. *Inventory Management, Pharmacy Management Program, Module 1*. Kirkland, Québec: Nordic Laboratories.

2.   Cunningham, G. "Lessons in 'Just-in-Time' Inventory Replenishment." *Drug Merchandising* 66 (April 1985): 43-44.

13

MERCHANDISE MANAGEMENT—
PURCHASING

INTRODUCTION

Purchasing, the activity of replenishing stock and introducing new products in the store, is closely related to inventory control and management. Products to be purchased must be selected on the basis of a number of criteria, from customer demand for the product, its turnover rate and profitability, and associated carrying costs, to its suitability for the store's merchandise mix. The dangers of both under- and overstocking; have already been discussed. The choices facing the pharmacist-owner in the process of investing inventory dollars wisely is equally important.

PURCHASING DECISIONS

There are a number of factors that a pharmacy owner or manager must consider when making purchasing decisions. One decision that can be complex—and should not be based solely on price—is whether to purchase through a wholesaler or directly from the manufacturer. When a product is available from either source, the manufacturer's price will generally be lower. This, however, is only one factor that should be considered along with the following:

- payment terms (including incentives for prompt payment or dating, credit terms, and penalties for late payment);

- minimum-order requirements (do you have to order more than you can sell in a reasonable period?);

- order cycle or time for delivery (that is, the lag time between order placement and actual delivery);

- pharmacy's cash flow;

- overall objectives of the pharmacy;

- supplier's policy on returned goods;

- range of services offered by the supplier and how well they meet the pharmacy's needs;

- effects of suppliers' incentive plans on the pharmacy's purchasing plans;

- time required to place individual (direct) orders;

- time/resources required to process individual invoices and accounts payable functions.

In addition, all purchasing decisions must, of course, relate to the identified needs of the pharmacy's customers, and the inventory-control systems used by the pharmacy.

In the dispensary, many products are supplied by pharmaceutical manufacturers, whose prices are generally better than those of the wholesaler. (This is because wholesalers' prices include the cost of the functions they perform as middlemen, including consolidation of purchasing from several manufacturers, storing merchandise, and various other services.) Drug manufacturers also offer prompt delivery, and their minimum-order requirements, unlike those of non-drug product manufacturers, are sufficiently low that pharmacies are not forced to purchase excessive quantities in order to meet them. In addition, the manufacturers extend good payment terms and favourable returns policies. These features have made the decision regarding pharmaceutical suppliers relatively straightforward.

In recent years, however, some wholesalers have become more aggressive and are attempting to compete, even on price, with manufacturers. They are offering discounted prices on pharmaceuticals purchased in quantity, as well as further discounts when predetermined annual purchasing levels are reached. In addition, they may offer extended payment terms, personal servicing of the pharmacy's account by their customer-service representatives, and same- or next-day delivery. These changes in the wholesaler's approach have given the pharmacy owner a wider range of options in his or her choice of supplier—and by doing so, have introduced a wider range of factors to consider in making that choice.

Suppliers

WHOLESALERS

Full-service wholesale suppliers offer a wide range of services, that include:

- same- or next-day delivery (just-in-time merchandise management which allows better financial control);

- customer pick-up counters for emergency orders;

- a wide assortment of products from various manufacturers;

- regular visits by customer-service representatives;

- store-planning services, including traffic-flow analysis;

- convenient payment terms and reasonable return policies;

- co-operative advertising and promotional programs;

- lower rates on charge cards (because of negotiated lower administrative fees);

- inventory-control services;

- marketing and merchandising information and assistance;

- incentive programs providing additional discounts on volume purchases.

For low-volume pharmacies, wholesalers represent a "one-stop" shopping opportunity. Through some of their programs, they also represent an opportunity for these pharmacies to compete (to some extent, at least) with larger pharmacies. Wholesalers meet the smaller pharmacy's needs with respect to inventory control and cash flow as well. For larger pharmacies, they represent an attractive supplier alternative to manufacturers, especially since they have recently improved their approach to the servicing of larger accounts. Many wholesalers are adding value-added services to assist their members in customer service. Wholesalers can also provide advanced technology to aid in ordering and merchandise management.

MANUFACTURERS

The role of manufacturers in the pharmaceutical industry and the pharmacy profession involves more than offering good prices on drug products to pharmacies. Through their medical service representatives, the innovative companies provide invaluable drug-information services. In addition, they are strong supporters of continuing-education programs in pharmacy and contribute, in both time and money, to the advancement of the health professions, as well as to the research and development of new drugs.

As suppliers, pharmaceutical manufacturers offer pharmacists the opportunity to "prestock" newly released prescription and non-prescription drugs. This means that the manufacturer and the pharmacy owner/manager have an understanding that a specified quantity of a new drug product will be shipped to the pharmacy automatically upon its release. Should physicians fail to prescribe the new product with any frequency, the pharmacy is free to return the stock to the manufacturer. On the other hand, prestocking ensures that the pharmacy will not have out-of-stock situations when physicians begin to prescribe the new product (or, in the case of non-prescription drugs, when customers begin to request it). Prestocking also gives the pharmacist time to assess the demand for the product and plan purchasing for the future.

As mentioned earlier, manufacturers of both drug and non-drug products can generally offer lower prices than wholesalers, and many pharmacies prefer to purchase directly from manufacturers for this reason. Some manufacturers, however, impose minimum-order quantity requirements that may make them unattractive to the smaller pharmacy, which, in many cases, would have to risk overstocking in order to meet the requirements. Furthermore, the pharmacy that purchases at lower prices from manufacturers is, in fact, choosing to undertake on its own certain services that are otherwise provided by the middleman. Absorbing these functions involves a cost to the pharmacy, which the owner or manager must recognize and assess.

THE MECHANICS OF PURCHASING[a]

Procedures for reordering merchandise often follow two basic principles: fixed quantities or fixed intervals. The principle of fixed quantities is based on the concept that an order is initiated whenever inventory of an item drops below a predetermined minimum level. It assumes that there are maximum and minimum levels of inventory for each item and that there is a mechanism in place to monitor this. In each case, the same quantity is ordered each time. This process may find use with paper goods. With the

[a]Some of this material was presented previously at a Front Store Management Workshop at the Koffler Institute for Pharmacy Management at the University of Toronto, April 22, 1992.

use of point-of-sale (POS) scanners, this information can be entered into the system and be programmed to flag appropriate items. A further refinement of this POS system is to have the system forward the information to the appropriate supplier, who in turn ships it. This works particularly well in situations where multiple units exist as a chain of stores and, while the data are individualized by store, they are aggregated before going to the supplier.

The fixed interval principle assumes a steady level of sales of an item and thus orders are placed at predetermined and precise intervals. The quantity ordered may vary each time depending upon the actual rate of sale between orders. Combining the two principles leads to the following method of calculating the maximum quantity for an inventory item:

(order cycle × rate of sale) + (lead time for order × rate of sale) + extra stock on shelf = maximum level of inventory

where:	order cycle = 2 weeks;
	rate of sale = 48 units per week;
	lead time = 1 week;
	extra stock = 12 units
thus:	(2 × 48) + (1 + 48) + 12 = 156 units
then:	every two weeks an order is placed for the difference between the maximum amount of stock (156 units) and the actual stock on hand.

Determining the Need for Products

The need for an assortment of products in a pharmacy is the result of what its customers are willing to purchase. This can be determined in a number of ways, including examining past sales, requests by customers, identifying what products other local merchants are stocking, talking with supplier's sales representatives, and keeping up to date on new product availability by reviewing trade magazines and papers. Perhaps the most reliable method among these is past sales. This can be done by utilizing stock cards or a similar method that tracks what is being ordered and sold; how often, and in what amount. Technology has progressed to the state where POS scanners, coupled with computers, can provide these data on demand.

As a by-product of the use of these scanners, judgements can be made about adding new products, deleting existing ones from stock, and the amount of units or dollar value to order. In addition, if one observes a particular popular item to be ordered frequently, but its sales are not being recorded through the scanning device, chances are high that there is a severe pilferage problem.

One mechanism to monitor this is a "cycle count" as illustrated in Figure 13.1. A cycle count is a process to validate inventory levels by reconciling an actual physical count with what is recorded on file. The difference indicates missing inventory that has disappeared from the shelf and should be accounted for due to breakage, in-store use, or transfers to other stores. It should be done with highly pilferable items more often. Produced via the POS system, the report validates your inventory units by means of comparing the book value of what should be on hand with an actual physical count. The discrepancy between the quantities represents stolen, or unsaleable merchandise that has been removed from the shelf.

The amount of product to order must be balanced by the breadth and depth of the mix of merchandise stocked. Remember, breadth concerns the variety of an item—specific brands, while depth is concerned with the number of units of each size to carry. Both of these considerations have implications for shelf space and dollar investment. These decisions must be made by the person responsible for the purchase function in consultation with the owner/manager.

Monitoring Stock Levels

The relationship between inventory management and purchasing becomes clearer when planning the amount of stock to carry. This planning function can be accomplished by using stock monitoring information such as a stock-to-sales ratio, weeks of supply, and inventory turnover.

Purchasing new or replacement stock depends on an expectation of sales. As a result, a sales forecast is necessary and, from this, a purchase plan can be formulated. In order to be realistic in the purchase plan process, a consideration of reductions must be taken into account. Reductions may result from employee discounts, stock shortages, mark-downs in retail price, or discounts taken in order to achieve competitive prices. All but the last of these factors should be recorded over time and calculated as a percentage of sales, and used in the purchase planning process.

Figure 13.1   Cycle Count Discrepancy Report (Sample)

JUNE 12/97 9:49

LEGEND: N—Item not Found in Product File; S—Serialized Item; F—Fixed Inventory;
O—Maximum Stock Overflow; I—Identification Stock on File for Adjustment

Excpt FNL	Item/UPC	Description	Size	Uom	ID	Date	Time	Counted	On File	Diff
Sales Dept: Department: Category:	COSMET CC 100	COSMETICS COLOR COSMETICS FACE & BODY COLORS								
524	02270014325	CG BAL CMPLXN MKUP BUFF BEIGE	30	ML	PD	06/12/97	09:48:01	1	1	
524	02270014315	CG BAL CMPLXN MKUP CRMY NAT	30	ML	PD	06/12/97	09:44:49	1		
					PD	06/12/97	09:47:29	3		
		TOTAL COUNT						4	4	
524	02270014305	CG BAL CMPLXN MKUP IVORY	30	ML	PD	06/12/97	09:46:50	3	4	1-
524	02270014320	CG BAL CMPLXN MKUP MED LIGHT	30	ML	PD	06/12/97	09:46:37	1		
					PD	06/12/97	09:47:44	5		
		TOTAL COUNT						6	15	9-

Notwithstanding purely seasonal items, basic levels of stock are kept on hand at all times as minimum assortments. This must take into account unanticipated demands on these levels, for example, unpredictable increases in product demand, slowdowns in delivery, and sales in future periods. As a result, there may be no relationship between stock on hand and sales activity. On the other hand, if one takes these factors into account, it is possible to create a relationship between stock on hand and sales. Stock levels are taken as of a specified date, and sales are those for a specified period of time. Generally, the first of the month is used to establish a stock-to-sales ratio, as sales are usually planned by calendar months.

Month	Planned Sales		Target Stock-to-Sales Ratios		Planned Beginning of Month Stock Level
January	$100,200	×	1.8	=	$180,360
February	$121,525	×	2.3	=	$279,508
March	$124,302	×	2.5	=	$310,755

Interpreting this information suggests only that in January, it is planned to have almost twice as much stock on hand, January 1st, as anticipated sales for the month. This ratio increases as sales are expected to increase.

The weeks of supply approach uses the concept of inventory turnover relating it to a number of "weeks of inventory supply." If, for example, turnover is targeted for five times per year, there should be approximately 52 weeks divided by five, or ten weeks of sales volume on the shelf at the beginning of the period.

Planned purchases (at retail) can now be calculated using a traditional formula:[1]

planned sales at retail	+	planned reductions	+	planned stock end of month	−	planned stock beginning of month

Its logic is this: these planned purchases represent the dollar amount to order to supplement stock on hand, and thus raise stock levels to the amount required for the month. This formula calculates the stock needed for the month from the planned sales ($180,360), reductions in value that will occur ($18,036), the value of stock desired at the end of the month ($503,114), and the stock on hand at the beginning of the month ($324,648).

Since the stock at the beginning of the month is already on hand, its value must be deducted in order to determine the amount to purchase.

If the dollar values are placed into the above formula, planned purchases at retail are found to be $376,862. At this point it is useful to compare the initial markup at retail to the actual markup earned, assuming that the cost of these purchases is found by taking the suggested retail price less one-third. For example, the cost is 100% − 33% × $376,862 = $252,498. Then:

value of planned purchases at retail	$376,862	100.0%
− value of planned purchases at cost	252,498	67.0
value of planned initial markup at retail or gross margin	124,364	33.0
− reductions		
	18,036	
value of actual markup at retail or gross margin	106,328	28.2

This serves to illustrate the importance of recognizing the dollar value of reductions and the effect they have on margins. If reductions, due to staff or courtesy discounts, are coupled with the cost of shrinkage—theft, product expiration, and damage—which is another form of reduction, the dollars left may not be enough to cover expenses, thus incurring a loss. Corrective action is to increase the initial markup and the retail price, buy more at lower costs, or make adjustments in reductions.

Financial Constraints

The pharmacy's financial constraints will affect its ability to purchase merchandise. One approach to control purchase budgets is the OTB budget, explained in Chapter 12 (p. 271). In its simplest form, an OTB budget can be formulated by the owner/manager and delegated to staff who have product category responsibility. Control of purchase budgets is maintained while allowing autonomy and purchase discretion to staff members.

The OTB budget can be administered by means of a notebook in which the monthly purchases are recorded, subtracting the value of each from the beginning monthly balance. In this way, management can control the total investment in merchandise, by increasing or decreasing the amount purchased in each of the various product categories in the pharmacy.

Creating Purchasing Policies and Systems

Purchasing policies should be established by owner/managers and communicated to staff who have purchasing responsibilities. These policies might range from using a list of "approved" suppliers to using purchase orders and an OTB budget.

Approved suppliers might be selected by owner/managers because of product availability, favorable credit, or delivery terms. Purchase orders (POs) act as a control mechanism and source of information. For example, if all purchases require a PO to be completed by the "buyer," it serves to identify that buyer and provides information on his or her ability to buy appropriately. This includes such factors as quantities, prices, deals, delivery dates, frequency of purchases, terms of payment, backorders, and suppliers selected. Managers or supervisors who monitor purchase orders are in a position to assess the purchase activity of their buyers and to alter purchase budgets as necessary.

POs (see Figure 13.2), should not be dismissed lightly, as they provide a mechanism of control. For example, because POs constitute a record of purchases, the incoming goods can be verified by a receiver—a person different from the buyer—and help prevent goods from being diverted. In addition, the monitoring of prices allows an opportunity to compare prices from other suppliers, and acts as control against an employee favoring a supplier for reasons other than the best price.

A PO essentially becomes a contract between vendor and purchaser, which must be signed by both. As such, it should be as clear and explicit as possible. It should include the following, more or less in the order they are listed:

- purchase date;
- date goods are to be received;
- supplier's name;
- quantity ordered;
- appropriate description of goods ordered;
- costs of goods (could appear as regular cost, net cost, net/net cost);
- suggested retail price;
- special retail price;

Figure 13.2   Purchase Order (PO)

Purchase Order

TERMS & CONDITIONS – SEE OVER

SUPPLIER   3

ADDRESS

DATE OF PURCHASE   1

DATE TO ARRIVE   2   VIA   PREPAID / COLLECT

TERMS OF PAYMENT

4			5		6			10
QUANTITY IN UNITS	# OF UNITS PER CASE	# OF CASE	ITEM & DESCRIPTION	SIZE	REG UNIT INVOICE COST	DEAL UNIT INVOICE COST	TOTAL INVOICE AMOUNT	

8   FOR STORE USE ONLY

7					
TYPE OF TICKET	UNIT NET NET COST	REGULAR SELLING PRICE	SPECIAL VALUE	DEPT. CODE	DISPLAY AREA

11   G.S.T.   TOTAL

THE COST CODE – LOWEST UNIT COST RECORDED

SPECIAL INSTRUCTIONS & COMMENTS

SALES REP. NAME PRINT

PHONE NO.

ALLOWANCES AND DISCOUNTS

CLAIM NO.   DATE   AMOUNT $

CLAIM NO.   DATE   AMOUNT $

SALES REP. SIGNATURE   BUYER'S SIGNATURE

- extension of cost price;
- and the total cost of the order.

Two other documents that should complete the pharmacy's process of establishing a system of purchasing policies are the receiving register and the claim form (see Figures 13.3 and 13.4, p. 292).

The receiving register is intended to record goods that are received by the pharmacy. It is also a mechanism of control. Ideally, cartons should be sealed on receipt, counted, and checked against the delivery firm's waybill that is signed by the receiver. As well, the information collected should include the date, supplier, number of pieces in the order, the corresponding packing slip number, and the signature of the receiver. Any shortages, damages, or opened cartons should be recorded and reported to the supplier and/or delivery firm as soon as possible. When the goods are unpacked, they should be checked against the purchase order, priced, marked, and moved to the appropriate selling area of the pharmacy.

During this "checking" process, any shortages should be noted as to quantity, description, and cost, and claimed using a claim form. This form also provides a record of other claims such as display or advertising allowances, overcharges on invoices, returned goods, or "free goods" offered with a purchase. The form should be signed, where applicable, by the sales representative and an authorized person in the pharmacy, and a copy given to the sales representative. When a claim is honored, it should be noted on the claim form. Periodically, these claim forms should be monitored as a check of having obtained the goods or payment claimed.

Identifying Sources of Supply

Essentially, purchasers can contact suppliers via trade shows, telephone, or mail orders, or suppliers can come to purchasers. To achieve the latter, suppliers have sales representatives who call on the trade and represent manufacturers, limited or full-line, full-service wholesalers, or rack jobbers.

The majority of goods sold in pharmacies is obtained from wholesalers, most likely of the full-line, full-service type. This type of wholesaler provides, in addition to products, services that include delivery, credit, market information, assistance with store design and fixtures, computer services, and merchandising programs. The limited line-wholesaler provides products and lets the pharmacy perform these other functions of storing goods, financing, delivery, and back-up services.

Figure 13.3   *Merchandise Received Register*

469277

Store No. 824   MERCHANDISE RECEIVED REGISTER

	Receiving Date	Receiv Initial	Supplier	# of Cart Cases	Carrier	Packing Slip No. or Waybill No.	Damages/ Shortages	Invoice No.	Amount	Claim No. and Comments
1	16 8 97	JB	Mattry (totes)	21	own	22359, 9/997,		487101 - 19		
2			Mattry	261	own			18532		
3			Province	10	own			884552		
4			Hoshm	21	own			485852	52	25605
5			KtF (shorts)	60	own	0470345,	0470394			
6			Aldrich	1	own			800234		
7			Isle	48	own			2975712 - 5		
8			NIVEL	11	PURO.			750345 -347		
9			CLEARY'S	10	CANPAR			0010047		
10			Metro News		own			208952, 04745		
11			Toy Sales	10	own			003165, 000754		
12			Anten	1	FTS			1035607		
13			Canan	2	"			250608		
14			Dist - Iris	2	"			208757		
15			Centura	15	"			44129, 44268		
16			York Um	1				54346		
17			K&F	2	Own			0470882, 0470900		
18										
19										
20										
21										
22										
23										
24										
25										
26										
27										
28										
29										
30										

RETURNED OR REFUSED MERCHANDISE ONLY								Claim No.	

Figure 13.4   Accounts Receivable and Claim Form

Accounts Receivable & Claim Form

WHITE – Supplier's Copy
CANARY – Attach to Packing Slip
PINK – Control Copy
GREEN – Manager's Copy

CJ#

To _____

From _____

Check One:

- ☐ Display & Promotion Allowance
- ☐ Advertising Allowances
- ☐ Credit for Damages & Shortages
- ☐ Overcharge on Invoice
- ☐ Goods Returned
- ☐ Inter-Store Transfer
- ☐ Private Accounts
- ☐ Third Party Receivables
- ☐ Other _____

- ☐ Rx
- ☐ OTC
- ☐ HBA
- ☐ Household
- ☐ Beverage
- ☐ Paper

- ☐ Confectionery
- ☐ Food
- ☐ Cosmetics
- ☐ Tobacco
- ☐ Expense

Date _____
Due Date _____
RE – Your Invoice No. _____
Dated _____
RE – Our Purchase Order No. _____
Dated _____

Quantity	Item No.	DESCRIPTION	Dept. Code	Cost Per Unit	Amount
				SUB TOTAL	
				G.S.T.	
				TOTAL AMOUNT CLAIMED	

Salesman's Authorization O.K. ☐

Store Signature

HOW TO BE PAID:
- ☐ CREDIT NOTE
- ☐ CHEQUE

- ☐ FREE GOODS
- ☐ OFF INVOICE

- ☐ REFLECTED IN COST
- ☐ NOT REFLECTED IN COST

Authorized Signature _____

Phone No. _____

FORM S-223 REV. 292   PRESS FIRMLY – YOU ARE MAKING MULTIPLE COPIES

Rack jobbers are usually specialty suppliers handling a limited number of goods. They arrange with a pharmacy to stock and maintain a specified selection of goods on a self-standing rack or special fixture. The items displayed for sale on this rack are selected by the jobber and changed by him to obtain optimum sales. Examples here might be sunglasses, hair care items, or panty hose. Retail prices are competitive and often guarantee a certain gross margin to the pharmacy. While the rack jobber services his or her "selling space," these racks may take up aisle space that could be utilized in some other way. As a result, it is useful to monitor both the merchandise and its profitability before using too many such suppliers.

Manufacturers may offer the opportunity of selling directly to pharmacies. What is gained in lower prices may be lost in wholesaler services that manufacturers don't supply. On the other hand, manufacturers' sales representatives are expected to be better trained about their own products, thus providing a useful source of information, not only about the product but its marketing and merchandising as well.

Purchasing through sales representatives or at trade shows allows certain advantages. It identifies a source of supply, provides an opportunity to inspect the product and solicit opinions from staff, and obtain marketing information. Also, inventory levels can be checked before ordering, which allows the purchasing function to proceed in an orderly manner.

Understanding Terms of Sale

The terms of sale are an important aspect in evaluating alternative opportunities of purchasing. Delivery terms are necessary to understand as they determine who has the risk of ownership while goods are in transit, and identify if the cost of transportation will be a significant part of the product's cost.

Among the terms of sale is the question of the change of title (ownership) from supplier to purchaser. The most common occurrence is referred to as "free on board" (FOB). This indicates that the supplier places the goods "free on board" the carrier at the designated point of shipment with the purchaser paying the transportation costs from that point. Further, the purchaser takes title at that designated point and assumes the risk of damage or loss. It is therefore advantageous to purchase FOB your pharmacy.

Part of the sales terms include discounts described as trade, quantity, seasonal, promotional, and cash. It has been common practice for many suppliers to no longer quote a "suggested list price," but rather a range of retail prices for an item. These prices serve as a base from which to calculate the discounts.

Trade discounts are designed to allow the purchaser a sufficient margin (the difference between the cost of the goods and its retail price) to cover operating costs and provide a profit. For example:

suggested price	$18.00	a dozen
customary retail price	$ 1.49	each
trade discount 35%		
net cost ($18.00 – 35%) ÷ 12	$ 0.975	each

This is the price to the retailer. If the supplier sells through a wholesaler, the trade discount may be expressed as "less 35 percent, less 15 percent" and interpreted as 35 percent to the retailer and 15 percent off that price to the wholesaler.

Often, trade discounts are expressed as a series of percentages (serial discount). This occurs when wholesaler price adjustments are made without charging the suggested price. For example, the discount could be stated as "less 35 percent less 10 percent and 2 percent":

suggested price	$14.00
– 35%	4.90
– 10%	0.91
	$ 8.19
– 2%	0.164
Net Cost	$ 8.026

In calculating these discounts, each discount must be taken in turn, not cumulatively.

A variation of the trade discount is the "deal." This can occur as an offer of "free goods" with an order. It is intended as a bonus, usually acting as an incentive to increase an order. For example, if a gross (12 dozen) is purchased, the supplier will ship another dozen of the same item at no extra charge. The actual unit cost is found as follows:

$$\begin{array}{c} \text{regular cost} \\ \text{per dozen} \end{array} \times \begin{array}{c} \text{number of dozens} \\ \text{paid for} \end{array} = \begin{array}{c} \text{total dollar} \\ \text{amount order} \end{array} + \begin{array}{c} \text{number of} \\ \text{dozens received} \end{array} + 12 = \text{unit cost}$$

$$\$18.00 \times 12 = \$216 + 13 + 12 = \$1.38$$

Yet another variation is for a supplier to offer a dozen of an item and bill for only ten or 11 of the items—referred to as 10/12 or 11/12 billing. The unit cost for this type of transaction is found as follows:

$$\begin{array}{c} \text{regular cost} \\ \text{per unit} \end{array} \times \begin{array}{c} \text{number of units} \\ \text{paid for} \end{array} = \begin{array}{c} \text{deal cost} \\ \text{per dozen} \end{array} + 12 = \text{unit cost}$$

$$\$1.50 \times 10 = \$15.00 + 12 = \$1.25$$

Quantity discounts are provided by suppliers to encourage large orders or volume purchasing. They are calculated as a trade discount or, if an extra discount is given for specified larger quantities, as a serial discount.

There are two types of quantity discounts: cumulative and non-cumulative. The former refers to the total amount of goods purchased over a predetermined period and is not concerned with the size or total number of orders. A non-cumulative quantity discount is based on the size of a one time only order.

Seasonal discounts are designed to encourage orders of seasonal items well in advance of a normal buying period. These discounts, by encouraging "early" purchases, assume that retailers have storage space available or will merchandise these products early.

Promotional allowances or discounts provide dollars that are intended to be used to promote or advertise a particular product. This can occur as broadcast ads, use of flyers or newspapers, or window or shelf space. Follow-up by the supplier may or may not occur, and thus the discount may not serve its intended purpose. It is good policy to monitor these discounts and file a claim for them as required.

Cash discounts act as a premium or incentive to pay invoices promptly. This type of discount is really an interest payment made by the supplier in exchange for settling the debt in advance of the due date. They are expressed as "2/10 net 30" and interpreted as follows: The supplier is extending credit for 30 days from the date of the invoice, at which time the net amount is due. If the purchaser settles the account within ten days of the invoice date, a two percent discount may be taken. Although this saving seems slight, it is substantial in dollars over a fiscal period and the annualized rate of interest is indeed substantial. An invoice amount of $5,000 with these terms is illustrated below.

If the discount is not taken within the ten-day period, the purchaser is paying for the privilege of having credit extended an additional 20 days at a cost of two percent per 20-day period. The actual annualized interest can be calculated as follows:

$$ I = \frac{D}{(G-D)(T+365)} = 37.2\% $$

where I = annual interest rate
       G = gross amount of invoice ($5,000)
       D = discount in dollars ($100)
       T = time between date discount due and final payment date (20 days)

As this rate of interest is in excess of the interest cost on money, a decision must be made whether to take these cash discounts, even if it means borrowing from the bank to do so. Until bank rates are 37.2 percent a year, it is better to borrow and take advantage of the discount.

Some other terms of sale include the concept of "dating" or the time limits that govern payment for purchases. There are two types: immediate payment—cash dating, and future dating. Cash dating includes cash on delivery (COD), where purchasers have poor credit ratings. Future dating involves extension of credit by suppliers. This is indicated on the invoice in several ways. For example, the designation end of month (EOM) indicates that the cash discount and net credit period begin on the first day of the following month, as opposed to the date of the invoice. The advantage here is that multiple purchases can be made during the month and paid for with one invoice.

This is illustrated with the following payment terms of 2/10 net 30 EOM. If the order is shipped and billed mid-month, the terms begin at the 1st of the following month with the cash discount being taken by the 10th, and the net amount due on the 30th. The advantage here is the extra amount of time available to settle the account, while having the goods available for sale.

In some instances, suppliers may provide what is referred to as "extra dating." The payment terms appear as "2/10 net 30 to 60 days extra" and are interpreted as having 60 days extra before the ordinary terms begin. Thus, there is a total of 90 days to settle the account without taking the discount.

Lastly, consignment sales may be offered by some suppliers. In this situation, the title or ownership of the product remains with the supplier until the goods are resold by the retailer. The unsold goods may be returned to the supplier. This may occur with new lines of merchandise or where a supplier wants to establish a base of retail distribution. It is always useful to understand clearly the arrangement with consignment sales as there may be high costs attached to returning unsold merchandise.

Receiving, Marking, and Stocking Shelves

The responsibility for receiving merchandise in a pharmacy should be assigned to one staff member. That person must ensure that all merchandise received agrees with the packing slip and purchase order, and that it is in good condition and suitable for sale. Errors in back orders or quantities received, and any damaged merchandise, must be reported immediately, following store policies and procedures. Items received but not invoiced, or invoiced but not received, must also be reported and a record kept, in order to maintain proper inventory control and, where appropriate, for re-order purposes. Good policy dictates that a record of a telephone call and person spoken with be kept, as well as copies of a fax or formal letter. Some pharmacies have specific receiving hours to ensure that staff is available to receive merchandise in accordance with established policies. Most stores have specific policies with regard to certain categories of merchandise, such as narcotics, high-ticket items, or perishable products.

The key to managing these "procedures" is control. Control is exercised by means of keeping records and following up on their use. The process begins with receiving goods into the pharmacy. For example, upon receipt of a delivery of five cases to the receiving door of the pharmacy, the delivery is accepted after counting the cases and signing the waybill. The person responsible for receiving goods verifies that a purchase order exists and the order has arrived within the "time window" of the expected date. The order is checked off against the packing slip and the purchase order.

These two documents are stapled together and passed along to the financial person who matches them to the supplier's invoice when it arrives via the mail. When the invoice does arrive, it is checked against the purchase order. The goods are then marked or ticketed on the cases and sent from the receiving area to the selling area after having been entered into the POS computer system. Regardless of the size, complexity, or sophistication of the pharmacy, an appropriate receiving procedure must be established and followed consistently.

Prior to the placement of merchandise on the shelves or in the stockroom, products must be priced correctly, employing the appropriate markups. Careful attention should be paid to avoid error in these procedures. Pharmacies with POS systems must follow specific procedures for the use of the system with regard to pricing.

It is important to note the difference between pricing and marking goods. Pricing is a managerial function, as it involves determining margins, whereas the act of marking is a delegated task of placing the selling price on the goods.

The task of marking goods for sale is a serious responsibility as the right price should appear on the right merchandise—both for competitive reasons and for margin preservation. Control of this function includes control of price stickers and marking guns as a guard against shrinkage through deliberate miss-pricing of selected items. In addition to the selling price, the price sticker should contain "coded" information as to the item's cost, supplier, and date received. This becomes useful in monitoring and managing one's inventory.

The importance of issuing a PO with each order placed cannot be overemphasized. As mentioned earlier, POs must be prepared consistently and according to specific guidelines, identifying the supplier correctly and listing the products ordered, the sizes and quantities of each, the unit costs, and the total value of the order. The PO is not only necessary for inventory control and bookkeeping purposes, but also helps to reduce errors in receiving procedures and can be used for pricing by staff. Also mentioned earlier, POS systems have the capability of generating POs and purchase reports— another invaluable aid.

Those responsible for placing merchandise on the shelves should ensure that stock is rotated properly, moving existing stock to the front of the shelves and new stock toward the back. Care must also be taken to see that each product is placed in its designated position on the appropriate shelf, in accordance with the pharmacy's merchandising plan or planogram.

Returning Goods to Suppliers

All suppliers have policies relating to accepting returned merchandise that may differ considerably. It is not unusual for suppliers to require prior authorization before accepting returned goods. Part of this process may require the retailer to justify the reasons for returning the goods, prepaying the freight, and perhaps absorbing a financial penalty by way of being charged a handling fee. A record of returned goods should be kept, such as the claim form discussed previously.

As suppliers usually do not like to accept returned goods, the entire process is slow, and the cash refund or credit given may be slow in coming as well. The best alternative to returning goods is to place them on sale, if appropriate, and pricing them to achieve quick movement and recovery of cash. It is useful to contact the manufacturer of goods that you wish to return, as they may reimburse the difference between your regular selling price and "special sale" price rather than accept the returned goods.

Terms of Payment, Dating, and Quantity-Purchase Deals

As part of their marketing approach, both manufacturers and wholesalers may offer a special payment provision known as "dating," which in this context refers to the practice of extending payment terms for 30, 60, or 90 days, or permitting the splitting of payments over that period of time. Dating deals are normally arranged on large-quantity purchases. Also, the supplier is likely to be most flexible about extending terms of payment with a long-standing and reliable customer who directs a significant portion of the pharmacy's business to him. (This is one reason why it is wise to develop a strong relationship with only a small number of suitable suppliers, rather than to spread the pharmacy's business too thinly among many sources of supply.) The secret to success with dating deals is to ensure that purchases are confined to quantities that can be sold by the time payment is due. Note that this is where inventory-control data is invaluable.

Some argue that opportunities for cash discounts should always be taken (even if funds must be borrowed for the purpose) because over a year's time, the total discount missed could amount to as much as 37.2 percent.

It is this argument that is in fact flawed, however, since cash-discount savings must be assessed in light of prevailing interest rates, and, at the time of writing, it is indeed more advantageous to opt for extended terms of payment than to earn a two percent discount through early payment. Caution should be exercised to ensure that suppliers ship the goods on an appropriate date that assures the pharmacy the full period of time to pay the invoice, even if one does not opt for the discount period. It should be noted, also, that some suppliers are now charging a monthly interest of 1.5 percent or more on overdue accounts.

There are a number of suppliers who also offer quantity-purchase "deals" or discounts. These deals, offered on large-quantity purchases, are often designed to introduce a new product or encourage the pharmacy to select a particular brand of product. The deals may take the form of offering "free goods," promotional allowances, co-operative advertising allowances, or extra discounts and premiums. Promotional allowances are in fact payments to the purchaser, which are intended to be used in association with the promotion of the particular product. Similarly, co-operative advertising allowances are allowances or payments toward the advertising of the product. In the case of non-prescription drug products, the supplier may support the offer with a backup media promotion as a further inducement for the customer to purchase in quantity. The decision to purchase "on deal" or in larger-than-normal quantities must be based on cash-flow and inventory-control considerations. Some pharmacies adhere strictly to established policies requiring that products purchased have a proven specified turnover rate or that they carry a dating advantage, so that they are sold by the time they must be paid for. Others will only take quantity deals on a consignment basis, and still others insist that products gain customer acceptance before they will buy in quantity. In general, while buying certain products in bulk can lower unit cost and help increase gross margins, it may also result in excess inventory levels, decreased gross margins, and too much money invested in inventory. Therefore, each individual pharmacy must carefully assess its ability to sell off the merchandise before engaging in large-quantity purchasing. Such an assessment is, of course, made easier with the help of a computer to provide timely information on the movement of products.

It should be noted here that POS systems are very helpful with regard to capitalizing on discounts and, generally, adhering to suppliers' terms of payment. The system stores information on when accounts are due for payment, ensuring that the pharmacy will take advantage of discounts where applicable. (It will even generate the cheques for payment.) The supplier files also contain relevant information on minimum-order requirements, prices, and other pertinent supplier information.

Central Purchasing and Co-operatives

In some chain pharmacies, much of the purchasing is done by a central office, in consultation with the managers of the chain's affiliated stores. Senior management in such situations believe that cost savings are made with this method and that better control of inventory is achieved. Merchandise is either distributed directly to the respective units of the chain (a system known as "drop shipment") or delivered to a central warehouse, from which it is redistributed to each unit. In these instances, the chain adopts some of the functions of a wholesaler.

To gain the advantages that come with large-quantity purchasing, a number of independent pharmacies will often combine to form a voluntary purchasing or buying group (examples include Pharmasave and Value Drug Mart). The resulting savings are shared among group members, helping them to compete with larger pharmacies or to increase their profitability (or both). In some cases, each member of a co-operative group will purchase specific products, so that no single member is unduly burdened by the process. These informal groups meet frequently, usually monthly, to plan purchases. In addition, these groups are in a good position to negotiate for funds with suppliers to pay for a portion of the cost in printing flyers and other promotional activities.

SUMMARY

Inventory is the largest single investment of a community-pharmacy practice. Mismanaged, it can become the greatest liability of the business, tying up funds that could be invested to upgrade or expand the business and incurring excess insurance, interest, rent, and labor costs. Properly managed, it can be the pharmacy's strongest asset, ensuring the profitability and future income of the operation.

Purchasing involves the investment of capital in saleable merchandise. It consists of identifiable functions. These have been described as a process that acts to obtain and maintain an appropriate level and assortment of merchandise when it is required and at the most desirable purchase terms.

Reference

1.   Davidson, W.R., Sweeney, S.J., and Stampfl, R.W. *Retailing Management.* 6th ed. Toronto: John Wiley and Sons, 1988.

14

PRICING

INTRODUCTION

The product mix in a pharmacy includes three distinct types of products: prescription drugs, non-prescription drugs, and non-drug products. The range and type of service provided differ with the sale of each of these product categories. Because of this, and because pharmacists are educated to make professional judgments in the sale of pharmaceutical products, methods of pricing for these product categories should be different.

Non-drug products, for example, are offered for sale in a wide variety of outlets, consumers are familiar with them, and little or no service is required in their sale. As a result, their selling price is determined by calculating a percentage of their cost and adding this amount (the markup) to the cost to arrive at a retail price. The percentage used may vary depending on competition, volume sold, and the retailer's pricing strategy.

Non-prescription drug products have traditionally been priced in a similar fashion. In this instance, however, a pharmacist may be involved, either at the customer's or the pharmacist's instigation. An example is the diabetic looking for a cough syrup. The pharmacist must first determine that the person is diabetic and then recommend an appropriate (sugarless) product. Even though the product is priced on the basis of its cost, the percentage added to represent the difference between the product's cost and its selling price should reflect the cost of services provided.

Prescription products highlight the uniqueness of pharmacy as a business. These products cannot be sold in the same way as ordinary merchandise, because the consumer must be advised on the proper way to consume or use them. Hence, pharmaceutical services based on professional judgment are involved. As a result, the final price of a prescription product must reflect the cost of the product plus a separate charge for this specialized and individualized service. A professional fee is the method of choice.

Although pharmacies handle the three distinct product categories, our discussion in this chapter shall focus on two—non-prescription merchandise (including drug and non-drug products) and prescription drugs. This will enable us to analyze the two main approaches to pricing—the first using a percentage markup, the second using the application of a professional fee.

PRICING NON-PRESCRIPTION PRODUCTS

The value of any product or service is its "exchange value" in the marketplace. In other words, it is worth only what someone is willing to pay for it at a given point in time. Hence, its price is its exchange value.

Individual preferences determine how much utility or gratification is represented by a specific product or service. Thus, consumers are faced with decisions as to what and how much to purchase. The price system helps them decide in that it influences the way in which they will disperse a fixed amount of money among an almost limitless number of products and services.

Consumers attempt to maximize the value of their purchases, and merchants attempt to set prices that will attract buyers. Price, then, becomes an important component of overall marketing strategy and results in a firm's ability to generate sales and earn a profit.

Pricing Objectives

Pricing objectives can serve many purposes. For example, some firms will place a very high price on a new or innovative product, for one or more of the following reasons: they believe this invests the product with value in the mind of the consumer; to recoup research and development costs as soon as possible; to take advantage of market exclusivity before competitors bring out a similar product; or simply to maximize profits.

Other firms will be committed to very low pricing. This, too, creates a certain image, attracts certain customer segments, may increase the volume of products sold, and may deter competitors from entering the marketplace.

Both of these approaches, with different effects but similar objectives, are employed in the pharmaceutical industry and, perhaps to a lesser degree, in community practice. Consumers have different expectations with regard to value, which translate into a willingness to purchase products only at what they think are appropriate prices. Pricing policies, therefore, must strive to find an equilibrium between a pharmacy's price levels and its consumers' expectations and perceptions of value at those prices.

Pricing Policies

There are a number of pricing policies available to the pharmacy owner or manager, which can be classified in the following general categories:

- market-oriented pricing;
- discount pricing, including leader and loss-leader pricing;
- traditional pricing, including markup on cost and gross-margin pricing.

Market-oriented pricing is most often applied to general pharmacy merchandise—that is, to products that can be purchased at most pharmacies. This type of pricing occurs in a competitive environment and is accepted, and even expected, by consumers. A market-oriented policy can involve setting the price on a product at, below, or above the prevailing market price.

Pricing at the market level serves to retain, but not necessarily increase, market share and may be applied to items such as cough syrups or certain analgesics, which are used by consumers regularly and are purchased as needed. Price reductions on such products would serve little purpose, as most pharmacies sell identical items at similar prices and consumers are unlikely to go out of their way to find bargains on them.

Pricing below the market level constitutes a discount policy and is used to attract traffic and increase sales. Competing outlets are likely to monitor prices in the market and may be forced to follow suit when they discover that discount prices are being offered elsewhere. Therefore, this type of pricing policy is most effective when implemented at random times in different categories of merchandise—for example, by holding theme sales. Health and beauty aids are examples of goods that are priced below market at random times. This approach has the advantage of drawing customers into the store, because they know that they can occasionally obtain items at lower-than-regular prices; it also stimulates impulse buying and may increase sales of selected items. The risk involved is that below-market pricing can create a discount-pharmacy image; consideration should therefore be given to the frequency and manner in which this approach is used.

Above-market pricing is used when it is unlikely that customers will shop elsewhere for the products sold or where service is required in the sale of the goods. Above-market pricing policies are most likely to be found in pharmacies that carry home health-care supplies, provide delivery service, or have extended store hours.

The main objective of discount pricing is a greater volume of sales— in either units sold or dollars generated, or both. There are several variants of discount pricing. Leader pricing is meant to create an image of an innovative, aggressive retail store that is a "leader" in setting competitive prices. It attempts to attract new customers as well as retain regular customers. Customer interest is maintained by promoting weekends or holidays as special sale days. Sale items must be selected carefully, to suit the particular theme of the sale, and the pharmacy must be able to purchase the merchandise in appropriate quantities at appropriate prices. An extension of leader pricing is loss-leader pricing, where certain products are priced *below cost* for an aggressive merchandising policy. This approach is intended to attract customers in large numbers, diminish stock levels of selected items, and discourage competition.

A continuous application of leader and loss-leader pricing will lead to the perception that the store is a discounter. Such pricing policies result in low-margin retailing and a dependence on high turnover and high sales volumes. Caution must be exercised to avoid creating the wrong impression in customers' minds: they may come to expect the so-called discount prices to extend to the dispensary for prescription drugs, if they perceive the operation to be a "discount drug store." If the two major departments of the pharmacy (the front store and the dispensary) do not have compatible pricing policies, customers may simply decide to shop in the front store f or the bargains and take their prescriptions elsewhere. Therefore, the pharmacy must attempt to communicate to the public the important relationship between price and value with regard to prescription products, in order to retain their loyalty and their patronage.

Pharmacies generally adopt a one-price policy for all consumers. This is reflected in the fact that a price sticker displaying a retail price appears on each item in the store, or on the shelf if the retailer uses a barcode scanner. In some instances, however, special prices may be offered to identified individuals or groups. For example, employees and certain groups of customers, such as senior citizens, may be given the privilege of purchasing items at special discounts.

Traditional or routine pricing refers to the practice among pharmacies of applying markups on the cost of goods. Two variants of the traditional method are gross-margin pricing and markup on cost. Traditional methods generally result in prices that are consistent with market levels; if they fail to generate sales at expected rates, they may be combined with a selective use of discount policies in order to stimulate business.

Gross-margin pricing has routinely been adopted by pharmacies. The cost of an item is taken as the base to which a markup value, calculated as a percentage of the selling price, is added, in order to obtain a desired gross margin.

In making this calculation, keep in mind the relationship among retail price, cost price, and markup at retail (which is the gross margin): Retail price = cost price + markup, *or* Cost price = retail price – markup, *or* Markup = retail price – cost price. Hence, if the cost of an item is $1 and the desired gross margin is 30 percent, the following formula would provide the appropriate selling price:

cost price + 30% of selling price (markup) = selling price

then:

$$1.00 + .30x = x$$
$$1.00 = x - .30x$$
$$1.00 = .70x$$
$$\frac{1.00}{.70} = x$$
$$\$1.43 = x.$$

Another way to approach this situation is as follows:

retail price: 100%
markup: – 30%
_____
cost: 70%

In dollar terms, the cost is $1.00, which represents 70 percent of the retail price x, therefore, $1.00 = 70%$ of $x = \$1.43$.

By definition, the gross margin is the difference between the selling or retail price and the cost of the item; in our example, then, the gross margin is 43 cents, or 30 percent of the retail price. (It should be noted here that, in practice, gross margins are generally set for product lines rather than individual products; for example, an average 30 percent margin might be required on the various sizes and formats of a particular brand of toothpaste.)

A markup may also be expressed as a percentage of the cost price, and hence is referred to as a "markup on cost." In our example, the markup on cost is 43 percent. As you can see, there is an important difference between a markup based on retail price and a markup based on cost price. The two should not be confused. There is, of course, a relationship between them as well. Let us illustrate this with a second example.

If a particular bar of soap costs the pharmacy $1 and the supplier's catalogue suggests it sell for $1.50, the gross margin is $0.50 – the difference between the selling price and the cost. In terms of a percentage markup, this $0.50 is $(0.50 \div 1.00) \times 100 = 50\%$ of cost or $(0.50 \div 1.50) \times 100 = 33.3\%$ of the retail price. Table 14.1 develops this principle for selected values.

An adaptation of gross-margin pricing is a sliding gross-margin policy. In this approach, a higher markup is applied to lower-cost items and a lower markup to higher-cost items. This reasonable approach to pricing serves to minimize the inequity that results from an "across-the-board" markup on all items.

Considerations in Cost-Based Pricing

As can be seen, price-setting is not a simple matter. Most retailers have now adopted cost-based pricing, as opposed to market-oriented or discount pricing, in order to ensure that at least product costs are recouped. Historically, manufacturers set the retail prices on their products and specified discounts to wholesalers and to retailers (known as trade discounts). The discounts represented payment for services provided in the distribution channels and in selling the products to the public. They were expressed as percentages of the retail price. Increased competition led to the decline of this system, as prices charged from store to store varied widely and the suggested retail price became meaningless. Also, when retail chains began to buy in bulk, the relationship between cost price and suggested selling price became less

Table 14.1   *Markup Conversion Values and Retail Price*

Percentage Markup on Cost	Percentage Markup on Retail (Gross Margin %)	Retail Price Using $1.00 as Cost
5.3%	5.0%	$1.05
11.1	10.0	1.10
14.9	13.0	1.15
17.7	15.0	1.18
19.9	16.6	1.20
25.0	20.0	1.25
33.3	25.0	1.33
50.0	33.3	1.50
66.6	40.0	1.67
100.0	50.0	2.00

The conversion from a cost base to a retail base and vice versa is facilitated by the following formulae:

$$\text{markup on cost} = \frac{\text{markup \% on retail}}{100\% - \text{markup \% on retail}}$$

$$\text{markup on retail} = \frac{\text{markup \% on cost}}{100\% + \text{markup \% on cost}}$$

important. However, the principle of using percentages in pricing has survived.

In many cases today, the only known values are the product cost and the retailer's required gross-margin percentage, which explains the importance of the data in Table 14.1. The process of establishing a price based on cost involves totaling all costs associated with an item offered for sale. Among these costs are the cost of the product itself, the freight cost, allowances for advertising, and the cost of labor involved in getting the product to the shelf and maintaining it. Although they no longer set the retail price on products, some manufacturers (and wholesalers) still provide a suggested range of prices, which can serve as a guide to the retailer and provide a level from which to discount. In addition, because suggested prices take into account the cost of the item to the retailer, they are useful in suggesting both a gross margin amount and a markup figure.

If a product does not come with a suggested retail price and the pharmacist-manager wishes to establish a markup (or verify the markup where a suggested retail price is given), the traditional formula for calculating initial markup (on retail) can be applied, as follows:

$$\text{initial markup percentage} = \frac{[(\text{expenses} + \text{profit}) - \text{cash discounts from suppliers}] + (\text{markdowns} + \text{stock shortages} + \text{employee discounts} + \text{customer discounts})}{\text{net sales} + (\text{markdowns} + \text{stock shortages} + \text{employee discounts} + \text{customer discounts}).}$$

Note, however, that:

- expenses + profit = gross margin;

- markdowns (i.e., any price reductions for the purpose of stimulating sales) + stock shortages (due to theft, breakage, or unsaleable items) + employee and customer discounts = reductions;

- gross margin – cash discounts from suppliers = maintained markup.

Therefore:

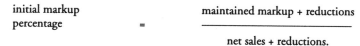

$$\text{initial markup percentage} = \frac{\text{maintained markup} + \text{reductions}}{\text{net sales} + \text{reductions}.}$$

The value of calculating an initial markup percentage is evident, for example, when a pharmacy owner or manager is planning to carry a new line of products. The planning procedure should involve the following steps:

1. Establish a sales goal for the new line over a specified period of time—for example, $20,000 in one year.

2. Calculate the expenses to reach this goal. They will include fixtures and a portion of staff salary and overhead for a cost of, say, $5,000.

3. Estimate the retail reductions, such as markdowns, employee discounts, and customer discounts. Let us say these total $1,000.

4.   Set a profit goal—for example, 6 percent of sales, or $1,200.

5.   Account for cash discounts on purchases, at, say, $500.

Remember that:

gross margin = expenses + profit: $5,000 + 1,200 = $6,200;
reductions = markdowns + stock shortages + employee and customer discounts: $1,000;
maintained markup = gross margin–cash discounts: $6,200 - $500 = $5,700.

Therefore, in order to meet the obligations of the business and earn a 6 percent profit, the initial markup on this new line of products must be:

$$\text{initial markup percentage} = \frac{\text{maintained markup + reductions}}{\text{net sales + reductions}}$$

$$= \frac{\$5,700 + \$1,000}{\$20,000 + \$1,000}$$

$$= 31.9\%.$$

If cash discounts do not appear as a separate item in the income statement, they must be subtracted from gross margin, because "cash-discount" dollars, earned as a result of the business's ability to pay its invoices on time, reduce the cost of the goods. If included, it would mean that they were in effect being counted twice, because the cost of the merchandise would be artificially inflated by the value of the discount taken, and any markup calculated on cost would be increased as well.

Reductions must be added back, because they represent discounts from the proposed retail price. If they are not added back, the resulting gross margin or markup based on retail price will be smaller, resulting in a lower markup on cost as well. Reductions are included in both the numerator and the denominator, to increase both elements of the equation relatively, in order that reductions will not affect the initial markup percent abnormally.

This formula may not be widely used in community pharmacies, because individual departments are often not sufficiently well defined in terms of allocation of overhead costs. The value of the formula is in its ability to define costs better and allow judgmental pricing decisions to be made when there is cause to deviate from full-margin pricing.

Importance of Cost Recovery in Pricing

All prices calculated at a full gross margin must cover the cost of the item plus the following expenses and profit:

- direct expenses incurred in operating the business (labor costs);

- indirect expenses incurred in operating the business (overhead costs);

- reductions in inventory (shrinkage) or reduction of markups (discounts);

- anticipated profit or return on investment;

- the actual cost of the item.

By calculating a correct retail price, the pharmacy owner will be able to recover these costs and expenses and earn the desired profit upon selling the merchandise. The only cost that is known with some certainty is the actual cost of the merchandise. The other costs must be determined as accurately as possible and reflected in the final price charged. Anything less will not ensure the recovery of all operating or overhead costs, let alone the anticipated profit.

PRESCRIPTION PRICE DETERMINATION: A COST-RECOVERY MODEL[1]
Historic Approaches to Prescription Pricing

The community pharmacist is both a health-care professional and a businessperson. This dichotomous role presents a dilemma in determining adequate, reasonable remuneration.

Traditionally, pharmacists were identified with a product—prescription medication. Deriving revenue was therefore a simple matter, since it was tied directly to the product. Indeed, the revenue collected represented a portion for the cost of the product and a portion for overhead expense, which included professional income and profit.

Over the years, the mechanisms used in determining prescription prices have been erratic. In the United States, for example, drug catalogues were in circulation as early as the 1760s, but the prices of products were not listed until 1828.[2] The 1828 catalogue was the result of three years of deliberations by several committees. Published under the title *Catalogue of the Materia Medica and of the Pharmaceutical Preparations with the Uniform Prices of the*

Massachusetts College of Pharmacy, it represents the first known attempt in North America to establish a uniform dispensing fee for prescription drugs on the basis of agreement by an association of pharmacists. This fee was to be added to the cost of ingredients.

Pharmacies were fairly quiet about their fees until 1908, at which time the National Association of Retail Druggists, aided by F. W. Nitardy, published a *Prescription Pricing Schedule*, which "called for a charge for the ingredients plus a charge equal to the cost of the ingredients."[3] It was believed that doubling the cost of ingredients for an average prescription would derive enough revenue to cover the cost of maintaining the prescription department, the pharmacist's salary, and a profit consistent with "respectability."

Two basic concepts emerged from this first organized approach to pricing: that a prescription was an article of merchandise, and that it was to be priced relative to its cost. It appears that this philosophy sparked further investigation and other methods of determining prescription prices. Both McEvilla[4] and Myers[5] have examined the historical beginnings of prescription pricing, tracing its evolution from a markup system to calculating a dispensing fee.

The major change in philosophy occurred in the early 1950s. As pharmacists became more sophisticated in their practice, moving from the compounding of prescriptions to the use of an ever-increasing range of manufactured dosage forms, their methods of pricing prescriptions started to reflect this change. Professor Swinyard of the University of Utah developed the "computation system," which involved calculating the price of each prescription "on the basis of the cost of material and the time required for filling."[6] The system was considered exact and fair, but it proved to have a disadvantage in that individual pharmacists did not dispense prescriptions at a uniform pace. With standardized dispensing times, the method became one of computing cost plus a flat rate for dispensing. The flat rates were simply taken from a predetermined list based on the quantity and type of preparation dispensed.

The computation system was significant in that it recognized the different cost factors involved in prescription-price determination. Swinyard identified these as the cost of material, container, and service. Thus, each pharmacy could set its own fee on the basis of its overhead, salary expense, and "professional skill rendered the patient."

A further refinement was described by H.J. Fuller in a 1957 report.[7] Most of the methods examined added a fixed gross margin to the cost of ingredients, then added in the cost of a container. To arrive at a final price, a dispensing fee was also added. Fuller observed that this method was unsound from a cost-accounting perspective.

At about the same time, Professor S.B. Jeffries of the Brooklyn College of Pharmacy identified the cost factors involved in pricing a prescription as the ingredients, the container, labor, and overhead. Jeffries defined the first three of these as variable costs and the last as a fixed cost (fixed for at least a certain period of time). A dispensing fee was added to these four costs.

The problem with such pricing methods was the determination of the cost of overhead. Fuller handled this by defining overhead as all expenses related to the pharmacy department (excluding materials and labor) for a specified period of time. He suggested dividing this total overhead amount by the total number of prescription transactions, to arrive at a standard overhead cost per transaction. This approach is reasonable since, in the long run, *all* costs must be recovered before any profit can be made. For an accurate determination of the dispensary's total overhead, however, the pharmacy's financial record-keeping must be organized in such a way that a proper and valid allocation of the store's overhead costs is made to the prescription department.

Today, with computerization of both the front store and the dispensary, this calculation is more likely to produce accurate results than could be obtained in the late '50s.

What set Fuller's method apart from the others was his philosophy for using a professional, or dispensing, fee, as follows:

- A prescription is not an article of trade, capable of being bought and sold by anyone.

- The services rendered by the pharmacist in dispensing and/or compounding a prescription are of a professional nature, requiring specialized knowledge and judgment and, therefore, the reward he gets for these services is a fee.

- The professional services rendered by the pharmacist are not, and never have been, a function of the cost of ingredients used.[8]

In 1962, R.E. Abrams distilled this approach to dispensing-fee determination: "The utilization of a percentage markup is an admission that the final price of a prescription is a function of the cost of the product. It is not and should not be. The ultimate consumer fee should be, in all fairness, related to the professional services rendered and the costs involved in making these services available."[9]

He further pointed out that, calculated properly, the fee is designed to meet all operating expenses and provide a reasonable return to the pharmacist. Therefore, each prescription, regardless of the costs of its ingredients, would bear the same charge for the professional services rendered, be based on each pharmacist's actual costs, and, probably, be competitive within most communities.

In an attempt to standardize a procedure for identifying a standard fee per prescription, Abrams put forward the following formula:

$$\frac{\left(\text{prescription sales as a \% of total sales}\right) \times \left[\begin{array}{c}\text{total pharmacy expenses}\\ \text{[excluding proprietor's salary]}\end{array}\right] + \text{proprietor's salary}}{\text{number of prescriptions dispensed in the year.}}$$

This was the first attempt at standardizing the method of allocation of expenses to the prescription department. This method, by first taking out the proprietor's (i.e., the pharmacist-owner's) salary and then putting it back in, is sound only if the ratio of prescription sales to total sales is very high. If this ratio is low, the cost of dispensing calculated in this manner will be disproportionately high, as the costs are spread over a relatively low number of prescriptions. Therefore, Fuller modified Abram's formula by not putting back the proprietor's salary, but adding a direct labor charge, which he originally set at $0.50 per transaction plus an arbitrary amount for net profit. (Abrams later added an amount for net profit to his formula as well.) The Fuller formula is:

$$\frac{\left(\text{prescription sales as a \% of total sales}\right) \times \left[\begin{array}{c}\text{total expenses}\\ \text{[excluding}\\ \text{proprietor's salary]}\end{array}\right] + \text{direct labor cost} + \text{net profit}}{\text{number of prescriptions dispensed in the year.}}$$

If similar data are applied to each formula, the resulting fee is somewhat different. Nevertheless, the value of these formulae is the breakthrough in thinking that they represent and the fact that they establish useful criteria for the calculation of a professional fee that does not take into account the cost of ingredients. They also recognized that overhead costs should be distributed equally over all prescriptions dispensed. The use of a standard overhead cost per transaction is supported by the fact that, on average:

- the time it takes to dispense each prescription is almost equal;

- the service provided with each prescription is almost equal;

- the responsibility assumed for dispensing each prescription is equal;

- the liability assumed for dispensing each prescription is equal.

The flaw in Fuller's approach is the arbitrariness with which the labor cost and the amount for net profit are assigned in his formula. These values can in fact be calculated to reflect the actual costs of labor and a legitimate return on investment. Calculation of dispensing fees must recognize the costs involved in stocking a basic inventory of prescription medication and the expense of a pharmacist's salary, which is incurred throughout the pharmacy's opening hours—whether prescriptions are being dispensed or not. The model described in the following section addresses these issues.

Dispensing-Cost Identification

As private and government insurance carriers became involved in paying claims on behalf of their subscribers, pressures to restrain prescription prices grew. The PARCOST (Prescriptions at Reasonable Cost) Program in Ontario was based in part on setting maximum professional (or dispensing) fees while allowing individual pharmacies to charge less than the negotiated maximum if they so wished.[10] It thus became critical for pharmacists to be able to accurately determine and document their dispensing costs, if only to verify that the maximum allowable fees under the program would compensate them adequately. In April 1971 the Ontario Pharmacists' Association (OPA) circulated an information letter explaining how to calculate the direct and indirect costs of dispensing, enclosing a special form for the purpose. To a large extent, the OPA's recommended method of calculation in itself legitimized the fact that the dispensing function could be broken down into fixed (direct) and variable (indirect) costs and that these costs would be different for each pharmacy operation.

The OPA's calculations are made by isolating the cost factors in the dispensing function, then assigning costs to them, as shown in Figure 14.1 (p. 318) (based on the amounts in the income statement in Figure 14.2, p. 319). This cost-recovery model also includes a cost factor, to allow for a return on investment in prescription-drug inventory, under the category "opportunity cost."

Professional labor cost is directly attributable to the dispensing function. It includes a pharmacist's salary for each hour the pharmacy is open. In our example, in Figure 14.1 (p. 318), the pharmacy is open 74 hours per week and employs one full-time pharmacist (40 hours per week), in addition to the pharmacist-owner. The pharmacist's hourly rate is as follows:

$$\frac{\$54,080}{40 \text{ hours} \times 52 \text{ weeks}} = \$26 \text{ per hour.}$$

for a total pharmacists' salary cost of 74 hours × 52 weeks × $26 = $100,048 (as represented in Figure 14.1, p. 318 by the pharmacist's full salary and a portion of the pharmacist-owner's salary—$54,080 + $45,968). Also included are the labor costs connected with any additional personnel working in the pharmacy department on a full-time or part-time basis. In our example, there is one pharmacy assistant. The other direct costs are the labels, containers, and forms required in the dispensing process.

The operational costs of the pharmacy department—the indirect costs—are represented by that portion of the pharmacy's total expenses (excluding salaries) that is attributable to the dispensary. For this discussion, it appears that the most appropriate way to allocate occupancy costs is on the basis of the relationship of prescription sales to total sales. Although certain other expenses should be allocated either according to different criteria (e.g., relative net investment) or entirely to the dispensary (e.g., professional licences, professional liability insurance), we have based the allocation of operational costs exclusively on relative sales, for the sake of convenience. Therefore, since prescription sales represent 54.2 percent of total sales, we have calculated the operational costs of the pharmacy department at 54.2 percent of total pharmacy costs.

Figure 14.1   Cost-Recovery Model
Professional-Fee Calculation

		Costs	Percentage of Total Costs
1.	Professional Labor Cost (Direct Cost)		
	Pharmacist:		
	$26/hr × 40 hrs × 52 wks =	$ 54,080	
	Pharmacist-owner:		
	$26/hr × (74 − 40 = 34 hrs) × 52 wks =	45,968	
	Pharmacy assistant:		
	$12/hr × 40 hrs × 52 wks =	24,960	
	Labels, containers, etc.: $0.50 × 45,703 =	22,851	
	Total Direct Cost	$ 147,859	44.2%
2.	Operational Costs of Pharmacy Department (Indirect Costs)		
	Rent	$ 51,311	
	Heat, light, power	12,542	
	Accounting, legal, professional fees	9,006	
	Taxes and licences	9,415	
	Insurance	5,478	
	Interest paid	8,708	
	Repairs	7,274	
	Delivery	4,741	
	Advertising	26,156	
	Depreciation	16,947	
	Bad debts	1,367	
	Telephone	4,516	
	Miscellaneous	102,615	
		$260,076	
	Total Indirect Cost ($260,076 × 54.2%)	$140,961	42.1%
3.	Opportunity Cost		
	Prescription inventory $80,200 × 35% =	28,070	8.4%
4.	General and Administrative Cost of Pharmacy Department (54.2% of the portion of proprietor's salary earned as manager)		
	$(1.5 × \$26/hr) × (50 − 34 = 16 \text{ hrs}) × 52 \text{ wks} × 54.2\%$ =	$ 17,587	5.3%
5.	Total Costs (1. + 2. + 3. + 4.)	$334,447	100.0%
6.	Cost to Dispense One Prescription		

$$\frac{\text{Total costs}}{\text{Number of prescriptions dispensed}} = \frac{\$334,477}{45,703} = \$7.31, \text{ rounded to } \$7.35$$

Figure 14.2   Income Statement
Hypothetical Pharmacy Limited

Sales		$2,164,553
Prescription	$1,173,543	
Other	991,010	
Cost of Goods Sold		1,524,897
Gross Margin		639,656
Expenses		
Pharmacist-owner's salary	$ 80,920*	
Pharmacist's salary	54,080	
Other salaries (including pharmacy assistant)	190,782	
Rent	51,311	
Heat, light, power	12,542	
Accounting, legal, professional fees	9,006	
Taxes and licences	9,415	
Insurance	5,478	
Interest paid	8,708	
Repairs	7,274	
Delivery	4,741	
Advertising	26,156	
Depreciation	16,947	
Bad debts	1,367	
Telephone	4,516	
Miscellaneous	102,615	
Total expenses		585,858
Profit (before tax)		$ 53,798

Other Pertinent Information
   Total number of prescriptions dispensed annually:
   (approximately 125/day)   45,703
   Hours open per week: Mon.-Fri.   5 × 12 = 60
                                  Sat.   1 × 9 = 9
                                  Sun.   1 × 5 = 5
                                                          ___
                                                           74

   Total hours worked per week by
      pharmacist-owner: 50
   Prescription inventory value: $ 80,200

* The pharmacist-owner's salary breaks down as follows: $45,968 as a pharmacist, $34,952 as manager, part of which is attributable to the dispensary.

The calculation of indirect costs for the purpose of professional-fee calculation should be a simple matter for pharmacy owners who insist that monthly financial reports reflect the activities of the front store and dispensary separately.

Opportunity costs are the dollar costs involved in maintaining an inventory of prescription drugs, viewed as a return for risk on invested capital. In other words, if these dollars were not invested in prescription inventory, they could be invested elsewhere to earn a return commensurate with the risk; the opportunity cost factor in the model compensates for that foregone return. (Another way to interpret opportunity cost is as profit. Contrary to popular belief, businesspeople are not entitled to a profit; profit is the financial reward for effective management of resources or assets. This return on investment, then, is justified on the basis of capital invested at risk and of efficient management of that investment.) The rate is arbitrary, but it must be in line with alternative opportunities for return on investment in the marketplace, modified to reflect the greater risk associated with investment in a business enterprise. We have chosen a rate of 35 percent in our example, which is considered an acceptable rate of return for the risk of investment in prescription inventory among community pharmacies at present.

The general and administrative costs of the pharmacy department are the management time invested in administering this area. For example, a typical pharmacy employs two pharmacists, an employer or manager (often the pharmacist-owner) and an employee or staff pharmacist. During the week, the manager or owner divides his or her time between dispensing and administrative or management tasks. It is this latter function that represents the base from which the pharmacy department's general and administrative cost is calculated. To be fair, only that portion of the manager's salary attributable to dispensary administration can be charged to this category. This portion can be calculated either on the basis of time or as a proportion of prescription sales to total sales (we have followed the second option in our example). Note that the remuneration for management activities is calculated at a higher rate (150 percent of the pharmacist's rate of pay, in our example) to compensate for effective management and increased responsibility.

This general and administrative cost category may also be viewed as representing a profit, earned on the basis of efficient purchasing, inventory control, and cost control (including bulk-purchase savings, taking cash discounts on accounts payable, and collecting receivables on time, thus preventing a drain on working capital and possibly saving interest on borrowed funds). The difference that usually exists between the actual acquisition cost of prescription inventory and "published costs" in government benefit lists and formularies is explained by the purchasing advantage that pharmacies are able to achieve with suppliers. This is one aspect of effective management that is being recognized in the general and administrative cost category. The profit represented here should certainly not be construed as a markup based on the cost of ingredients, or arbitrarily added to it as an entitlement.

All the costs we have described are finally totaled to reflect the dollar amount expended in operating the dispensary for a given period of time. The fee or "burden rate" per prescription is then calculated by dividing the total costs by the number of prescriptions dispensed during the period. The result is the average cost of dispensing a prescription. This model can be applied either on the basis of historical data for purposes of financial assessment or on the basis of forecasted costs in financial planning for a future period of time.

The professional fee determined for any particular pharmacy must be reviewed periodically, to ensure that it continues to reflect current costs. This can be accomplished only by recalculating the fee at regular intervals, perhaps annually or semi-annually. Possibly the most reasonable approach to fee review would be to identify a cyclical period whose end point coincides with a change in costs—for example, when employees are due for performance reviews and labor costs are anticipated to rise, or when overhead costs are expected to increase because of increasing rent or utility costs.

It is also useful to monitor the proportion of each of the cost categories relative to the total fee. For example, in our professional-fee calculation in Figure 14.1 (p. 318), direct costs account for 44.2 percent of total costs; indirect costs, 42.1 percent; opportunity cost, 8.4 percent; and general and administrative costs, 5.3 percent. In this way it can be demonstrated that the majority of the professional fee goes to remunerate labor (direct costs and administrative costs are 49.5 percent of the total) and overhead (42.1 percent of the total). Inventory overhead costs represent only 8.4 percent of the total.

The cost-recovery model we have just described has been criticized by some pharmacists, who, under agreement with their provincial government, add a markup of approximately 10 to 15 percent of the cost of ingredients, in addition to the dispensing fee. These pharmacists argue that when the cost of the ingredients in a prescription is already high, the professional fee calculated using the cost-recovery model appears too small in relation to the total cost of the prescription, and must therefore represent too small a gross margin. (It should be noted that during the '80s the cost of prescription drugs did indeed rise rapidly, outstripping the rate of increase of overhead-cost components in the professional fee, and resulting in lower gross margins than were typical for prescription products in the past.) Another objection arises in cases where pharmacies are required to pay a percentage of their sales for rent. This percentage of sales is sometimes equal to or even greater than the percentage of the total cost of the prescription represented by the dispensing fee, on prescriptions whose ingredients are costly. In such cases the pharmacy is dispensing prescriptions at a loss.

These perceived problems, although they appear to be related to the cost of the prescription ingredients, are really not a function of the product or its cost. In the first instance, the professional fee may appear to be small in dollars, but the method by which it is calculated takes into account the service, responsibility, and liability of the pharmacist and remunerats him or her equitably. These are not, after all, functions of the ingredient cost. Neither is the rent-related dilemma associated with ingredient cost: it is a problem rooted in lease negotiation and, although an important cost consideration, it should not be confused with the process of professional-fee calculation. Notwithstanding the practical financial implications for the pharmacy, the situation in which landlords in effect share in one's business must be questioned seriously, particularly from the perspective that, in pharmacy, the situation amounts to a form of profiteering from illness.

Inventory costs are taken into account in calculating a professional fee by applying the concept of return on investment. If the inventory investment—and with it the element of risk—increases, the rate of return should be increased to reflect these changes. It thus becomes critical that inventory be monitored periodically—perhaps monthly—to track increases in investment and adjust the fee accordingly.

It should be stressed that if a markup-on-cost pricing system is selected for prescriptions, the cost of the product will be recovered only if and when it is dispensed and paid for. A markup on cost makes no provision for earning a return on the inventory that remains on the shelf. The cost-recovery model, however, provides for a return on investment on the average value of prescription inventory and amortizes it equally over all prescriptions dispensed and paid for. Thus, the entire inventory generates a return.

In summary, the dispensing fee—currently more accurately referred to as the professional fee—in prescription pricing has historically been determined either as a percentage of the cost of ingredients or as a distinct entity representing the cost of the service component in dispensing. Recently, the latter approach has found favor among pharmacists, as it attempts to identify and separate the professional functions from the commercial ones. It also allows the pharmacist to charge all clients fairly and equally for the service provided, and, on average, the service provided to each client is the same. Furthermore, since the professional fee is based on the total number of prescriptions dispensed, the cost of the service is amortized and passed along equally to its users. In short, each user is charged an equal fee for the accessible, convenient, and responsible pharmacy services provided by the pharmacist, who, in turn, is able to recover the costs involved in providing those services.

CHARGING FOR MEDICATION MANAGEMENT, DISEASE MANAGEMENT, AND COGNITIVE SERVICES

Market Changes[11]

Pharmacy practice has changed dramatically during the decade of the '90s and continues to do so at a seemingly even faster pace. In part, this has come about from the growth in third-party plans that pay for prescription medication and the resulting pressure to reduce the cost paid out to pharmacies/pharmacists. Changes are also occurring in the ownership of practices, from independent entrepreneurs to franchises and corporate chains, bringing greater pressure to apply appropriate management principles for survival and growth. Another change is occurring in the role of the pharmacist, with increasing emphasis on pharmaceutical service and decreasing attention to the distribution or dispensing function. This role is focused on the patient and the services that pharmacists can provide with respect to intelligent and appropriate drug use.

Thus the '90s have required a re-evaluation of business strategies and practices, with managers and owners struggling to find new ways of remaining competitive while controling costs and adding new services. It is estimated that in Canada 80 percent of prescription medications are paid for by a combination of public and private insurance programs. This has created a situation wherein convenience and additional services have replaced the price of a prescription as reasons to patronize a particular pharmacy. These factors have become the "value added" to the core service of the pharmacist, the core service being the distributing or dispensing function.

The concept of value clearly is a perception of the customer and becomes part of a pharmacy's customer service and its key to survival. While retail organizations believe they offer customer service, many tend to forget that you cannot have customer service without the customer. Further, customer service, or health care, is produced and consumed at the same time. Its consumption offers immediate feedback as to its understanding or appropriateness, and thus it can be modified instantly to meet customer demand. It is neither uniform nor predictable, but must be tailored for each consumer, comprising basic and similar components of information, knowledge, care, and compassion. The pharmacist's dilemma is how to charge for this added package of values.

Value-Added Services

During the '60s, North American society valued disposable products. Mass produced, widely available, and inexpensive, these "disposables" were not intended for repeated or long use. As energy-dependent resources came into short supply in the '70s, due to the unavailability of oil, North Americans changed their attitudes toward disposable products: they wanted quality-made, long-lasting products, and they were prepared to pay for them.

This change in the value system spilled over into the retail sector, and with the recession of the late '80s came expectations of greater value from retailers, in terms of both quality and service. Today, we accept the concept of products that are slightly more costly, use them longer, and even recycle some of them. Consumers look for and expect good value. Retailers have responded by providing consumers with the choice of a full-service/full-price specialty retailer or a low-price/low-service discounter. Those retailers who did not re-examine and reposition their business have, by and large, disappeared, because of lost market share, revenue, and profits. This evolution in retail practice has forced pharmacists to assess the services they provide. Observers of the profession refer to it as a change of role, with a focus on the patient. The days of differentiating one's product offering solely on the basis of price are gone. Service must now be factored into the equation.

Customers purchase products and services to address a specific need or solve a particular problem, and pharmacists must satisfy those expectations. This requires an understanding of each category of customer who buys prescription services; cash paying, third-party insurer, and pharmacy-benefit manager. Value-added services help to achieve this by providing an enhanced product that reflects a cluster of characteristics. The end point is that a total product—physical product plus services—is the expected norm. Anything less at the price charged is now unacceptable to the customer, and if the consumer is not willing to pay for the product, it has no value.

Value-Based Pricing

The reality of operating a business is that in order to generate a profit, revenues must exceed costs. Further, prices should reflect the perceived value of the product or service. M.T. Rupp argues that "third-party payers do not understand what pharmacist services they are paying for, let alone how they might benefit from them."[12] It is necessary, then, for pharmacists to demonstrate their value, based on service outcomes to everyone who wishes to receive them.

For the most part, price determination is based on a cost-plus approach; thus, the cost recovery model used to determine dispensing fees may have some utility as an approach to pricing medication management services. It must be remembered that costs do not determine prices, as the function of costs in setting prices is to determine the profit consequences of alternative prices.[13] Key to the consideration of costs, however, is a clear identification of the professional tasks, overhead, and time involved in producing and delivering the service. This will facilitate the emergence of a clearer definition of the pharmacist's role, indicating how it differs from the role of other health providers. This in itself gives value to the pharmacist's services and highlights their need.

Toward Pricing of Pharmacist's Service

While, traditionally, dispensing has generated revenue through a fee-for-service mechanism, it is not without its difficulties. It provides no reward for cognitive services, it is volume driven, it is essentially piece work, and it places little value on services not related to a distributive function.

An alternative that has not been a great success is the concept of capitation. "Capitation is a pricing strategy that can be offered to (employer clients) by pharmacy benefit managers and other managed care organizations that provide pharmacy benefits."[14] Capitation can also be offered by pharmacies that have the opportunity or ability to organize groups, called rostering, of potential medication users. This concept has its benefits and risks.

Among the benefits are:

* the capping of payer's budgets, determined by defining how much it will pay per capita for services for a defined period;

* freedom of choice of patients to register with a provider;

* payment is based on the number of patients registered, not the number of services performed, which offers an opportunity to provide as few or as many services as are needed per patient;

* valuing the pharmacist as a member of the health-care team.

Among the risks are:

* underestimating the capitation fee, thus generating less than adequate operating revenue;

* having more "problem patients" than healthy ones, thus having to provide a disproportionate level of service to each;

* assuming an incorrect drug utilization rate and not being able to control total drug costs.

One approach to making the situation more equitable is having the payer agree to share the risks.

Capitation does offer an opportunity to practise somewhat free of solely a distributive function, to observe outcomes from continuity of care, and to document and assess the services provided. It is this last issue, documentation, that is believed to be the key to service, recognition, and reimbursement for the pharmacist.

Recent studies of pharmacist interventions intended to prevent inappropriate drug use report that pharmacists will fulfil this function and document it if they are rewarded for doing so.[15] Further, a favorable benefit-to-cost ratio often results from these interventions; the value of intervention being the cost of medical care avoided.[16]

In Canada, the province of Québec has been the pioneer, establishing a precedent in charging for non-distributive services. Called a "pharmaceutical opinion," it is a "judgment by the pharmacist concerning the therapeutic value of one drug or a drug regimen, as a result of the analysis of a patient profile."[17] Pharmacists can request payment for a pharmaceutical opinion from the government-paid prescription plan. To be eligible, the pharmacist must include at least one prescribed drug covered by the plan. The key to reimbursement is a "recommendation that concerns the patient and either modifies or interrupts the prescribed treatment."[17]

Problems of reimbursement for medication-management service remain the question of the value-added system; the documentation and price charged must still be resolved to the satisfaction of the payer, the provider, and the regulatory body.

SUMMARY

Determining price for products or services is not a straightforward exercise. The process must consider objectives, productivity, and costs. Recognition of costs in pricing pharmaceutical services is critical to the longevity of the practice and thus should not be overlooked. Regardless of the method selected to determine pricing, a price-quality relationship must be established, and it must provide consumers with both a perceived and real value added.

References

1. Segal, H.J. "Prescription Pricing: Financial Considerations." Invited paper, presented at the Annual Meeting of the Association of Faculties of Pharmacy Research. Halifax, Nova Scotia, 27 May 1985.

2. Griffenhagen, G. "Fair Trade in 1828." *Journal of the American Pharmaceutical Association* 20 (March 1959): 156.

3. Nitardy, F.W. "Prescription Pricing Schedule." *NARD Notes* 6 (30 July 1908): 17.

4. McEvilla, J.D. "Pharmacy and the Professional Fee in Theory and Practice." *Journal of the American Pharmaceutical Association* NS2(9) (September 1962): 520.

5. Myers, M.J. "Professional Fee: Renaissance or Innovation?" *Journal of the American Pharmaceutical Association* NS8(12) (December 1968): 628.

6. "Rx Pricing by Computation Plus Flat Rate Favoured by Educator." *Drug Topics*, 2 January 1950.

7. Fuller, H.J. "Prescription Pricing Methods." *Canadian Pharmaceutical Journal* 90(2) (February 1957): 42.

8. Fuller, H.J. "The New Philosophy of Professional Fees." *American Professional Pharmacist* 26(8) (August 1960): 503.

9. Abrams, R.E. *Focus on Pharmacy.* Detroit: Wayne State University College of Pharmacy, March 1962.

10. Segal, H.J. "PARCOST: Its Origins, Mechanics, and Impact." *Medical Marketing and Medica* 8(8) (August 1973): 11.

11. Shepherd, M.A. "Pharmaceutical Care: Adding Value to the Future." *American Pharmacy* NS31(4) (April 1991): 55.

12. Rupp, M.T. "Strategies for Reimbursement." *American Pharmacy* NS32(4) (April 1992): 79.

13. Wentz, T.E. "Realism in Pricing Analysis." *Journal of Marketing* 30 (April 1966): 26.

14. Wentz, T.E. "Capitation." *Drug Topics* 39(2) (23 January 1995): 40.

15. McCormack, J., Reinhardt, G., Hastings, J., and McGuirt, R. "Arkansas Study Shows Pharmacists Who Get Paid Document More Interventions." *NARD Journal* (March 1996): 39.

16. Dobie, R.L., and Rascati, K.L. "Documenting the Value of Pharmacist Interventions." *American Pharmacy* NS34(5) (May 1994): 50.

17. Poirier, S. "Reimbursement of Cognitive Services: Québec's Experience." *American Pharmacy* NS32(5) (May 1992): 56.

15

RISK MANAGEMENT

INTRODUCTION

In addition to the difficulties in effectively operating a business, there are identifiable risks in running a business. Some of them are fire, flood, vandalism, disability, and death. Such occurrences can overwhelm even the best-managed business. There are various approaches to risk management.

One definition of risk management is "the identification, analysis and economic control of those risks which can threaten the assets or earning capacity of an enterprise."[1] In this definition the risks must be identified so that we can determine if further examination of the risk is needed. This requires that we look at a large number of potential risks and analyze each for its impact on the business. Some risks will be substantial and immediate, others will be important but very unlikely, and many will be unimportant but deserve consideration. In devising ways of dealing with the risk, the key element is to balance the cost of the action against the potential for damage. If there is a small risk of a potential loss of $100, there is little point in preventive measures that cost $200 or insurance of $50 per year.

This approach is emphasized as there is a tendency to look to insurance as the only method of dealing with risk. While insurance is still the preferred method, it needs to be used wisely and only where it is the most economical approach.

Sometimes risk can be avoided by taking action, such as installing a sprinkler system. Another approach might be to have the building owner assume some of the risks for fire or natural disaster. If, in the judgment of the manager, the risk is small, one could assume the risk and bear the cost. In Alberta, hospitals as a group assume the risk for fire, on the assumption that this approach is less costly than insurance. Most commonly, risk is shared, and this is realized through insurance. The degree of risk associated with loss by fire or the elements can be greatly reduced by insurance. Insurance is available to protect real estate, saleable assets, and receivables; it can even provide for a continuation of income in the event that the business is temporarily closed as a result of fire, damage by the elements, or some form of impact.

ESSENTIAL BUSINESS INSURANCE
Insuring Assets

The major part of a pharmacy owner's investment in a practice is its fixed assets (land, building, fixtures, and equipment) and its inventory. Each of these assets can be insured for its replacement value by what is known as simply "replacement insurance."

If you own the building that houses the pharmacy, replacement insurance is essential. It will provide the full replacement value of the building (i.e., the cost of rebuilding, which may be more or less than the current market value of the building) in the event that it is destroyed: the insured does not have to settle for the depreciated value of the building at the time of the loss. In the normal course of events, a building will depreciate, for accounting purposes, at the rate of 5 percent per year. After 20 years, it is assumed to have depreciated to a value of zero. However, a loss requires replacement of the building, which, despite depreciation, was adequate for the operation of the business. Replacement insurance is therefore required to provide the necessary capital in the event of loss. Replacement insurance requires that the building be insured to the replacement value.

Inventory is the major asset of a pharmacy. An inventory of $100,000 destroyed by fire must be replaced if the pharmacist is to continue in business. Without replacement insurance, the $100,000 might have to be borrowed, placing the pharmacist in a difficult financial situation.

Furniture, fixtures, and equipment are the means by which a pharmacist displays inventory, dispenses efficienly, facilitates proper record keeping (in recent times, by computer), and generally enhances the pharmacy's ability to provide a range of services. In short, the pharmacist would be unable to function without furniture, fixtures, and equipment. How much are these assets worth? A rule of thumb says $20 per square foot, at the very least. Hence, in a pharmacy that occupies 5,000 square feet, furniture, fixtures, and equipment will be worth at least $100,000. For accounting purposes, these assets depreciate at 10 percent per year, so that in ten years, at "book value," they are worth nothing. In reality, however, they are still functional and, if destroyed, must be replaced. Once again, replacement insurance protects the pharmacist from this expenditure.

Cash and valuables (bonds and other important papers) are similarly insured and, if lost or stolen, will be replaced at insured value and policy limits would apply. Notwithstanding the above, the pharmacy owner should recognize that while it is hazardous to underinsure, it is wasteful to overinsure.

Insurance policies have a "co-insurance" clause, which applies to a partial loss. It states that you must insure your building, stock, equipment, and fixtures to the agreed amount, normally 80 or 90 percent of their value. If your building is insured to the co-insurance amount and you suffer a partial loss (this is the normal situation), the insurance company will fully cover the loss. If your insurance is less than the co-insurance clause amount and you suffer a partial loss, you will become a co-insurer of the loss and the insurance company will pay only a portion of the loss. It is important that you discuss the co-insurance clause with your insurance agent or broker to fully understand the policy limits.

SECURITY

Community pharmacies have been increasingly victimized by burglary. "Break and enter" (commonly referred to as B&E) claims have reached an alarming level. The prime targets for theft in pharmacies are narcotic drugs, cigarettes, and postage stamps.

Insurance companies now require that pharmacies be protected against robbery with "adequate security,"which implies alarm systems in addition to reliable double locks on front and back entrances. Failure to provide adequate security could result in an inability to secure "all risk" insurance coverage. The implementation of various security measures has reduced but not eliminated the incidence of burglary among community pharmacies. Your insurance professional should be able to advise you on the type of system that will qualify as adequate security from the insurance company's point of view.

Business Interruption Insurance

In the event of fire or other insured peril—for example, sewer backup, severe hailstorm, or impact by a vehicle—the pharmacy may be unable to render services for periods ranging from a few days to several months. No income will be generated, but interest on loans will accumulate, taxes will continue, and creditors will insist on being paid. How can the pharmacist meet these continuing obligations with no income? The simple answer is business interruption insurance. This type of insurance is based sometimes on earned profit, but more often on gross margin. If, for example, annual sales are $1 million and gross margin is 30 percent, the gross margin for the year will be $300,000. The pharmacist and the insurance professional agree that even in a major catastrophe the pharmacy should be able to resume operations in six months or less. Therefore, a business interruption insurance policy valued at half the annual gross margin—$150,000—is purchased. This protection will allow the pharmacist, during the period when the pharmacy is closed, to pay:

- interest on loans;
- taxes;
- debts to creditors;
- his or her own salary;
- the salaries of key staff members, to prevent them from taking jobs elsewhere.

Failure to secure business interruption insurance is the most common reason why pharmacies that experience a major catastrophe never reopen.

Comprehensive General Liability and Shop Malpractice Insurance

It is important that you investigate and understand the nature of the coverage offered under comprehensive general liability and shop malpractice insurance. (Note that the term "comprehensive general liability" is now gaining favor in the insurance industry.) Ensure that both the corporation as an entity and all its employees, full-time, part-time, and occasional, are covered for legal liability and shop malpractice, for cases such as the following:

- an alleged dispensing error;

- alleged misinformation or insufficiency of information: for example, an allegation that a patient became pregnant because the pharmacist failed to make clear that the inert tablets in the birth-control prescription were to be taken faithfully for seven days, in addition to the 21 active-ingredient tablets;

- an incorrect sale: for example, selling oil of wintergreen when castor oil was requested;

- injury caused by an employee-owned vehicle when used on company business.

In other contexts, this type of coverage may be referred to as a third-party liability insurance or casualty insurance, which are defined as protection against financial loss arising out of injury to persons or out of damage, loss, or destruction of property caused by negligent, fraudulent, or criminal acts. (The term "casualty insurance" does not normally appear in a "fire and all-risk" certificate of insurance: it is commonly used in automobile insurance contracts and in policies for the types of business where "casualty" damage is likely to occur.)

It should be noted that in pharmacy, as in other health-related professions, there is ultimately no form of malpractice insurance that can fully protect the practice. Some cases of malpractice may be ruled by professional peers to be so gross as to disqualify the practitioner and thus force the business to close.

PURCHASING INSURANCE

All necessary insurance coverage should be purchased upon setting up or taking over a practice. Most pharmacists will need to borrow a considerable amount of money to launch a pharmacy. The lending institution will require a copy of the insurance contract, not only to verify that its investment will be protected, but also to ensure that it is named as the first loss payable up to the amount of the loan.

The pharmacy owner should purchase insurance from a reputable firm with competitive prices and a proven record of satisfactory claims settlement. Locate a firm that provides advice and quotes premium rates and comparisons; above all, an agent should not only understand pharmacy practice as a business, but also be trustworthy and communicative. Note that a qualified insurance professional can be either an agent or a broker. An agent is essentially a sales and service representative for a particular insurance company. A broker, on the other hand, is not tied to one company but acts on a freelance basis and monitors the policies offered by many companies. A broker may be able to locate the particular policy that best suits a client's needs. Insurance is a complex subject and the new pharmacy owner cannot expect to be an expert in its various terms, conditions, and costs. The following guidelines will assist the pharmacist in choosing a reliable insurance professional:

- *information:* Ask the insurance professional to fully explain the suggested coverage and the company's claims procedures. Be certain to ask what risks are not covered in your contract. Too often, policyholders with inadmissible claims find themselves helplessly arguing, "I thought I was covered." The pharmacist should ensure that the insurance covers any theft of money and securities, whether on the way to the bank, robbery of the pharmacy, or employee fraud.

- *service:* Select an insurance professional who represents a company (or companies) with a proven track record in fair and prompt claims settlement, ready availability of information, and knowledgeability in the full range of adjustment problems that might arise.

- *price:* Obtain quotes from several companies; your selection should be not necessarily the lowest quote but the one that best addresses your needs and offers the most satisfactory and clear presentation of the coverage.

Insist that the insurance professional review your coverage annually, at the very least. Consider the following example: at a 3 percent annual rate of inflation, a pharmacy's inventory, as listed in the original policy, will have increased in value at least 30 percent in ten years; in addition, the pharmacy may have opted to expand and carry a larger base of inventory. In other words, without proper monitoring and discussion, inventory could reach a replacement value of $200,000 during the time that premiums are being paid faithfully on a policy providing protection for only $100,000. Because the owner and insurance professional have not reviewed events as they occurred, a claim for $200,000 will not be honored, since the increased value of the inventory is not reflected in the policy.

Interprovincial Pharmacy Group Insurance Program

A special insurance plan for community pharmacies is offered through the Interprovincial Pharmacy Group Insurance Program. The plan is available in seven provinces: British Columbia, Alberta, Saskatchewan, Manitoba, New Brunswick, Newfoundland, and Prince Edward Island, sponsored by provincial pharmacy associations. The insurance agent and the pharmacist complete a worksheet that sets out the basic rates per $1,000 of coverage for (1) the building, and (2) "other," including inventory, fixtures, the unamortized value of lease improvements, and accounts receivable. The basic rates vary, depending on the construction of the building (masonry vs. frame) and the community in which the pharmacy is located. The rates for the building and the assets will differ, because, for example, while stock and fixtures might be destroyed in a fire, the building itself could remain essentially unharmed.

The worksheet also sets out a series of rate credits that can result in a substantial reduction of the basic rate. Credits are granted for features that put the pharmacy in a lower risk category—for example, "less than 5,000 square feet," "less than 30 years old," "one storey in height," "concrete floor," "heating standard," "electrical standard." At the time of writing, credit-adjusted rates per $1,000 in coverage could range from approximately $0.04 for the building and $0.06 for assets (masonry building, lowest-risk location, eligible for all credits) to $0.44 for the building and $0.47 for assets (non-masonry building, highest-risk location, ineligible for credits— a case unlikely to occur in actuality as almost all pharmacies would be eligible for at least some of the rate credits).

Finally, a premium is added to the calculated rate according to a "loading" factor. This relates to the quality of security in place in the pharmacy: the lower the level of security, the higher the premium will be.

The insurable values for the building and assets are supplied by the pharmacist and then multiplied by the adjusted base rates. The policy also provides for the calculation of business interruption insurance, comprehensive general liability and shop malpractice, and money and securities. The total monthly premium may be paid annually, semi-annually, or quarterly, with no penalty.

The information thus gathered is set out in detail in Figure 15.1 (p. 336). In addition to the certificate, the policyholder receives a set of "wordings," which specifies exactly what is and what is not insured.

Figure 15.1   Certificate of Insurance (Sample)

GRAIN INSURANCE AND GUARANTEE COMPANY

CERTIFICATE OF INSURANCE
INTERPROVINCIAL PHARMACY GROUP
INSURANCE PROGRAM

Policy #:   028-0000B

Insured: 000000 Alberta Ltd. o/a
                       Best Value Drug Mart
Mailing address: YOURTOWN AB TOW 1NO

Location: Main Street Mall, Yourtown, AB

Policy period: Effective 12:01 am Standard time 08/30/96 at the
                       address of the insured and continuous until cancelled.

N O T E:

This policy is amended to read that TOBACCO products in the retail area of the
pharmacy are insured for an amount not exceeding $300.00, when the pharmacy is
not open for business.

This is to certify that in consideration of the payment of the premium charged the
insured is covered for:

SECTION 1:   BUILDING(S)   0

SECTION 2:   COMMERCIAL PROPERTY
                BUSINESS INTERRUPTION   1,250,000

SECTION 3:   COMPREHENSIVE GEN. LIABILITY
                SHOP MALPRACTICE AND
                TENANT'S FIRE LEGAL LIABILITY   5,000,000

Figure 15.1   (cont'd)

SECTION 4:	MONEY AND SECURITIES	10,000
	COSTUME JEWELRY & WATCHES	5,000

LOSS PAYABLE, if any,
TO: CIBC
           Box 100
           Yourtown AB T0W 1N0
           Alberta Gaming and Liquor Commission
           50 Corriveau Ave., St. Albert AB T8N 3T5

DEDUCTIBLE: $250,000

Warranted Protection: Full to central

NOTE: The 100% Values declared in this application or as revised annually will be used in the Settlement of Loss or Damage.

EFFECTIVE: 01/01/97

Signature of Insured: _____ Phone: 123-9876

Authorized Representative: _____

Courtesy of the Grain Insurance and Guarantee Company, Winnipeg, Manitoba.

The Interprovincial Pharmacy Group Insurance Program is of particular interest because its policies are designed specifically to meet the needs of pharmacist-owners. However, various firms across the country offer equally suitable, comprehensive coverages, and pharmacists are encouraged to explore the available options in their areas. Provincial pharmacy associations can generally offer assistance in this regard.

OTHER INSURANCE APPLICABLE TO BUSINESS
Life Insurance

Life insurance is relevant in business from a number of perspectives. Consider the following types of insurance and how they might contribute to success in business.

- *"Key Person" life insurance:* The success of many businesses depends on the leadership of one key person. That person's death may cause a serious financial setback, until such time as a qualified replacement can be found. If the business owns, and is named the beneficiary of, a life insurance policy on the key person, funds will be provided to attract, educate, and train the right candidate to replace the deceased and to keep the business in operation in the interim, ensuring stability and continuity and protecting the jobs of existing staff members.

- *partnership insurance:* The death of a business partner can result in the withdrawal of his or her investment in the business. The spouse may not be interested in continuing in the business, may wish to relocate, or, in any event, may liquidate the late partner's share. Furthermore, the goodwill assets of the partner may be lost. Partnership insurance covers the financing of reorganization into a new partnership or a sole proprietorship.

  Partnership insurance usually goes hand-in-hand with a buy-sell agreement. This agreement should be drawn up by a lawyer and provide for the succession of a business in the event of a partner's death. It can specify either a value of the business or a formula to assess the value. This value is then insured by means of a life insurance policy, owned by the company, on each partner for the proportion of the business that he or she owns. The company is the beneficiary of the policy but is bound by the buy-sell agreement to transfer the funds to the deceased partner's family in return for their shares in the company. In this way, the business can proceed and money is available to purchase the shares.

Life insurance has become so sophisticated in recent years that it can virtually be tailored to meet the needs of each individual business owner. The policyholder may choose to name several beneficiaries, from family members, to the company itself, to lending institutions and other parties that may have an interest in the business. Different types of insurance (such as whole-life, term, reducing-term, and endowment insurance) are designed for different circumstances and needs: your insurance professional will be able to advise you on the terms and benefits of each. You should also explore with the agent or broker the circumstances under which insurance premiums may be tax-deductible.

Automobile Insurance

Automobile insurance is compulsory in Canada. This area of insurance is complex, both in its personal and corporate applications, and requires the pharmacist's close attention (especially if the pharmacy owns a delivery vehicle). Automobile insurance is not normally part of a "fire and all-risk" insurance package. It is important, however, and should be discussed with an expert in the field.

Long-term Disability Insurance

Disability insurance is as important as life insurance. During the course of our working lives, most of us will experience an illness or accident that will keep us out of the workforce for a period of days, months, or years. Employers generally extend two weeks' pay, meaning that, on average, the disabled employee must locate income for the balance of the period of disability. In a pharmacy practice, a six-to-eight-week disability would involve replacing the owner-manager at a cost of $4,000 to $6,000 per month. The disabled manager's salary would also have to be paid. The solution is personal-income replacement or long-term disability insurance.

As surely as fire insurance protects against loss of property, disability insurance protects against loss of income, by providing for its continuance when the loss is caused by illness or accident. Neither an owner or an employee should be without it, because to neglect this area of protection is to court financial disaster. Young pharmacists are encouraged to obtain disability insurance at a low rate, based on their age, and to maintain their policies throughout their career, even if thir employer does provide disability insurance.

SUMMARY

Insurance can be seen as a way of transferring risk. For a relatively small amount of money, it affords protection against major loss. Insurance is vital to the pharmacist-owner's survival in business, and it is good business practice for a corporate pharmacy.

Find a reliable insurance professional in whom you have confidence. Ensure that he or she represents a company with a proven track record for competitiveness, fairness, and know-how. Review your coverage regularly. As a policyholder you will not find it necessary to change agents or companies if your demands, based on business acumen, are being met to your satisfaction.

Reference

1.   Dickson, G.C.A. *Corporate Risk Management.* London: Witherby, 1989.

Recommended Reading

A Guide to Buying Life Insurance. Toronto: Canadian Life and Health Insurance Association,1996.

Catherwood RH., ed. *Life Insurance and the Businessman.* Toronto: Maclean-Hunter Ltd.

Facts of the General Insurance Industry in Canada. 16th ed. Toronto: Insurance Bureau of Canada, 1988.

Synder J.C. *It's Your Money.* 6th ed. Toronto: Stoddard, 1989.

Most provincial governments publish consumer guides to insurance, e.g., *Insurance: A Basic Guide for Consumers,* Ministry of Consumer and Commercial Relations, Government of Ontario.

16

SECURITY

INTRODUCTION

The Retail Council of Canada Loss Prevention Survey annually reports the tremendous losses suffered by retailers from both external and internal theft. Its most recent report, 1997, states that $4 billion was lost to retailers in one year alone. "An ounce of prevention" will result in great savings to the profitability of a business. Ranging from armed robbery to shoptheft, from burglary to employee theft, and from prescription forgery to credit-card and cheque fraud, there is ample evidence to suggest that every pharmacy can expect to be victimized in one way or another.

The reality is that pharmacies are particularly vulnerable to criminal attack because of their attractive mix of desirable items: cash, tobacco, and drugs. An additional feature is that they are open late; losses, however, can be suffered at any time of day or night.

While taking steps to prevent these crimes may seem at first glance an expensive proposition, the ongoing benefit to a store's profitability will justify the expense many times over. According to the Retail Council of Canada's 1997 Loss Prevention Survey, pharmacies lose 2.2 percent of sales to theft and related losses. As losses come out of profits, sales will have to increase by $1,904,800 to make up for this loss.[a]

While numbers may vary due to various other influences (e.g., location of the pharmacy, number of employees, degree of implementation of policy and procedures), it is thought that 60 percent of loss is employee theft and 40 percent is shoplifting. The fact is that security should be an essential part of doing business in today's world.

[a] Based on Figure 5.1 (p. 97), profit in 199y was reported to be 2.5% of the pharmacy's $2,164,553 sales. At 2.2% of sales, loss due to shrinkage would be $47,620. Therefore, in order to make up for this loss, sales must increase by (2.5% of x = $47,620) $1,904,800.

Many common crime-prevention techniques can be used to protect pharmacists, staff members, customers, and property. Exterior security measures, interior security devices, and internal procedures help minimize security risks and are essential aspects of effective policies and systems. It cannot be stated strongly enough that a security program against internal or external theft must be considered as an all-exclusive package. Internal theft refers to theft by employees, while external theft refers to theft by customers. A strong area of security will be compromised by allowing another area to be weak.

SECURITY HARDWARE
Exterior Security Measures

Any initial review of a potential pharmacy site must consider the surrounding physical environment. While many pharmacies are located on busy, well traveled streets or in malls, others are located in relatively isolated areas, with little pedestrian or vehicular traffic, that require more inventive crime-prevention measures, especially with regard to exterior security.

An analysis of the streetscape should include the types of neighboring businesses such as bars, coffee shops, and game arcades, and their operating hours, the local crime rate, and the prognosis for the future. Input of this nature should be obtained from any available source such as the local police. A careful inspection of the site itself—interior walls, ceilings (especially in malls), and basement construction—can uncover weak links in the security potential of the premises.

Properly placed exterior lighting can provide a powerful deterrent to crime and will also serve to enhance the appearance of the premises. It is best to illuminate the entire property, including the roof, entrances, and loading areas. Exterior lighting fixtures should be protected from vandalism and bulbs should be replaced regularly.

A commercial timer should be installed to control the exterior lighting and other functions such as heating systems and window display lighting. Photo-electric switches can also be used to automatically turn on the lighting system as darkness approaches.

Landscaping should be evaluated with a view to eliminating concealment and climbing opportunities for a burglar. Shrubbery and trees should be trimmed to a maximum height of three to four feet above the ground to permit natural surveillance of the property. Consider both vehicular and pedestrian traffic in your review, both in daylight hours and after dark. Debris, such as empty boxes or garbage containers, should be cleared away or situated so that it does not provide a hiding place. If fencing is required, chain-link fences are recommended because they do not restrict visibility for police officers and other observers.

Ensure that the pharmacy address is displayed prominently on both front and rear of the pharmacy, to enable the police to locate the pharmacy quickly in an emergency. Unlabeled rear doors can cause confusion and delay when police officers need to go to the rear exit as well as the front. Many police departments require an up-to-date contact list for these purposes.

Doors, Windows, and Roof Openings

Doors, windows, and roof openings are the most common entry points for pharmacy break and enter. Exterior doors should be of 1-3/4 inch (4.5 cm) solid-wood core construction, or 16-gauge steel or aluminum alloy. A solid door is a waste of money unless the frames are of comparably solid construction. On rear receiving-style doors, multiple sliding dead bolts should be applied, both high and low, or a night drop bar considered.

Particular attention should be paid to hinges, ensuring that they are mounted on the inside of the frame or have non-removable hinge pins. A locking pin can also be installed in an existing hinge plate. A low-tech solution would be to tack weld the pin.

All exterior doors should be fitted with a good-quality single-cylinder dead-bolt lock with a minimum one-inch (2.5 cm) extension into the frame. Do not rely on key in the knob locks. (The National Building Code of Canada prohibits the use of double-cylinder or interior key locks for public buildings in which the door is deemed a fire exit.) Pivoting bolts can be replaced with hook bolts to provide extra protection. Thumbturn locks (sometimes used in mall locations) should be protected by a firmly attached metal plate to block exterior reach to the thumbturn; alternatively, the thumbturn lock could be replaced by a keyed cylinder.

Since sliding glass doors can be lifted from the tracks and set aside, additional security measures such as pins, shims, or commercial locks especially designed for sliding doors are recommended. Bay or receiving doors should be equipped with protective devices such as slide bolts, cast-iron keepers and pins, or cylinder bolts and/or padlocks. If padlocks are used, it is recommended that they include such features as hardened-steel shackle, heel-and-toe locking, a minimum of six tumblers in the chamber, and a solid one-piece body. Any chain or hasp must be made of high-quality hardened steel.

While a more expensive option, glass windows may, where warranted, be strengthened with unbreakable glass or an aftermarket film. Such windows must be sealed and/or bonded to the frame to prevent them from being kicked in. Because the once prolific metal security bars are such a visual blight, conveying an armed camp mentality, it is difficult to recommend their use. Seldom-used windows should be secured permanently with tamper-proof screws or bolted from the inside.

Roof openings, such as skylights and hatchways, require special attention. Skylights should be covered with iron bars or a securely fastened steel grill. Hatchways should be secured from the inside with a slide bar or slide bolts and equipped with non-removable pinion outside hinges and padlocked.

Air ducts or air-vent openings exceeding eight to 12 inches (20 to 30 cm) should be covered with iron bars or a steel grill. Undertake regular inspections of all access points to ensure that security devices have not been tampered with. Good key control is not costly and cannot be stressed enough. Establish policies that specify which employees are permitted to have keys to entry or office doors. Use of a "protected" key way—that is, one that may not be duplicated without authorization—is highly recommended. Assign and record all key distribution; collect keys from employees who leave the business, changing lock cylinders where the circumstances of leaving seem to warrant it or where keys have gone "missing." Some interior doors (i.e., locker rooms or doors off the sales floor) may be fitted with a numbered keypad lock that can be altered at will, thereby avoiding key issuance.

Safes

Because of the nature of their business, pharmacies need three styles of safe containment. An office or cash safe should be a heavy-gauge (3/8-inch steel or better) burglary-resistant unit. If it weighs less than 500 lbs it must be bolted to the floor. Light, fire-rated units are not noted for their bolt work strength and are often removed from a store in their entirety.

The second unit is a narcotics safe. While the Narcotic Control Regulations require that only "reasonable" steps be taken with this inventory, it is recommended that the safe be of at least 3/8-inch steel with some form of substantial bolt work. Although it may appear that the cost of the drugs does not warrant this expense, you should consider the damage and lost sales that could result from break and enter the fact that if you are attacked successfully once, the perpetrators will likely return, and your moral obligation to keep these drugs safe. Finally, in most provinces a tobacco locker or safe of some form is recommended. There are many manufacturers, of many different styles, depending on store layout and design. Regardless of exterior appearances, they should be of at least light-gauge metal with a locking mechanism resistant to substantial force. In recent years the tobacco black market has rivaled, and in some cases surpassed, the illegal prescription drug trade.

Alarm Systems

Regardless of the installation of security devices to "harden" a site, the lure of drugs, cash, and tobacco will always prompt burglars to penetrate a pharmacy's barriers by force. The relative insecurity of walls and ceilings is common in today's construction. For example, in both strip malls and enclosed malls the common ceiling area can be used to advantage by burglars. In addition, "peeling" of corrugated metal roofing or exterior block removal is not uncommon. Therefore, extra vigilance is required with regard to the installation of systems or equipment to help reduce the risk of break-in.

A store in which no alarm system is evident is especially vulnerable.

An alarm system for a pharmacy should include one or a combination of the following elements:

- contact devices to protect all doors, windows, and other access points, including the narcotics safe as a separate area;

- motion detection and glass-break sensors that indicate when external security barriers have been breached, with specific coverage of high-risk areas (i.e., cash and narcotic safe, tobacco, etc.) being recommended;

- exterior and/or interior camera surveillance or closed-circuit television systems, which should include a time/date feature for playback purposes;

- safe protection by means of contacts, with a separate zone that may be used to restrict access (i.e., narcotics);

- emergency signaling features that permit a hostage victim to send a silent "Duress" alarm.

Additionally, an alarm system should be relatively user-friendly, with the ability to alter names and/or PIN numbers as staff changes or a number becomes known. Many systems allow separate zone coverage so that selected areas, such as the narcotics safe, may be accessed only by designated individuals.

High-risk sites may not be secure enough, with the use of regular telephone-line communication, for alarm transmission. To eliminate the danger of alarm attack, consider a dedicated line (DVACS), or cellular backup.

Recent decisions by local police boards to charge administration fees or response fees has resulted in an increase in private-sector alarm response. Consult with the crime-prevention officers of local law-enforcement agencies for advice related to your particular location. Obtain equipment recommendations and price quotations from two or three reputable security firms. Check all areas of the store before extinguishing lights and locking up.

Installation of an adequate alarm system will serve to deter burglars, detect undeterred burglars, and provide special protection for currency and high-risk merchandise such as narcotics, cosmetics, and stamps. In addition, many insurers provide premium reductions for a monitored, ULC-approved system.

EXTERNAL THEFT

The types of crimes to which pharmacies are vulnerable from outside elements include break and enter, robbery, prescription forgery, and shop theft. In each case, a range of security measures should be taken—from precautions and preventive procedures to appropriate conduct in the face of crimes—to reduce the potential for injury to staff members and customers. We shall discuss some of these precautions and procedures in this section.

Break-ins and Robberies

Five important steps should be taken upon the discovery of a break and enter:

1.   Do not interfere if the offence is in progress.

2.   Notify the police.

3.   Note the description, licence-plate number, and direction of any vehicles seen leaving the crime scene.

4.   Do not touch or disturb any evidence.

5.   Request that any other witnesses remain at the scene to assist police with the investigation.

A detailed record of all missing products or equipment will be required, and should include any lot numbers, serial numbers, or personally added markings (i.e., etchings or black-light ink) that may assist the police in later identification.

As opposed to break and enter or burglary, robbery is defined as the theft of property under the threat of force (regardless of whether the robber actually has a weapon). Well-trained store personnel who follow robbery-protection steps can greatly reduce the threat of robbery.

Important measures to be taken:

- ensure that staffing is adequate relative to store size, and have at least two employees present when the premises are closed for the day;

- reduce the target size by making frequent bank deposits and taking regular inventory of narcotic and controlled drugs;

- install a surveillance camera and ensure that front windows are not obscured with displays and signage;

- report suspicious persons and make eye contact with all customers;

- vary the time at which night deposits are made and ensure that two people are present;

- always be discreet when handling cash.

Such measures will help "tell" potential robbers that robbery-prevention procedures are being followed.

One useful security measure is to store "marked" money in the cash register—a few identifiable bills to be given to a robber along with the remainder of the cash-register contents. Should the robber be apprehended with the money, the bills can be positively identified as the property of your store. Separate out a few bills and note their serial numbers, then keep them in the register in an envelope labeled, for example, "Christmas Fund." A similar measure that has proved helpful in obtaining convictions is to identify merchandise and containers with special pens. Other marking techniques for money or merchandise can be suggested by the crime-prevention division of your local police force.

If a robbery occurs, remain calm and avoid rapid movement that could be perceived as a threat. The individual will most likely be frightened, or may be on an unknown substance, and reducing the amount of time in the store is the safest route. Co-operate with the robber, but do not volunteer to do more than asked. Observe the individual(s) as closely as possible and note anything handled or touched in order to give police a clear description later on. Give the robber the marked money, if available, from the cash register. When the robber leaves, note the direction of travel, the type of vehicle, and the licence-plate number, if it is safe to do so. Call the police immediately, and be prepared to give a description of the robber and the getaway vehicle. Close and lock the pharmacy and preserve the scene for evidence. Request all witnesses to remain at the scene and make separate written notes of descriptions and other important information (i.e., rings, tattoos, speech, mannerisms, etc.). A suspect-identification form will be helpful in this regard. A hold-up can be a terrifying experience, and the attending police may be able to help locate trauma counseling, if required.

Prescription Forgeries

Constant vigilance in detecting and intercepting prescription forgeries has a hidden payoff: The "street" intelligence network will spread the word that a certain pharmacy should be avoided when it comes to this type of fraud.

When presented with a prescription, pharmacists and other dispensing personnel should ask themselves the following 11 questions:

1.   Do I know this patient?

2.   Do I know this prescriber?

3.   Is this the right physician identity number?

4.   Is this the prescriber's handwriting?

5.   Is the prescription for a commonly abused drug?

6.   Is this a usual quantity, dosage, and direction for use?

7.   Are these the usual abbreviations?

8.   Is this prescription written using one pen?

9.   Is this an original prescription blank, not a photocopy?

10. Am I sure that nothing about this prescription looks suspicious?

11. In provinces where the triplicate-prescription-form-program[b] is in effect, is the prescription written on the appropriate form?

If the answer to any of the questions is "No" or "I don't know," the situation warrants some investigation. Always call the prescriber using a telephone number from your files or from the official telephone directory. Do not accept the telephone number on the prescription form as valid.

Some provincial licensing organizations have established phone networks, through which other pharmacies are notified of any reported attempts to pass forged prescriptions. Contact your provincial licensing body for further information (see the Directory at the end of this book).

Shoptheft and Fraud

The *Criminal Code of Canada* has no section on shoplifting. The criminal charge is either theft, pure and simple, or fraud. Because of the wide variety of products available, pharmacies are a favorite target for such offences.

Both professional and amateur thieves employ a diverse array of techniques to achieve their objectives. Some of the common ones are:

*   removing an item from a counter by covering it with a shopping bag, coat, or umbrella and dragging it off the counter into another bag;

*   distracting a sales clerk: one member of a shoplifting team feigns illness, a seizure, or a fight inside or immediately outside store premises while an accomplice removes the merchandise;

*   placing small objects into coat linings, gloves, hats, or other items of clothing;

*   running from the premises with valuable items that have been removed by the clerk from secure display cases.

---

[b] A program designed to reduce "multi-doctoring" and the abuse of narcotic and controlled drugs.

Examples of fraud are:

• switching the contents of an expensive product into the box or container of a less expensive product;

• changing a price ticket or signage to reflect a lower price;

• selecting an expensive item off the shelf unobserved and boldly requesting a refund at the cash desk;

• attempting to pass a bad cheque.

A number of simple techniques can be used to deter such acts. One of the most important (and least expensive) techniques is to make eye and verbal contact with each customer. "May I help you?" are words a potential thief does not want to hear. Good customer service is a powerful tool. Sales clerks should be trained to be alert and observant while they are attending to routine tasks such as stocking shelves and taking inventory. Watch for individuals more interested in looking at staff than at the merchandise. Neatly faced-up shelves improve sales and easily identify selected merchandise. The removal of discarded empty packages will help discourage the "everybody does it" rationalization of some customers.

Store layout should ensure clear visibility, elimination of blind spots that might provide cover for a shoplifter, and location of the check-out counters near entrances and exits. (Have only one entrance/exit if possible, and require customers to pass through a check-out area on leaving the store.) The installation of convex mirrors and/or surveillance cameras has a deterrent value.

Valuable inventory such as glucometers should be placed in locked display cases, in view of the check-out counter but not near entrances or exits. Sample units are often provided to allow customers to "touch and feel" appliances before purchasing items stored behind the pharmacy counter.

Post signs that tell customers shoplifters will be prosecuted. Consistent enforcement of this policy will also have a deterrent effect.

Develop and enforce a cheque-cashing policy requiring specific identification, and attempt bank verification on high-dollar first-time writers. Current runs of counterfeit currency may necessitate the purchase of detection pens or lights.

Larger pharmacies frequently employ security agencies to provide "floor walkers" or plain-clothes investigators. Section 494 of the *Criminal Code of Canada* allows a person to make a citizen's arrest and to deliver the offender to a police officer. However, it is critical that you know the conditions under which you can make a citizen's arrest, to avoid a false-arrest lawsuit.

These conditions are:

- you must see the offence being committed with your own eyes and are not merely accepting the word of another person;

- you must see selection from the store shelves of the item about to be stolen;

- you must see concealment, thus proving that the person is stealing and it is not just a case of forgetfulness;

- you must have a constant, unimpeded view of the person;

- you must see the person leave the store without paying for the item;

- you must notify the police and request assistance.

As a retailer, you have the right, through the *Trespass to Property Act* to prohibit undesirable individuals from entering your premises. Returning parties may be fined or charged through police involvement. While each province has its own statute on this matter, a storekeeper does have the right to ban a person from the store. However, you must show fairness and have just cause that the person's presence adversely affects your business. This type of ban is routinely applied to shoplifters after they have been arrested. Ask the head office or a lawyer to draft a properly worded letter to serve on the person.

Electronic Article Protection

No discussion of controlling external theft would be complete without mention of the use of electronic deterrence systems. The concept of electronic article surveillance (EAS) systems is relatively straightforward. A tag, filament, or wafer is inserted in a theft-prone product, activating an alarm at a store exit unless the article has been deactivated at the point of purchase.

Three technologies currently available are radio frequency, electro-magnetic, and acousto-magnetic. While each has its advantages and disadvantages, they all require a substantial financial commitment. It is therefore recommended that you carefully consider whether a system is suited to your store's environment. Keep in mind that these systems are intended as a means not to apprehend thieves, but to deter them. Never accuse an individual of theft based solely on the strength of an alarmed device. These systems are labor-intensive to maintain due to tag application, but some product suppliers are beginning to offer pre-tagged or "source-tagged" goods directly to the store. Future availability of these products, and which technology is used, may influence the choice of EAS supplier.

INTERNAL THEFT

According to security experts employed for retail businesses, theft by employees accounts for a much larger percentage of total losses than shoplifting or other external crimes. Inventory shrinkage through internal theft may account for as much as 80 percent of a store's losses.

Internal theft can occur within any division of a business—cash, accounting, or receiving. The key to preventing losses of this nature lies in having strong loss-prevention systems and procedures and in maintaining alert store supervision at all times. The active involvement of the proprietor or supervisor will either create obstacles or give cause for suspicion about possible internal theft.

Hiring Practices

The first step in controlling internal losses is to hire honest and dependable employees. Application forms should request information that the employer can verify. Length and dates of employment, along with gaps in employment, should be verified. Never hire on the strength of a résumé alone. An application form should be clear in stating that any falsehoods reported will result in dismissal. Always remember that a résumé is intended to put the applicant in a positive light and does not require applicants to report all of their jobs or any gaps in employment. A call to the licensing body to confirm the good standing of a pharmacist is always in order before an offer of employment is made.

Loss-Prevention Procedures

The second step in an effective internal security program is to establish strong loss-prevention systems and procedural programs. Such programs should include:

- surprise register audits;
- front store supervision;
- lottery/stamp reconciliation;
- staff-purchase procedures;
- safe controls;
- secure store openings and closings;
- review of exception reports;
- receiving controls;
- night-crew supervision;
- bank-statement reconciliation/accounting procedures;
- pharmacy controls;
- post office controls (if applicable).

Two basic principles apply for the setting up of control systems:

1. Reduce employee access to both money and merchandise, so that access is restricted on the basis of need.

2. Separate responsibility among employees: entrust the handling of money or merchandise to one employee, independent accountability and record-keeping to another.

The majority of reported employee thefts involve cash; therefore, the implementation of the above systems is paramount in discouraging or reducing internal theft.

SURPRISE REGISTER AUDITS

Cash registers should be audited without notification. A register reading is taken, the opening reading and starting cash are subtracted, and the resulting figure is compared to the cash on hand (which should be counted in the cashier's presence). Voids and refunds are then subtracted.

Too much money in the register may indicate that the cashier has not rung in each sale, but rather has accepted money from customers, failed to record it, and waited for a chance to remove the excess cash. This simple, obvious, and hard-to-detect method is employed by almost all employees who steal from the cash register.

A cash shortage could also indicate employee theft. A cashier may extract cash by preparing a false refund form or creating a void purchase slip and pocketing the equivalent amount in cash. A supervisor's approval for such transactions should therefore be required.

Repeated errors may indicate that a clerk is merely incapable of handling money and making change. In short, out-of-balance registers point to the need for close attention to the employee in question. As a surprise register audit is a useful indicator, you should not discuss the results of an audit with any cash-handling person. The results should be used to guide you if there is a problem.

FRONT STORE SUPERVISION

Internal theft can occur with amazing speed and deftness, so alert supervision is paramount to the successful operation of the front store area. Supervisors should be trained to be conscious of the possibility of internal theft. The presence of calculators or "countdown sheets," or the turning of cash register turrets (which display the price to the customer as the cash register rings up the sale) away from the customer's view are strong indicators of a problem.

LOTTERY/STAMP RECONCILIATION

Lottery tickets and stamps should be treated as money. Cashier accountability should be required including a cashier float, with a reconciliation at the end of each shift. It is also important to control and reduce excess lottery tickets and stamps in the cash safe.

STAFF-PURCHASE PROCEDURES

Staff purchases present an opportunity for internal theft. All sales to employees should be handled by an approved supervisor. An employee other than the purchaser should be charged with wrapping and shipping the merchandise, and the purchaser should not be able to pick up the merchandise at a secure collection area until the end of the work shift. In larger operations it may be necessary to restrict staff purchasing to non-business hours. Employees are less likely to steal if they are given a substantial discount on purchases; however, a clear, written policy should be established to ensure that all employees are aware that this privilege is restricted to their own needs and those of their immediate family. "Bag checks" of regular staff purchases can help prevent abuse and establish routine control. Employees should be informed of the policy, and a signed acknowledgment should be placed in each employee's personal file. Other security measures include forbidding employees to place merchandise behind the counter or elsewhere for "future" purchase, and providing lockers in designated areas for purses and personal property.

Safe Controls

Never leave keys or combinations in readily available locations. Because a safe is a necessary tool for control, access to it should be restricted. Alter safe combinations when unauthorized users have obtained it, or when authorized users have terminated their employment. Keep the narcotics safe locked at all times. A common mistake is to leave it open during the day and lock it only in the evening.

Secure Store Openings and Closings

To ensure staff safety and store security, avoid opening or closing the store alone. Make sure that at least two people are present and are aware of the procedure. Never leave a door ajar or unlocked before the store opens, as this will provide an opportunity for a robber to gain access. Take down the licence-plate number of any suspicious looking vehicle during opening and closing times. Always control staff access at these times.

Review of Exception Reports

Exception reports produced from point-of-sale (POS) equipment can be a valuable tool. Regular review and discreet follow-up of any trends in exceptional cash-handling transactions will be very useful in identifying employees involved in theft. In analyzing these reports, do not be overly concerned with individual instances, but, rather, concentrate on trends.

RECEIVING CONTROLS

Ensure that the receiving door is always secure, with both day- and night-alarm contacts. Never leave the door open except shipping or receiving. All merchandise received should be recorded in a receiving log, which should be reconciled through the accounting process. Secure valuable product such as tobacco in a locked room. Pre-numbered purchase orders, on which all details (including unit price, number of units ordered, and name of employee who ordered the merchandise) have been noted and approved, allows for easier supervision.

NIGHT-CREW SUPERVISION

More and more stores are using a night crew to restock their shelves to facilitate customer shopping comfort durind the day. Such persons must be supervised; drop-in visits by management are recommended.

BANK-STATEMENT RECONCILIATION/ACCOUNTING PROCEDURES

Monthly bank statement reconciliations should be completed by a person other than the employee who prepares the bank deposits. Periodic record audits will act as a further deterrent. It is also wise to insist that every purchase or expense be accompanied by an invoice or other documentation. Responsibility for purchasing, receiving, and paying bills should, if possible, be assigned to different individuals.

PHARMACY CONTROL

Not surprisingly, of all the merchandise carried by pharmacies, dispensary inventory presents a special temptation for employees. Such theft can involve either large or small quantities of desirable drugs. Continuous supervision of the dispensary is highly recommended. Establish a policy of restricting access to authorized dispensary personnel, and enforce this policy strictly. The development of rigorous inventory control methods, including frequent periodic reconciliations may be necessary to prevent or detect shortages.

POST OFFICE CONTROLS

Ensure accountability of the clerks in handling both cash and merchandise. Ensure that drawers containing stamps are always secured, to discourage snatch-and-grab theft. Establish adequate controls over the safe so that access is restricted to supervisory staff. Strive to maintain a minimal stock position, to reduce exposure and help identify problems more readily. Stamps should be treated as cash.

INTEGRITY OR MYSTERY SHOPPING

Many merchants employ a commercial shopping service to evaluate their store's retail sales practices. Random visits by individuals or teams of "shoppers" making a series of test purchases from each employee will result in reports of any dishonest practices, in addition to such problems as poor service and discourtesy as well as positive feedback.

FIRE SECURITY

Protection against fire damage is another area that pharmacists and their store planners need to consider. Because fire-protection regulations vary from one jurisdiction to another, pharmacists are advised to consult local authorities to determine the prevailing requirements. Exits, sprinkler systems, smoke detectors, and fire extinguishers, as well as the safe storage of flammable chemicals, are a few of the areas that must be considered.

Fire extinguishers are designed for use during the early stages of a fire. They should be located in several areas of the store (dispensary, stockroom, and front store area), and they must be serviced at least annually to ensure that they are in good operating condition. Some local fire departments provide hands on training in the use of these units. Water, as well as Multi Purpose extinguishers, may be required; however, never use water on an electrical or gas fire. Attempt to fight a fire only after contacting the fire department, and only if you keep an escape route at your back.

A sprinkler system might help prevent extensive fire damage. However, it may be costly and may not be required locally. As well, depending on product mix and utilization of computer components, water damage can be as severe as fire damage. Early detection by smoke or fire sensors, routed through an alarm system, can provide an economical alterative.

If a fire erupts during business hours, the plan of action should include locating the fire, safely evacuating staff and customers, and calling the fire department. Frequently, the prompt removal of a fuel source (i.e., unplugging an electrical cord, shutting down a gas supply) can minimize both spread and losses.

Even if drug inventory bears no obvious signs of heat damage (scorch marks, smoke deposits), the pharmacist must consider the possibility of invisible damage by heat, toxic fumes, or smoke penetration of containers, necessitating the disposal of the entire drug inventory.

SUMMARY

Review the following 36-point Security Checklist to ensure that you have taken into consideration all the security measures necessary for the protection of your operation.

Security Checklist

1.   Are all entrances and exits well lit?

2.   Is the address prominently displayed on the front and rear of the premises?

3.   Have areas of concealment for burglars been eliminated?

4.   Are good key-control procedures being followed?

5.   Are all exterior wood doors of solid-core construction?

6.   Are the door frames reinforced at the strike area?

7.   Are the exterior doors hinged on the inside?

8.   Are the exterior doors equipped with a dead-bolt lock?

9.   Have glass panels been fitted with unbreakable glass or covered by a mesh grill or bars?

10.   Are double glass doors equipped with a cylinder dead-bolt?

11.   Have glass windows and sliding glass doors been equipped with additional security devices?

12.   Have all access points (skylights, hatchways, air ducts, loading bays, and outside walls) been considered?

13.   Are routine maintenance checks performed to ensure that security arrangements are intact and alarm systems are functional?

14.   Is the interior of the pharmacy well lit to ensure visibility both inside and outside?

15. Are windows free of display cards and advertising clutter?

16. Are narcotic and controlled-drug inventories and reconciliations being carried out regularly?

17. Are surprise register audits being conducted?

18. Is there alert front store supervision?

19. Is there adequate control over lottery tickets and stamps?

20. Are there adequate controls in the post office?

21. Is access to all safes controlled on an as-needed basis?

22. Are there appropriate store opening and closing procedures in place and being adhered to?

23. Are exception reports reviewed and reacted to regularly?

24. Is the receiving door controlled and are incoming shipments being properly recorded?

25. Is the night crew supervised?

26. Are cash-handling functions divided among several employees to ensure accountability?

27. Is a commercial shopping service employed to evaluate employees' sales practices?

28. Are strict purchasing and receiving accountability procedures being followed?

29. Does the proprietor or a designated individual take an active supervisory role?

30. Are employees trained to prevent and respond to shoplifting attempts?

31. Have all staff members received training in what to do in the event of an armed robbery?

32. Are dispensary staff members instructed in detecting and intercepting prescription forgeries?

33. Are crime-prevention decals and posters displayed in the dispensary and front store area?

34.   Has liaison been established with local law-enforcement agencies?

35.   Have all fire extinguishers been inspected in the past 12 months?.

36.   Does the pharmacy have a good insurance policy?

A large number of negative responses to these questions indicates a need to enhance the security of the premises and store operation. Improving security will not eliminate pharmacy crime, but it will discourage intruders and other criminals, who tend to choose the least-secure locations as their targets.

17

CONSIDERATIONS FOR
SUCCESSION PLANNING

INTRODUCTION

While larger corporate practices have succession plans in place, family-owned businesses seldom do; herein lies the problem or choice for continuity or dissolution. The solution is not found in size, but in a business' ability to continue. The biggest threat to owners of a family-owned business is themselves. The real dilemma is the lack of plans for that time when the principal owner is no longer part of the business. If there is a plan, it is likely in the mind of the principal owner and not available when needed.

Succession of a business or a professional practice is simply the transition of management or ownership and the circumstances under which it occurs. Further, it may include the transfer of assets in the event of death, disability, or retirement. All of this should occur in the most orderly and tax-effective manner. It is estimated that . . . "only about 30 percent of family businesses . . .continue into the second generation and a scant 10 percent make it to the third."[1] The reasons for this are tax law and the dynamics of family relationships. A successful transfer of management or ownership involves both a plan and the use of outside advisors. This latter group comprises a lawyer, accountant, banker, and estate planner who may be an accountant. Because of the income tax implications, it is critical to seek professional advice, and structure the transfer in a way that takes advantage of the Income Tax Act.

WHY SUCCESSION PLANNING?

The major reasons for planning succession are the following:
*   partnership disagreement;

- marriage break-down;
- death of the owner/manager;
- retirement of the owner/manager;
- disability of a partner or owner;
- extended absence of a partner or owner.

Succession planning is an issue that should ideally be considered as soon as the practice opens. There are basically four choices:[2]

1. The practice can be left to a spouse or children.

2. A pharmacist can be hired to operate it.

3. It can be sold.

4. It can be liquidated.

A final decision may be dependent upon the Pharmacy Act of the province in which the practice exists. Appropriate advice should therefore be sought before any action is taken.

Succession of a pharmacy is simply the orderly transfer of the practice's assets in the most tax-effective manner. As a result of the asset transfer, capital may be required to operate the practice while this occurs. This need for capital is to cover any loans and outstanding invoices, pay salaries, and any taxes due. Sources of capital may be difficult to locate owing to an owner's death. In such circumstances, life insurance proceeds provide immediate funds for this.

It is not uncommon that older pharmacists/owners face a serious illness or die before retirement. Appropriate planning, often called a crisis plan, can be implemented quickly and prevents untoward upheaval while retaining the confidence of creditors. A key element of a crisis plan is to identify the person to be in charge and who will have signing authority for business and financial matters.[3] Planning in this instance cannot be over-stressed. "The best time to consider various options for a major decision is before the decision has to be made."[4]

Choices in Succession Planning

Before establishing a timetable for the transfer of assets and/or management responsibility, it is useful to determine objectives for the succession plan.[5] For example, the objective can be as straightforward as the owner's desire to reduce the amount of the time spent actively in the pharmacy, to an outright sale of the practice.

Having established objectives, a timetable needs to be developed in order to have the transition occur in an orderly fashion. A planned retirement and sale of the practice by the owner should begin about two to three years before the target date. A change of management may require less lead time but just as rigorous a planning process. For a sale, potential purchasers must be identified, the practice valued, legal forms completed, and the details of these activities attended to. Any change, planned or not, should be carried out with minimum disruption to the practice and its clientele.

Key issues of succession planning are control of the business and value of the business. Control of a family-owned business can be directed to heirs (if they are pharmacists, and able to operate it profitably), to employees or associates (if they are able to purchase it at a reasonable price from heirs), or to competitors (who will only pay whatever is necessary). The value of the practice can be calculated as discussed previously. Remember, however, that this is an estimate, and the true value is determined at the time the assets are realized.

Like any product, a business has a life cycle. It is neither predictable nor uniform, but unique to each individual business.

According to Hyde, the "appropriate approach" to attaining succession goals is linked to the relationship between the fair value of a business and its growth stage. As illustrated in Figure 17.1 (p. 364), a well-operated business increases in value over time. It reaches its peak value as it approaches maturity and then revenues and earnings begin to decline. This model represents Hyde's argument for establishing a succession strategy while the business is still in its growth stage, and then implementing it before the business matures. Failing to do this has potential adverse effects for the business and its owner. They are as follows:[6]

- If succession occurs after the business begins to decline, one may find oneself owning an asset of decreasing value.

- The next generation of managers or owners may become dissatisfied.

- The possibility of early "burnout" may push the business into decline prematurely.

- It is possible that an orderly transition of ownership can be hindered if succession is left to the terms of a will.

Figure 17.1   Business Growth Cycle

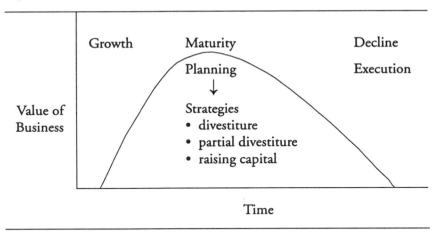

Source: Hyde, J., *Business Succession, The Enterpriser,* Autumn, 1996, Ernst & Young.

Hyde's advice is simple, "Exiting a business requires the same commitment, hard work, and sound decision making that it takes to establish and grow a successful venture."

The issue of using the equity in a business to fund one's retirement raises possible succession problems. One approach, that assumes transfer of ownership to a family member without putting the business into debt or mortgaging property, is suggested by Thibault.[7] The concept includes exchanging existing shares for a "frozen share," thus setting its value at an upper limit. The value can fall but never increase beyond its frozen amount. Income can be taken in two ways. First, dividends can be paid at regular intervals in amounts that do not adversely effect the business' cash flow. Second, frozen shares that pay no dividends can be retained and sold back to the business over a period of time.

If this strategy is selected, caution must be exercised in valuing the business so as not to alert Revenue Canada's suspicions about an artificially low transfer price. This possibility can be avoided by using the services of a chartered business evaluator who would provide an impartial evaluation of the business that should satisfy the tax authorities and all family members as to its reasonableness.

Should funding be required for the transition of assets from the existing owner to the new owner(s), one source may be the business' cash flow. It occurs as unsecured debt and is considered in the hierarchy of debt as being "between senior secured debt and equity."[8, 9] Although this type of funding is not for everyone, an established business that has a history of predictable earnings, strong working capital, and little existing debt is a good candidate. The cost to service this type of debt is high but this is balanced by the business's strong operating results. As always, when searching for funding, it is helpful to explore all possible sources.

As succession occurs in a family business, there is a high potential for conflict. This conflict takes place as a clash between family and business values. It is critical to prevent this from becoming a destructive force. Therefore, the conflict must be recognized and managed, by creating a code or charter of behavior that indicates how the business should operate.[10] This document should contain guidelines for resolving problems, values important to the family, rules for decision making, and criteria for family members' growth in the business. Most important is the fact that such a document should be constructed with the help of outside advisors.

In addition to the above, the charter should consider the following:

- criteria for joining the business;
- standards of performance, training, and personal growth;
- compensation;
- share ownership;
- responsibilities and decision making;
- conflict resolution;
- succession planning.

As in any sale of a business, assets or shares can be sold. The decision should not be taken lightly because of the resulting tax implications. It is always helpful to seek the advice of the appropriate professionals before signing any documents.

"Canada's Income Tax Act allows gains on sales of shares of a Canadian-controlled private corporation (CCPC) that has 90 percent or more of the fair market value of its assets in an active business primarily carried on in Canada to be tax exempt."[11] The extent of this tax saving is $500,000, composed of a basic exemption of $400,000 and as much of the $100,000 personal capital gains exemption that is unused. Called a superexemption, it was announced by the Minister of Finance in the February 1994 budget, and implied that it would be in effect for many years. It must be used in concert with careful background preparation in order not to trigger other taxes; thus the need for professional help. Its major advantage is that it "is a once-in-a-lifetime deal for each shareholder."[11]

SUMMARY

Most management books deal with professionally operated public companies. However, the majority of businesses are owned and operated by family members. Consequently, most succession discussions deal with this type of business. The importance of creating a succession plan early on in the life of the business cannot be stressed enough. The knowledge and expertise of professional advisors are critical in implementing these plans successfully. Not to be forgotten is the issue of integrating the succession plan with financial and tax planning. The key to a smooth transition of management and assets is recognition that the "family" must serve the business rather than attempting to have the business serve the family.

References

1. Viger, S. "How to Beat the Business Succession Blues." Royal Trust Money Guide, April 1997.

2. McCaslin, B. "Succession Planning." *Pharmacy Post*, March 1993.

3. McFarland, J. "When the Boss Dies." *The Globe and Mail*, 21 February 1996.

4. *What Happens if the Pharmacy Owner Dies?* Advertisement for "Safeguarding Your Pharmacy's Legacy." National Association of Retail Druggists, Alexandria, VA, 1992.

5. Tootelian, D.H. "Reducing the Traumas of Management Transition." *California Pharmacist*, July 1989.

6. Hyde, J. "Business Succession." *The Enterpriser*. Toronto: Ernst and Young, Autumn 1996.

7. Thibault, D. "Business Succession: More than a Feeling." *Business Advisory Review*. KPMG, Summer 1995.

8. Church, E. "Financing Deal Tackles Succession Snarl." *The Globe and Mail*, 17 March 1997.

9. Partridge, J. "Bank of Montreal Unveils Credit Line for Small Business." *The Globe and Mail*, 11 April 1997.

10. Title, A. "Family Business Charter Stave Off Conflict." *The Globe and Mail*, 7 October 1996.

11. Title, A. "The $500,00 Superexemption: Big Deals for Small Business." *The Globe and Mail*, 15 March 1996.

GLOSSARY

Accounts payable: a term applied to the aggregate of amounts owed to the creditors of a business.

Accounts receivable: a term applied to the aggregate of amounts due from the customers of a business.

Assets: those items owned by a business.

Automated counting system: automatic system for counting tablets or capsules by which technical personnel can obtain the exact count of the medication prescribed.

Average collection period: average length of time required to collect accounts receivable.

Average inventory: the amount calculated when the beginning inventory and ending inventory are added together and divided by two.

Average payable period: average length of time taken to pay invoices.

Balance sheet: a statement of the financial condition of a business at a certain date showing its assets, liabilities and capital.

Basic law of investment: a principle which holds that a return on investment will vary directly with the degree of risk involved and inversely with the liquidity of the investment.

Bay shelving: a storage facility of open shelving found in the prescription department.

Beginning inventory: the total inventory on hand at the beginning of a specified period.

Blister package: a protective package of clear plastic that conforms roughly to the shape of the contents and is attached to a firm cardboard or plastic backing allowing the entire contents to be displayed.

Book value: the dollar worth of an asset appearing on the balance sheet after deducing a specified percentage per year for depreciation.

Break-even analysis: a procedure that determines the degree of business volume at which total revenue equals total expense or, in other words, at which sales equal fixed costs plus variable costs.

Business interruption insurance: a type of insurance that provides a continuation of income to the pharmacy in the event of fire or other serious disruption that causes the pharmacy to be unable to render services for a period ranging from a few days to a few months.

Business plan: a report that consists of a descriptive section outlining the nature of a business and the marketing approach that is planned for it, as well as a financial report detailing past operations and the latest interim monthly financial statement, together with projected monthly income statements and projected monthly cash flow statements for the upcoming year.

Capital: wealth (money or property) which is used or capable of being used to produce more wealth.

Capital gains: gains that result from the disposition of capital property.

Capitation: a method of determining fees, by which a pharmacist claims a fixed fee per patient for a specified time, regardless of the amount of care required.

Carrying costs: the costs associated with holding products in inventory (also called holding costs or maintenance costs).

Cash flow: a summary of cash receipts and disbursements of a business, for a defined period of time.

Cash management: freeing up funds for operating purposes by minimizing assets and maximizing liabilities, specifically accounts payable.

Census Agglomeration (CA): the main labor market area of an urban area of at least 10,000 population.

Census Metropolitan Area (CMA): the main labor market area of an urban area of at least 100,000 population.

Central computer system: a computer system by which the pharmacist contracts for full service with a computer service company and thereby transfers the responsibility for management reports to that company.

Citizen's arrest: a provision (Section 449) of the Criminal Code of Canada which allows any person to make a citizen's arrest and to deliver that person to a peace officer. The citizen must see the crime occur to make such an arrest.

Collective ownership: a form of business enterprise popularly known as a co-operative, by which interested parties band together to buy or sell products or services.

Comprehensive general liability and shop malpractice insurance: a type of insurance that covers both the corporation as an entity and all its employees for legal liability in case of a possible suit (may also be referred to as third-party liability or casualty insurance).

Computer hardware: the physical equipment of a computer system.

Computer software: the programs that instruct the computer hardware to perform various functions.

Consumer market: the potential of a selected group of consumers to purchase the goods or services offered to them.

Continuing education unit (C.E.U.): terminology used in the field of continuing education. One C.E.U. approximates one contact hour of involvement in continuing education. In provinces and states where continuing education is mandatory, the pharmacist must complete a given number of C.E.U.'s in a prescribed period of time.

Corporation: a form of business enterprise in which ownership is represented by stock or shares in the firm. Shareholders are not financially liable for the business beyond the cost of the shares they have purchased (limited liability).

Cost of goods sold (COGS): the cost of merchandise sold to customers during a specific period, usually one year, calculated by adding the net cost of purchases during the period to the beginning inventory, and deducting the ending inventory.

Cost-based pricing: the process of establishing a price based on costs by totaling all the costs associated with an item offered for sale, including the product cost itself, the freight cost, allowances for advertising, and the cost of labour involved in getting the product to the shelf and maintaining it.

Current assets: assets that can be converted into cash within a twelve-month period.

Current liabilities: liabilities that will be paid within a twelve-month period.

Current ratio: a key ratio that bankers use to determine the liquidity of a business; calculated by dividing the total current assets by the total current liabilities.

Debt capital: the amount of money that must be borrowed to finance a business.

Depreciation: the decrease in value of a fixed asset due to wear and tear or obsolescence.

Destination store: stores which generate most of their own traffic, i.e., customers consciously choose the store as their destination.

Diagnostic kit: a test kit which can monitor for a specific disease or medical condition and which is designed for use at home by the patient or in a laboratory.

Disability-free life expectancy (DFLE): the age to which the average person lives free of chronic illness or other disabilities.

Disability insurance: a type of insurance which protects against loss of income by providing for its continuance, when the loss is occasioned by illness or accident.

Discount pricing: pricing below market levels; used to attract traffic and increase sales.

Dividend: a distribution of profits to the shareholders of a corporation.

Dollar control: Any approach to controlling inventory that focusses on the amount of money invested in inventory rather than on the number of units or the particular products involved.

Dump bin: a self-standing container with a header card into which a promoted product is "dumped" randomly. They are located in high traffic aisles of the retail outlet.

Earnings multiplier: the reciprocal of the percentage return on investment that a business should be expected to bring its owner. The indicated earnings of the pharmacy are multiplied by the "earnings multiplier" factor to determine the theoretical value of the operating assets.

Economic order quantity (EOQ): the dollar volume of purchases or level of inventory at which combined procurement and carrying costs are lowest.

End displays: displays at the ends of gondolas.

Entrepreneur: someone who organizes a business, assuming all the inherent risks, for the purpose of obtaining a profit.

Environmental scanning: the process of continually noting current events and analyzing them for their impact on the business environment.

Equity capital: the amount of money invested in a business.

Exchange value: the value of any product or service in the marketplace as determined by what an individual will pay in dollars for it.

Financial leverage: the relationship between equity capital and debt capital.

Financial ratio analysis: a simple ratio or series of ratios calculated from data in the financial statements. The ratios provide indications of how well managers are utilizing the resources available to them by comparing current year's ratios to past year's and to industry averages.

Financial statement: a statement, comprised of an income statement and a balance sheet, which provides a picture of the financial status of a business at a point in time.

Fiscal year: a twelve-month period ending with the last day of any month.

Fixed assets: assets more or less permanent in nature whose useful life is more than one year.

Franchise: a form of licensing by which the owner (franchisor) of a product, service or method obtains distribution at the retail level through affiliated dealers (the franchisees).

General partnership: a grouping of two or more people coming together to form a business. Each partner is individually liable for the business debts.

Generic products: products that are copies of an original brand-name product.

Gondolas: free-standing fixtures that hold retail merchandise for sale.

Good will: the value of an intangible asset; usually the difference between the purchase price of a business and the appraised value of its physical assets.

Gross margin: the difference between the selling price and the cost of the item sold (also referred to as gross profit).

Gross-margin pricing: the percentage by which the selling price exceeds the cost price.

Gross margin return on inventory investment (GMROI): a ratio that is used to assess the effectiveness of inventory management by determining the productivity of the inventory, i.e., the gross margin dollars that are generated by each dollar invested in inventory.

Halo effect: a term used to describe a phenomena by which an interviewer is biased in favour of a particular personality or physical attribute on the part of interviewees over other factors which may be more relevant to the position in question.

Hot-spot cross: the product placement area in the centre of a gondola; associated with the highest sales.

Impulse items: items that a consumer had not planned on purchasing.

Income splitting: the reduction of overall income tax which the owner of a business achieves by paying other family members a salary or making them shareholders of the business who then receive dividend income.

Indicated pre-tax earnings: pre-tax income after reasonable wages and all operating expenses have been paid; based on a review of the business' previous financial statements.

Intercept store: stores which are located between people in a 'trading area' and their traditional source of goods or services.

Inventory control: the monitoring of stock on hand in terms of stock-keeping units or dollar value and cost.

Key-person insurance: a type of insurance which upon the death of a business' 'key person' will provide the funds to attract, educate and train a replacement and keep the business in operation until this occurs.

Leasing: a financing mechanism for the acquisition by a business of premises, equipment, shelving, fixtures and computers, an alternative to renting or purchasing.

Letter of Intent: a document to be signed by interested parties that procedes the drawing up of a formal purchase agreement (to buy an established pharmacy); should include the basic elements of the purchase—price, terms of payment and structure—and an indication that the closing will be subject to the purchaser's obtaining the necessary financing.

Liquidity: the ability to turn assets into cash quickly, in order to repay debt from short-term capitalization.

Load shedding: the reduction by a government of its subsidization of certain services, i.e., privatization.

Marked money: a security measure by which identifiable bills are stored in the cash register, to be given a robber along with the remainder of the cash register contents.

Market area: sub-area, within a geographic region, that can be defined by population, transportation networks, and economic characteristics.

Marketing: the process by which the demands of the public for goods and services are not only satisfied, but also—by means of collecting and analyzing market information—predicted and enhanced.

Market research: the study of the attitudes and beliefs that shape the consumer's response to a product or service.

Markup on cost: a method of pricing by which the markup is expressed as a percentage of the cost price.

Net/net/net/lease: a lease which makes the tenant responsible for core rent and, separately, for all other expenses defined in the offer to lease, with the possible exception of major repairs.

Net worth (individual): the value of personal assets less personal liabilities.

Occupancy costs: expenses incurred as a result of a business occupying a specific premise, i.e., rent (or the interest on a mortgage and depreciation of the building), utilities, property taxes, repairs and maintenance.

Offer to lease: a document which covers the basic terms (rent, definition of the space, any additional costs for common maintenance and property taxes) that will be included in the actual lease of a premise.

Open-to buy (OTB) budget method: a dollar-control system based on establishing overall monthly purchase budgets in advance, monitoring actual sales and purchases during each month, and adjusting the purchase budget for the following month to compensate for documented overspending or underspending and sales declines or increases in the previous month.

Operating loan: a form of working capital financing; also referred to as a demand loan or "line of credit"; used to finance current assets.

Operational plan: the foundation for the business plan; involves gathering, analyzing and planning action around information that will assist in meeting the pharmacy owner's personnel and business goals.

Original packaging: the prepackaging by a manufacturer of a product (often prescription drugs) on the basis of a therapeutic course of treatment for which it is commonly prescribed.

Partnership insurance: a type of insurance that in the event of death of a partner provides funds to finance a purchase from the deceased's family.

Pareto's Law: a guideline of inventory control which holds that 20 per cent of all products stocked generates 80 per cent of total dollar sales, 15 per cent of inventory generates another 15 per cent of sales, and the remaining 65 per cent of the stock generates only 5 per cent of sales.

Password system: a computer security system using appropriate passwords in order to control and limit access to information to authorized personnel only.

Pegboard: a hard backing with symetrical holes that can hold movable hooks; used to display merchandise.

Performance review: an evaluation by an owner/manager or supervisor of an employee's performance in his or her job.

Periodic inventory control systems: a manual unit-control system; involves monitoring sales of product items over specific time periods.

Perpetual system: an inventory control system that records sales as they occur, continually calculating increases in the value of inventory as products are received into stock and reductions as products are sold.

Planogram: a precise, detailed scheme for merchandise display within given product categories.

Point-of-sale system: a combination of computer software, hardware and cash register that captures product information at time of sale or when it is received into inventory.

Policy and procedures manual: written guidelines communicating store policy and procedures for the benefit of both management and staff.

Post-marking surveillance: monitoring of new drugs after market introduction.

Procurement costs: the costs associated with purchasing merchandise.

Product facing: a product package on the shelf, facing out to the customer, with stock of the product lined up behind the front package.

Professional fee: a fee representing the cost to the pharmacy of the service component (labour, operational, general and administrative costs) in dispensing prescriptions.

Profit and loss statement: a financial statement of point in time showing the income and expenses of a business.

Profitability: the ability of the business to generate sufficient revenue not only to pay its expenses but also to reward its owner(s).

Reorder point: the minimum level to which stock of a product is permitted to drop before it is reordered.

Replacement insurance: a type of insurance that provides the full replacement value for fixed assets (land, building, fixtures, equipment).

Retained earnings: profits of a firm that are reinvested in the business.

Shareholders' agreement: a contractual agreement which establishes the ground rules of the relationship between a business (owner) and investors.

Shareholder's equity: shareholders' investment in a business.

Shrinkage: the variance between the book value of inventory and the physical count.

Slat wall: a slatted or grooved backing that can be fitted with either shelves or rows of hooks; used to display merchandise.

Smart card: a plastic card the size of a credit card that carries a computer chip; it can carry large amounts of information regarding its bearer, e.g., the person's complete medical and drug history.

Sole proprietorship: a business which is wholly owned by one individual, the proprietor.

Sole proprietorship insurance: a type of insurance that provides the necessary funds for a sole proprietor's surviving family members to reorganize, carry on, or sell the business in the event of his or her death.

Solvency: a measure of a firm's ability to repay debt from long-term capitalization.

Stand-alone system: an in-house computer system which includes both hardware (the microcomputer) and the rights to a software package(s).

Stock-keeping unit (SKU): the smallest distinguishable packaged unit in a product category.

Strategic planning: a plan which sets the overall direction or goal of the pharmacy and outlines the philosophy by which the pharmacy will operate.

Suscipient business: a principle of location analysis; holds that a store need not generate its own traffic nor depend on neighbouring stores for its customers but that having a location in a place where people circulate for reasons other than shopping can bring in its business.

Term loan: a type of loan used primarily to finance the purchase of capital or long-term assets, such as buildings, fixtures, and equipment, whose value will not fluctuate, but will depreciate over time.

Trial balance: a list taken of the account balances in the general ledger to prove the accuracy of the postings to the ledger and to establish a summary of data for the preparation of financial statements.

Turnkey operation: a type of franchise in which the franchisor undertakes all that is necessary to establish the operation, and the franchisee simply opens the door and begins doing business.

Turnover rate (TOR): a theoretical number of times during a specified period, usually one year, that inventory is bought and completely sold.

Unit control: any approach to controlling inventory that focuses on the number of units of particular products carried in inventory.

Universal Product Code (UPC): an identification code consisting of a series of bars and numerals located on a label or outer package which makes it possible to scan products on scanning counters in order to register all necessary product information and appropriate prices.

Venture capital: a source of capital for a new business, viable only if the business requires financing well in excess of $500,000 but shows promise of great profits in the future. Venture capitalists usually require a percentage of the ownership of the business, an annual return on their investment and a seat on the board of directors.

Visual balance: the appealing arrangement of products on shelves according to size or colour.

Visual system: a method of inventory control that consists simply of examining the merchandise on the shelves and reordering if it is below a desired level or out of stock.

Walk-in medical clinics: clinics often found in shopping malls which supply fast medical care without the need of an appointment.

Working capital: the value of current assets less current liabilities.

PERMISSIONS

Table 3.1   Reprinted with the permission of the Queen's Printer for Ontario, Toronto, Ontario.

Table 3.2   Reprinted with the permission of the Queen's Printer for Ontario, Toronto, Ontario.

Table 3.3   Reprinted with the permission of the Queen's Printer for Ontario, Toronto, Ontario.

Table 4.1   Statistics Canada information is used with the permission of the Minister of Industry, as Minister responsible for Statistics Canada. Information on the availability of the wide range of data from Statistics Canada can be obtained from Statistics Canada's Regional Offices, its World Wide Web Site at http://www.statcan.ca, and its toll-free access number 1-800-263-1136.

Table 4.2   Reprinted with the permission of John Wiley & Sons, Inc., New York, New York.

Table 4.3   Reprinted with the permission of the Minister of Public Works and Government Services Canada, 1998, Ottawa, Ontario.

Figure 4.1   Reprinted with the permission of *Drug Topics*, Medical Economics Company Inc., Montvale, New Jersey.

Figure 4.2   Reprinted with the permission of *Drug Topics*, Medical Economics Company Inc., Montvale, New Jersey.

Figure 5.4   Reprinted with the permission of John Wiley & Sons, Inc., New York, New York.

Figure 5.5   Reprinted with the permission of the South-Western Publishing Co., Florence, Kentucky.

Figure 7.1   Reprinted with the permission of the South-Western Publishing Co., Florence, Kentucky.

Figure 9.6   Reprinted with the permission of H.J. Segal, Toronto, Ontario.

Figure 9.7   Reprinted with the permission of the Drug Trading Company Limited, Scarborough, Ontario.

Figure 9.8   Reprinted with the permission of Hoffmann-La Roche Limited, Mississauga, Ontario.

Figure 10.1   Reprinted with the permission of BakerAPS, Montréal, Québec.

Figure 10.2   Reprinted with the permission of BakerAPS, Montréal, Québec.

Figure 11.1   Reprinted with the permission of BakerAPS, Montréal, Québec.

Figure 11.2   Reprinted with the permission of BakerAPS, Montréal, Québec.

Figure 11.3   Reprinted with the permission of BakerAPS, Montréal, Québec.

Figure 11.4   Reprinted with the permission of Innovative Medical Services, El Cajon, California.

Figure 11.5   Reprinted with the permission of BakerAPS, Montréal, Québec.

Figure 11.6   Reprinted with the permission of BakerAPS, Montréal, Québec.

Figure 12.2   Reprinted with the permission of Hoffmann-La Roche Limited, Mississauga, Ontario.

Figure 12.3   Reprinted with the permission of H.J. Segal, Toronto, Ontario.

Figure 12.7   Reprinted with the permission of the Ontario College of Pharmacists, Toronto, Ontario.

Figure 12.8   Reprinted with the permission of the Business Development Bank of Canada, (formerly known as the Federal Business Development Bank), Montréal, Québec.

Table 12.1   Reprinted with the permission of the Ontario College of Pharmacists, Toronto, Ontario.

Figure 15.1   Reprinted with the permission of the Grain Insurance and Guarantee Company, Winnipeg, Manitoba.

Figure 17.1   Reprinted with the permission of Ernst & Young, Toronto, Ontario.

APPENDIX

LEASE
(COMMERCIAL)

Made the 19th **day of** September, 199x

BETWEEN

(the "Landlord")

- and -

(the "Tenant")

In consideration of the rents, covenants and obligations stipulated herein the Landlord and the Tenant have agreed to enter into a Lease of the premises known municipally as Street West, Toronto, Ontario at which is located a building containing approximately six thousand six hundred and sixty (6,660) square feet on the ground floor and a basement.

1. GRANT OF LEASE

(1) The Landlord leases the Premises to the Tenant:

(a) at the Rent set forth in Section 2;

(b) for the Term set forth in Section 3; and

(c) subject to the conditions and in accordance with the covenants, obligations and agreements herein.

(2) The Landlord covenants that he has the right to grant the leasehold interest in the Premises free from encumbrances except as disclosed on title.

2.   RENT

(1)   Rent means the amounts payable by the Tenant to the Landlord pursuant to this Section and includes Additional Rent.

(2)   The Tenant covenants to pay to the Landlord, during the Term of this Lease rent as follows:

(a)   during the first Three years of the Term, the sum of $79,920.00 per annum, payable monthly in advance in equal instalments of $6,660.00 on the first day of each and every month, commencing on the first day of the Term;

(b)   during the 4th year of the Term, the sum of $86,580.00 per annum payable monthly in advance in equal instalments of $7,215.00 on the first day of each and every month, commencing on the first day of October, 1999; and

(c)   during the 5th year of the Term, the sum of $93,240.00 per annum, payable monthly in advance in equal instalments of $7,770.00 on the first day of each and every month, commencing on the first day of October, 2000; and

(d)   during the 6th year of the Term, the sum of $99,900.00 per annum payable monthly in advance in equal instalments of $8,325.00 on the first day of each and every month, commencing on the first day of October, 2001.

Note: The tenant shall be responsible for the Goods & Services Tax if imposed on any rent payable by the tenant.

(3)   The Tenant further covenants to pay all other sums required by this Lease to be paid by him and agrees that all amounts payable by the Tenant to the Landlord or to any other party pursuant to the provisions of this Lease shall be deemed to be additional rent ("Additional Rent") whether or not specifically designated as such in this Lease.

(4)   The Landlord and the Tenant agree that it is their mutual intention that this Lease shall be a completely carefree net lease for the Landlord and that the Landlord shall not, during the Term of this Lease, be required to make any payments in respect of the Premises other than charges of a kind personal to

the Landlord (such as income and estate taxes and mortgage payments):

(a) and to effect the said intention of the parties the Tenant promises to pay the following expenses related to the Premises as Additional Rent;

    (i) business taxes and licenses;

    (ii) utilities (including but not limited to gas, electricity, water, heat, air-conditioning);

    (iii) services supplied to the Premises, provided that this does not in any way oblige the Landlord to provide any services, unless otherwise agreed in this Lease;

    (iv) property taxes and rates, duties and assessments;

    (v) maintenance;

    (vi) insurance premiums;

    (vii) sales tax, and any other taxes imposed on the Landlord respecting the Rent;

    (viii) all other charges, impositions, costs and expenses of every nature and kind whatsoever;

(b) and if any of the foregoing charges are invoiced directly to the Tenant, the Tenant shall pay same as and when they become due and shall produce proof of payment to the Landlord immediately if requested to do so;

    (i) but the Tenant may contest or appeal any such charges at the Tenant's own expense;

(c) and the Tenant hereby agrees to indemnify and protect the Landlord from any liability accruing to the Landlord in respect of the expenses payable by the Tenant as provided for herein;

(d) and if the Tenant fails to make any of the payments required by this Lease then the Landlord may make such payments and charge to the Tenant as Additional Rent the amounts paid by the Landlord;

    (i) and if such charges are not paid by the Tenant on demand the Landlord shall be entitled to the same remedies and may take the same steps for recovery of the unpaid charges as in the event of Rent in arrears.

(e) and if the Tenant enjoys the use of any common areas and facilities not included in the Premises, the Tenant shall pay his proportionate share of the foregoing expenses relating to such common areas and facilities.

(5) Additional Rent shall be payable in monthly instalments in advance on the same dates stipulated for payment of Rent in Section 2 (2) and the Landlord shall at least once each year provide the Tenant with a statement providing such information as may be required to calculate accurately the amounts payable by the Tenant as Additional Rent:

(a) prior to the first such statement being delivered the payments of Additional Rent shall be based on the Landlord's estimate of the expenses chargeable to the Tenant;

(b) in the event that any such statement indicates that the amounts paid by the Tenant for Additional Rent are either more or less than the amount required pursuant to the statement then an adjusting statement shall be delivered within thirty days;

(i) and if the Tenant has overpaid in respect of Additional Rent the adjustment may be made by way of reduction of the next ensuing instalments of Rent.

(6) All payments to be made by the Tenant pursuant to this Lease shall be delivered to the Landlord at the Landlord's address for service set out in Section 15 or to such other place as the Landlord may from time to time direct in writing.

(7) The Tenant agrees to pay in advance to the Landlord at the commencement of the Term the first and last months' Rent payable under Section 2 (2) of this Lease.

(8) All Rent in arrears and all sums paid by the Landlord for expenses incurred which should have been paid by the Tenant shall bear interest from the date payment was due, or made, or expense incurred at a rate per annum equal to the prime commercial lending rate of the Landlord's bank plus two (2) per cent.

(9) The Tenant acknowledges and agrees that the payments of Rent and Additional Rent provided for in this Lease shall be made without any deduction for any reason whatsoever unless expressly allowed by the terms of this Lease or agreed to by the Landlord in writing; and

    (a) no partial payment by the Tenant which is accepted by the Landlord shall be considered as other than a partial payment on account of Rent owing and shall not prejudice the Landlord's right to recover any Rent owing.

3. TERM AND POSSESSION

(1) The Tenant shall have possession of the Premises for a period of six years, commencing on the first day of October, 199x and ending on the 30th day of September, 200x.(the "Term").

(2) Subject to the Landlord's rights under this Lease, and as long as the Lease is in good standing the Landlord covenants that the Tenant shall have quiet enjoyment of the Premises during the Term of this Lease without any interruption or disturbance from the Landlord or any other person or persons lawfully claiming through the Landlord.

(3) If the Tenant fails to take possession of the Premises or to open for business on or before the date specified for commencement of the Term of this Lease, the Landlord shall, in addition to any other remedies, have the right to terminate this Lease upon 24 hours written notice to the Tenant, and to recover from the Tenant the cost of all work done by the Landlord on behalf of the Tenant.

4. ASSIGNMENT

(1) The Tenant may assign or sublease part or all of the leased premises at any time during the lease term and any renewal thereof for use as medical suites and postal station without the consent of the Landlord and without having to notify the Landlord.

(2)   Other than the situation in sect. 4(1) above, the tenant shall not assign this Lease or sublet the whole or any part of the Premises unless he first obtains the consent of the Landlord in writing, which consent shall not unreasonably be withheld;

   (a)   and the Tenant hereby waives his right to the benefit of any present or future Act of the Legislature of Ontario which would allow the Tenant to assign this Lease or sublet the Premises without the Landlord's consent.

(3)   The consent of the Landlord to any assignment of subletting shall not operate as a waiver of the necessity for consent to any subsequent assignment or subletting.

(4)   Any consent granted by the Landlord shall be conditional upon the assignee, subtenant or occupant executing a written agreement directly with the Landlord agreeing to be bound by all the terms of this Lease as if the assignee, subtenant or occupant had originally executed this Lease as Tenant.

(5)   Any consent given by the Landlord to any assignment or other disposition of the Tenant's interest in this Lease or in the Premises shall not relieve the Tenant from his obligations under this Lease, including the obligation to pay Rent and Additional Rent as provided for herein.

(6)   If the party originally entering into this Lease as Tenant, or any party who subsequently becomes the Tenant by way of assignment or sublease or otherwise as provided for in this Lease, is a corporation then:

   (a)   the Tenant shall not be entitled to deal with its authorized or issued capital or that of an affiliated company in any way that results in a change in the effective voting control of the Tenant unless the Landlord first consents in writing to the proposed change;

   (b)   if any change is made in the control of the Tenant corporation without the written consent of the Landlord then the Landlord shall be entitled to treat the Tenant as being in default and to exercise the remedies stipulated in paragraph

10 (2) of this Lease and any other remedies available in law;

(c) the Tenant agrees to make available to the Landlord or his authorized representatives the corporate books and records of the Tenant for inspection at reasonable times.

5. USE

(1) During the Term of this Lease the Premises shall not be used for any purpose other than full service drug store and pharmaceutical dispensary and ancillary uses in accordance with existing zoning by-laws and permitted uses.

(2) The Tenant shall not do or permit to be done at the Premises anything which may:

(a) constitute a nuisance;

(b) cause damage to the Premises;

(c) cause injury or annoyance to occupants of neighbouring premises;

(d) make void or voidable any insurance upon the Premises;

(e) constitute a breach of any by-law, statute, order or regulation of any municipal, provincial or other competent authority relating to the Premises.

6. REPAIR AND MAINTENANCE

(1) The Tenant covenants that during the term of this Lease and any renewal thereof the Tenant shall keep in good condition the Premises including all alterations and additions made thereto, and shall, with or without notice, promptly make all needed repairs and all necessary replacements as would a prudent owner:

(a) but the Tenant shall not be liable to effect repairs attributable to reasonable wear and tear, or to damage caused by fire, lightning or storm.

(2) The Tenant shall permit the Landlord or a person authorized by the Landlord to enter the Premises to examine the condition thereof and view the state of repair at reasonable times:

(a) and if upon such examination repairs are found to be necessary, written notice of the repairs required shall be given to the Tenant by or on behalf of the Landlord and the Tenant shall make the necessary repairs within the time specified in the notice;

(b) and if the Tenant refuses or neglects to keep the Premises in good repair the Landlord may, but shall not be obliged to, make any necessary repairs, and shall be permitted to enter the Premises, by himself or his servants or agents, for the purpose of effecting the repairs without being liable to the Tenant for any loss, damage or inconvenience to the Tenant in connection with the Landlord's entry and repairs;

(i) and if the Landlord makes repairs the Tenant shall pay the cost of them immediately as Additional Rent.

(3) Upon the expiry of the Term or other determination of this Lease the Tenant agrees peaceably to surrender the Premises, including any alterations or additions made thereto, to the Landlord in a state of good repair, reasonable wear and tear and damage by fire, lightning and storm only excepted.

(4) The Tenant shall immediately give written notice to the Landlord of any substantial damage that occurs to the Premises from any cause.

7. ALTERATIONS AND ADDITIONS

(1) If the Tenant, during the Term of this Lease or any renewal of it, desires to make any alterations or additions to the Premises, including but not limited to: erecting partitions, attaching equipment, and installing necessary furnishings or additional equipment of the Tenant's business, the Tenant may do so at his own expense, at any time and from time to time, if the following conditions are met:

(a) before undertaking any alteration or addition the Tenant shall submit to the Landlord a plan showing the proposed alterations or additions and the Tenant shall not proceed to make any alteration or addition unless the Landlord has approved the plan, and the Landlord shall not unreasonably or arbitrarily withhold his approval;

    (i) and items included in the plan which are regarded by the Tenant as "Trade Fixtures" shall be designated as such on the plan;

(b) any and all alterations or additions to the Premises made by the Tenant must comply with all applicable building code standards and by-laws of the municipality in which the Premises are located.

(2) The Tenant shall be responsible for and pay the cost of any alterations, additions, installations or improvements that any governing authority, municipal, provincial or otherwise, may require to be made in, on or to the Premises.

(3) No sign, advertisement or notice shall be inscribed, painted or affixed by the Tenant, or any other person on the Tenant's behalf, on any part of the inside or outside of the building in which the Premises are located unless the sign, advertisement or notice has been approved in every respect by the Landlord.

(4) All alterations and additions to the Premises made by or on behalf of the Tenant, other than the Tenant's Trade Fixtures, shall immediately become the property of the Landlord without compensation to the Tenant.

(5) The Tenant agrees, at his own expense and by whatever means may be necessary, immediately to obtain the release or discharge of any encumbrance that may be registered against the Landlord's property in connection with any additions or alterations to the Premises made by the Tenant or in connection with any other activity of the Tenant.

(6) If the Tenant has complied with his obligations according to the provisions of this Lease, the Tenant may remove his Trade Fixtures at the end of the Term or other termination of this

Lease and the Tenant covenants that he will make good and repair or replace as necessary any damage caused to the Premises by the removal of the Tenant's Trade Fixtures.

(7)   Other than as provided in paragraph 7 (6) above, the Tenant shall not, during the Term of this Lease or anytime thereafter remove from the Premises any Trade Fixtures or other goods and chattels of the Tenant except in the following circumstances:

(a) the removal is in the ordinary course of business;

(b) the Trade Fixture has become unnecessary for the Tenant's business or is being replaced by a new or similar Trade Fixture; or

(c) the Landlord has consented in writing to the removal; but in any case the Tenant shall make good any damage caused to the Premises by the installation or removal of any Trade Fixtures, equipment, partitions, furnishings and any other objects whatsoever brought onto the Premises by the Tenant.

(8)   The Tenant shall, at his own expense, if requested by the Landlord, remove any or all additions or improvements made by the Tenant to the Premises during the Term and shall repair all damage caused by the installation or the removal or both.

(9)   The Tenant shall not bring onto the Premises or any part of the Premises any machinery, equipment or any other thing that might in the opinion of the Landlord, by reason of its weight, size or use, damage the Premises or overload the floors of the Premises;

(a) and if the Premises are damaged or overloaded the tenant shall restore the Premises immediately or pay to the Landlord the cost of restoring the Premises.

8.   INSURANCE

(1)   THE TENANT agrees that during the whole of the said term or any renewal thereof, it will pay to the Landlord the full cost of fire and extended coverage insurance (including sprinkler leakage) maintained by the Landlord providing insurance cov-

erage for an amount up to full replacement value or for not less than the amount required by any mortgagee holding a mortgage on the premises with the loss payable under such policy or policies to the Landlord and/or such person or persons as the Landlord may designate, as their interest may appear. The policy or policies of insurance referred to above shall also include insurance on boilers, machinery, unfired pressure vessels, air-conditioning equipment, electrical apparatus and other like objects, including insurance against loss or damage caused by the explosion, rupture or failure thereof.

(2) THE TENANT shall maintain in respect of its property on the demised premises, fire insurance with extended coverage and water damage insurance, including sprinkler leakage or discharge, and where applicable, boiler and pressure vessel insurance to cover all of its improvements, furniture, fittings, fixtures and stock in trade, in amounts adequate to cover fully any loss that the Tenant could sustain.

(3) THE TENANT shall further maintain a policy or policies of insurance against loss of rental income and taxes payable under this lease to the full amount of such rental income and taxes for a Twelve (12) Month period with loss payable to the Landlord. If such insurance coverage is added to the insurance coverage maintained pursuant to subparagraph (1) above, the Tenant shall pay to the Landlord the costs of same.

(4) UNLESS other provision satisfactory to the Landlord is made to cover loss in regard thereto, the Tenant shall maintain insurance upon all glass and plate glass in or forming part of the demised premises including the store front, if applicable, against breakage or damage from any cause including the elements, war and riots and civil commotion.

(5) THE TENANT shall maintain for the mutual benefit of the Landlord and the Tenant, liability insurance against claims for personal injury, death or property damage occurring upon, in or about the demised premises, such insurance to afford protection to the limit of no less than TWO MILLION ($2,000,000.00) DOLLARS for all deaths, injuries or loss of or damage to property.

(6)   ALL such policies shall waive recourse and any other rights of subrogation against the Landlord, shall be on terms and conditions and with insurers satisfactory to the Landlord, and shall provide (or the insurer shall agree) that no policy shall be cancelled or its overage reduced without Thirty (30) days prior written notice to the Landlord. The Tenant agrees to maintain all such insurance in good standing at all times and to pay premiums thereon as and when same become due. The Landlord shall at all times be supplied with proper evidence of such insurance being in force and the Tenant shall supply to the Landlord evidence of such insurance being in force and the Tenant shall supply to the Landlord evidence of the continuation of such insurance coverage at least Thirty (30) days prior to the expiry of such policy or policies of insurance. In the event that the Tenant shall fail to make payments on any such premium as and when the same becomes due, then the Landlord shall be entitled to pay such premium and shall be entitled to collect the amount thereof from the Tenant in the same manner as herein provided for the collection of rent in arrears.

(7)   THE TENANT shall be the option of insuring the demised premises through its own insurers for the coverage required pursuant to paragraph 8 (1).

(8)   THE TENANT shall have the option of being self-insured for any of the coverages it must maintain herein except for fire and extended coverage insurance for the premises and except for liability insurance coverage.

(9)   THE TENANT covenants to keep the Landlord indemnified against all claims and demands whatsoever by any person, whether in respect of damage to person or property, arising out of or occasioned by the maintenance, use or occupancy of the Premises or the subletting or assignment of same or any part thereof. And the Tenant further covenants to indemnify the Landlord with respect to any encumbrance on or damage to the Premises occasioned by or arising from the act, default, or negligence of the Tenant, its officers, agents, servants, employees, contractors, customers, invitees or licensees:

(a) and the Tenant agrees that the foregoing indemnity shall survive the termination of this Lease notwithstanding any provisions of this Lease to the contrary.

(10) THE TENANT shall carry insurance in his own name to provide coverage with respect to the risk of business interruption to an extent sufficient to allow the Tenant to meet his ongoing obligations to the Landlord and to protect the Tenant against loss of revenues.

(11) THE TENANT shall carry insurance in his own name insuring against the risk of damage to the Tenant's property within the Premises caused by fire or other perils and the policy shall provide for coverage on a replacement cost basis to protect the Tenant's stock-in-trade, equipment, Trade Fixtures, decorations and improvements.

(12) THE TENANT shall carry public liability and property damage insurance in which policy the Landlord shall be a named insured and the policy shall include a cross-liability endorsement;

(a) and the Tenant shall provide the Landlord with a copy of the policy.

9. DAMAGE TO THE PREMISES

(1) If the Premises or the building in which the Premises are located, are damaged or destroyed, in whole or in part, by fire or other peril, then the following provisions shall apply:

(a) If the damage or destruction renders the Premises unfit for occupancy and impossible to repair or rebuild using reasonable diligence within 120 clear days from the happening of such damage or destruction, then the Term hereby granted shall cease from the date the damage or destruction occurred, and the Tenant shall immediately surrender the remainder of the Term and give possession of the Premises to the Landlord, and the Rent from the time of the surrender shall abate;

(b) If the Premises can with reasonable diligence be repaired and rendered fit for occupancy within 120 days from the happening of the damage or destruction, but the damage renders the Premises wholly unfit for occupancy, then the rent hereby reserved shall not accrue after the day that such damage occurred, or while the process of repair is going on, and the Landlord shall repair the Premises with all reasonable speed, and the Tenant's obligation to pay Rent shall resume immediately after the necessary repairs have been completed;

(c) If the leased Premises can be repaired within 120 days as aforesaid, but the damage is such that the leased Premises are capable of being partially used, then until such damage has been repaired, the Tenant shall continue in possession and the Rent shall abate proportionately.

(2) Any question as to the degree of damage or destruction or the period of time required to repair or rebuild shall be determined by an architect retained by the Landlord.

(3) Apart from the provisions of Section 8 (1) there shall be no abatement from or reduction of the Rent payable by the Tenant, nor shall the Tenant be entitled to claim against the Landlord for any damages, general or special, caused by fire, water, sprinkler systems, partial or temporary failure or stoppage of services or utilities which the Landlord is obliged to provide according to this Lease, from any cause whatsoever.

10.   ACTS OF DEFAULT AND LANDLORD'S REMEDIES

(1) An Act of Default has occurred when:

(a) the Tenant has failed to pay Rent for a period of 15 consecutive days, regardless of whether demand for payment has been made or not;

(b) The Tenant has breached his covenants or failed to perform any of his obligations under this Lease; and

(i) the Landlord has given notice specifying the nature of the default and the steps required to correct it; and

    (ii)   the Tenant has failed to correct the default as required by the notice;

(c) the Tenant has;

    (i)   become bankrupt or insolvent or made an assignment for the benefit of Creditors;

    (ii)   had its property seized or attached in satisfaction of a judgment;

    (iii) had a receiver appointed;

    (iv) committed any act or neglected to do anything with the result that a Construction Lien or other encumbrance is registered against the Landlord's property;

    (v)   without the consent of the Landlord, made or entered into an agreement to make a sale of its assets to which the Bulk Sales Act applies;

    (vi) taken action if the Tenant is a corporation, with a view to winding up, dissolution or liquidation;

(d) any insurance policy is cancelled or not renewed by reason of the use or occupation of the Premises, or by reason of non-payment of premiums;

(e) the Premises;

    (i)   become vacant or remain unoccupied for a period of 30 consecutive days; or

    (ii)   are not open for business on more than thirty (30) business days in any twelve (12) month period or on any twelve (12) consecutive business days;

    (iii) are used by any other person or persons, or for any other purpose than as provided for in this Lease without the written consent of the Landlord.

(2) When an Act of Default on the part of the Tenant has occurred:

(a) the current month's rent together with the next three months' rent shall become due and payable immediately; and

(b) the Landlord shall have the right to terminate this Lease and to re-enter the Premises and deal with them as he may choose.

(3)   If, because an Act of Default has occurred, the Landlord exercises his right to terminate this Lease, and re-enter the Premises prior to the end of the Term, the Tenant shall nevertheless be liable for payment of Rent and all other amounts payable by the Tenant in accordance with the provisions of this Lease until the Landlord has re-let the Premises or otherwise dealt with the Premises in such manner that the cessation of payments by the Tenant will not result in loss to the Landlord:

(a)   and the Tenant agrees to be liable to the Landlord, until the end of the Term of this Lease for payment of any difference between the amount of Rent hereby agreed to be paid for the Term hereby granted and the Rent any new tenant pays to the Landlord.

(4)   The Tenant covenants that notwithstanding any present or future Act of the Legislature of the Province of Ontario, the personal property of the Tenant during the term of this Lease shall not be exempt from levy by distress for Rent in arrears:

(a)   and the Tenant acknowledges that it is upon the express understanding that there should be no such exemption that this Lease is entered into, and by executing this Lease:

(i)   the Tenant waives the benefit of any such legislative provisions which might otherwise be available to the Tenant in the absence of this agreement; and

(ii)   the Tenant agrees that the Landlord may plead this covenant as an estoppel against the Tenant if an action is brought to test the Landlord's right to levy distress against the Tenant's property.

(5)   If, when an Act of Default has occurred, the Landlord chooses not to terminate the Lease and re-enter the Premises, the Landlord shall have the right to take any and all necessary steps to rectify any or all Acts of Default of the Tenant and to charge the costs of such rectification to the Tenant and to recover the costs as Rent.

(6)   If, when an Act of Default has occurred, the Landlord chooses to waive his right to exercise the remedies available to him under this Lease or at law the waiver shall not constitute

condonaton of the Act of Default, nor shall the waiver be pleaded as an estoppel against the Landlord to prevent his exercising his remedies with respect to a subsequent Act of Default:

(a) No covenant, term, or condition of this Lease shall be deemed to have been waived by the Landlord unless the waiver is in writing and signed by the Landlord.

11. TERMINATION UPON NOTICE AND AT END OF TERM

(1) If the Landlord desires at any time to remodel or demolish the Premises or any part thereof, to an extent that renders continued possession by the Tenant impracticable, the Tenant shall, upon receiving one hundred and eighty (180) clear days' written notice from the Landlord:

   (a) surrender this Lease, including any unexpired remainder of the Term; and

   (b) vacate the Premises and give the Landlord possession.

(2) If the Premises are subject to an Agreement of Purchase and Sale or if the Premises are expropriated or condemned by any competent authority:

   (a) the Landlord shall have the right to terminate this Lease by giving ninety (90) clear days' notice in writing to the Tenant; or

   (b) the Landlord may require the Tenant to vacate the Premises within thirty (30) days from payment by the Landlord to the Tenant of a bonus equal to three months' rent.

      (i) but payment of the said bonus shall be accompanied or preceded by written notice from the Landlord to the Tenant advising of the Landlord's intent to exercise this option.

(3) The Tenant agrees to permit the Landlord during the last three months of the Term of this Lease to display "For Rent" or "For Sale" signs or both at the Premises and to show the Premises to prospective new tenants or purchasers and to permit anyone

having written authority of the Landlord to view the Premises at reasonable hours.

(4) If the Tenant remains in possession of the Premises after termination of this Lease as aforesaid and if the Landlord then accepts rent for the Premises from the Tenant, it is agreed that such over holding by the Tenant and acceptance of Rent by the Landlord shall create a monthly tenancy only but the tenancy shall remain subject to all the terms and conditions of this Lease except those regarding the Term.

12.   ACKNOWLEDGEMENT BY TENANT

The tenant agrees that he will at any time or times during the Term, upon being given at least forty-eight (48) hours prior written notice, execute and deliver to the Landlord a statement in writing certifying:

(a) that this Lease is unmodified and is in full force and effect (or if modified stating the modifications and confirming that the Lease is in full force and effect as modified);

(b) the amount of Rent being paid;

(c) the date to which Rent has been paid;

(d) other charges payable under this Lease which have been paid;

(e) particulars of any prepayment of Rent or security deposits; and

(f) particulars of any subtenancies.

13.   SUBORDINATION AND POSTPONEMENT

(1) This Lease and all the rights of the Tenant under this Lease are subject and subordinate to any and all charges against the land, buildings or improvements of which the Premises form part, whether the charge is in the nature of a mortgage, trust deed, lien or any other form of charge arising from the financing or re-financing, including extensions or renewals, of the Landlord's interest in the property.

(2)   Upon the request of the Landlord the Tenant will execute any
form required to subordinate this Lease and the Tenant's rights
to any such charge, and will, if required, attorn to the holder of
the charge.

(3)   No subordination by the Tenant shall have the effect of permitting the holder of any charge to disturb the occupation and
possession of the Premises by the Tenant as long as the Tenant
performs his obligations under this Lease.

14.   RULES AND REGULATIONS

The Tenant agrees on behalf of itself and all persons entering the
Premises with the Tenant's authority or permission to abide by such
reasonable rules and regulations that form part of this Lease and as
the Landlord may make from time to time.

15.   NOTICE

(1)   Any notice required or permitted to be given by one party to
the other pursuant to the terms of this Lease may be given

To the Landlord at:

To the Tenant at the Premises or at:

(2)   The above addresses may be changed at any time by giving ten
(10) days written notice.

(3)   Any notice given by one party to the other in accordance with
the provisions of this Lease shall be deemed conclusively to
have been received on the date delivered if the notice is served
personally or seventy-two (72) hours after mailing if the notice
is mailed.

16.   REGISTRATION

The Tenant shall not at any time register notice of or a copy of this Lease on title to the property of which the premises form part without consent of the Landlord.

17.   INTERPRETATION

(1)   The words importing the singular number only shall include the plural, and vice versa, and words importing the masculine gender shall include the feminine gender, and words importing persons shall include firms and corporations and vice versa.

(2)   Unless the context otherwise requires, the word "Landlord" and the word "Tenant" wherever used herein shall be construed to include the executors, administrators, successors and assigns of the Landlord and Tenant, respectively.

(3)   When there are two or more Tenants bound by the same covenants herein contained, their obligations shall be joint and several.

18.   SCHEDULES "A" & "B" ATTACHED HERETO FORM PART OF THIS LEASE.

In Witness of the foregoing covenants the Landlord and the Tenant have executed this Lease.

Witness

_____   _____

                                                                                    Landlord

_____   per   _____

                                                                                    Tenant

Schedule "A"

1) The Tenant shall not allow any ashes, refuses, garbage or any other loose or objectionable material to accumulate on or about the said demised premises and will at all times keep the said demised premises in clean and wholesome conditions and shall be responsible for the removal of all garbage or loose or other objectionable material.

2) Lease Renewal – Provided the Tenant is not in default in any of its obligations under the terms of the lease, the Tenant shall have the option to renew the lease for two further terms of five (5) years each. The Tenant will be required to give written notice to the Landlord of its intention to renew at least three months prior to the expiration date of the lease for the first renewal and three months prior to the expiration date of the first renewal term for the second renewal term.

   The first renewal term shall be on the same terms and conditions as the sixth year of initial lease term, except for rent which shall be set at the prevailing market rent and no greater than $15.00 per square foot.

   The second renewal term shall be on the same terms and conditions as the first renewal term, except for rent which shall be set at the prevailing market rent for similar properties in size, use and purpose. In the event the parties are unable to agree upon a market rent, a submission shall be jointly made to arbitration at the shared cost of the parties.

3) Net Lease – The Tenant acknowledges that the lease shall be an absolute net lease to the Landlord, and the Tenant shall be responsible for all costs, charges, outlays or other expenditures relating to the premises and the Tenant's occupation thereof, which may include any tax in the nature of the Goods and Services Tax which is levied on the Landlord as a result of Tenant's use and occupancy of the premises and in respect of the use by the Tenant of the common facilities and the lands.

4) Option to Purchase – The Tenant is hereby granted a first right of refusal to purchase the property, so that in the event Landlord receives a third party offer for the property, the Landlord shall notify the Tenant in writing immediately, who shall have seventy-two (72)

hours from receipt of notice to enter into an acceptance Agreement of Purchase and Sale with the Landlord.

5)   Warranty – Landlord warrants that the existing building, equipment and premises are in good repair and working order at the time of occupancy by the Tenant and that any and all environmental concerns have been addressed and the Tenant shall be permitted to operate its business upon occupancy without regard to such environmental controls as same are the responsibility of the Landlord who shall indemnify and save the Tenant harmless from all costs and business loss that may result from any non-compliance by the Landlord.

6)   The Landlord covenants to repair structural defects or weaknesses. "Structural repairs" shall be deemed to include repairs to roof, roof membrane and deck, foundations, load bearing walls, columns, downpipes, damage to exterior walls, and damage to drains, electrical, plumbing and drainage works leading up to and from the demised premises, but not within the demised premises. If any structural repairs can be covered by insurance obtainable by a normal, prudent landlord at a reasonable cost, then the Tenant must maintain or pay for such insurance as provided in paragraph 8 of this lease. To the extent not covered by insurance, charges for structural repairs shall be at the Landlord's sole cost and expense and shall not be charged to the Tenant, except to the extent caused by the willful or negligent act or omission of the Tenant or those for whom in law the Tenant is responsible.

7)   Advance Rental – Landlord acknowledges receipt of $14,985.00 as a deposit on rental, which is applied to the first and last month's net rent.

8)   It is agreed that this lease agreement supersedes the previous signed offer to lease dated _____

Schedule "B"

SCHEDULE OF RULES AND REGULATIONS
FORMING PART OF THIS LEASE

The Tenant shall observe the following Rules and Regulations (as amended, modified or supplemented from time to time by the Landlord as provided in this Lease):

1. The sidewalks, entrances, elevators, stairways and corridors of the building shall not be obstructed or used by the Tenant, his agents, servants, contractors, invitees or employees for any purpose other than access to and from the Premises.

2. The floors, sky-lights and windows that reflect or admit light into passageways or into any place in the building shall not be covered or obstructed by the Tenant, and no awnings shall be put over any window.

3. The toilets, sinks, drains, washrooms and other water apparatus shall not be used for any purpose other than those for which they were constructed, and no sweepings, rubbish, rags, ashes or other substances, such as chemicals, solvents, noxious liquids or pollutants shall be thrown therein, and any damage resulting to them from misuse shall be borne by the Tenant by whom or by whose employees, agents, servants, contractors or invitees the damage was caused.

4. In the event that the Landlord provides and installs a Public Directory Board inside the building, the Tenant's name shall be placed on the said Board at the expense of the Tenant.

5. The Tenant shall not perform any acts or carry on any activity which may damage the Premises or the common areas or be a nuisance to any other tenant.

6. No animals or birds shall be brought into the building or kept on the Premises.

7. The Tenant shall not mark, drill into, bore or cut or in any way damage or deface the walls, ceilings or floors of the Premises. No wires, pipes or conduits shall be installed in the Premises without prior written

approval of the Landlord. No broadloom or carpeting shall be affixed to the Premises by means of a non-soluble adhesive or similar products.

8.   No one shall use the Premises for sleeping apartments or residential purposes, for the storage of personal effects or articles other than those required for business purposes, or for any illegal purpose.

9.   The Tenant shall not use or permit the use of any objectionable advertising medium such as, without limitation, loudspeakers, public address systems, sound amplifiers, radio, broadcast or television apparatus within the building which is in any manner audible or visible outside of the Premises.

10.   The Tenant must observe strict care not to allow windows to remain open so as to admit rain or snow, or so as to interfere with the heating of the building. The Tenant neglecting this rule will be responsible for any damage caused to the property of other tenants, or to the property of the Landlord, by such carelessness. The Tenant, when closing the Premises, shall close all windows and lock all doors.

11.   The Tenant shall not without the express written consent of the Landlord, place any additional locks upon any doors of the Premises and shall not permit any duplicate keys to be made therefore; but shall usle only additional keys obtained from the Landlord, at the expense of the Tenant, and shall surrender to the Landlord on the termination of the Lease all keys of the Premises.

12.   No inflammable oils or other inflammable, toxic, dangerous or explosive material shall be kept or permitted to be kept in or on the Premises.

13.   No bicycles or other vehicles shall be brought within the Premises or upon the Landlord's property, including any lane or courtyard, unless otherwise agreed in writing.

14.   Nothing shall be placed on the outside of windows or projections of the Premises. No air conditioning equipment shall be placed at the windows of the Premises without the consent in writing of the Landlord.

15. The moving of all heavy equipment and office equipment or furniture shall occur only between 6:00 p.m. and 8:00 a.m. or any other time consented to by the Landlord and the persons employed to move the same in and out of the building must be acceptable to the Landlord. Safes and other heavy equipment shall be moved through the Premises and common areas only upon steel bearing plates. No deliveries requiring the use of an elevator for freight purposes will be received into the building or carried in the elevators, except during hours approved by the Landlord.

16. The Landlord reserves the right to restrict the use of the building after 6:00 p.m.

17. Canvassing, soliciting and peddling in the building is prohibited.

18. The Tenant shall first obtain in writing the consent of the Landlord to any alteration or modification to the electrical system in the Premises and all such alterations and modifications shall be completed at the Tenant's expense by an electrical contractor acceptable to the Landlord.

19. The Tenant shall first obtain in writing the consent of the Landlord to the placement by the Tenant of any garbage containers or receptacles outside the Premises or building.

20. The Tenant shall not install or erect on or about the Premises television antennae, communications towers, satellite dishes or other such apparatus.

21. The Landlord shall have the right to make such other and further reasonable rules and regulations and to alter, amend or cancel all rules and regulations as in its judgement may from time to time be needed for the safety, care and cleanliness of the building and for the preservation of good order therein and the same shall be kept and observed by the Tenant, his employees, agents, servants, contractors or invitees. The Landlord may from time to time waive any of such rules and regulations as applied to particular tenants and is not liable to the Tenant for breaches thereof by other tenants.

Notes